D1499180

THE BIRDS OF TIKAL

The Natural History Press, publisher for The American Museum of Natural History, is a division of Doubleday & Company, Inc. Directed by a joint editorial board made up of members of the staff of both the Museum and Doubleday, the Natural History Press publishes books and periodicals in all branches of the life and earth sciences, including anthropology and astronomy. The Natural History Press has its editorial offices at The American Museum of Natural History, Central Park West at 79th Street, New York 24, New York, and its business offices at 501 Franklin Avenue, Garden City, New York.

THE BIRDS OF TIKAL

FRANK B. SMITHE

Published for
The American Museum of Natural History

The Natural History Press
GARDEN CITY, NEW YORK
1966

The line illustrations for this book were prepared by the Graphic Arts Division of The American Museum of Natural History. The photographs are by the author, unless otherwise indicated.

Color illustrations by H. Wayne Trimm.

FOREWORD

The Mayan temples and pyramids of Tikal are being recovered from the jungle by a cooperative project sponsored by the Government of Guatemala and The University Museum of the University of Pennsylvania. The fascinating monuments of that once powerful civilization are attracting tourists in steadily increasing numbers. The Mayan ruins will always be the chief attraction, but wildlife, which is under strict government protection, will add to the enjoyment of those visiting Tikal. Even the splendid Ocellated Turkey is now easily seen.

The Birds of Tikal will add still further to the pleasure of visitors. Its author, Frank B. Smithe, a retired businessman and engineer, was, at the time of the first of many visits, an amateur archeologist and ornithologist. His interest in the birds of the area caused local authorities to urge him to make a comprehensive study, and to write a report on them. Mr. Smithe undertook this task with a thoroughness which, more than eight years later, resulted in this volume.

This is far more than a local field guide, although that is its primary purpose. It is a complete handbook of the birds of the Petén and contains a list of all the species recorded in that vast region and not merely those seen at Tikal. In the absence of other semi-popular works on the birdlife of the area, it will serve as a handbook to the birds of the lowlands of Central America.

It includes descriptions of the color of bills, eyes, legs, and other quickly fading soft parts, which are sometimes essential to identification, and which add to the scientific record. Descriptions of bird songs and calls, admittedly a difficult subject, are also given and will serve as a basis for further improvements. Vocalizations are often one of the most reliable means of identification. The book gives a chart of daily rainfall and temperature records at Tikal, made over a period of four consecutive years, a constructive addition to the published knowledge of the climate of these lowlands.

The color plates by Wayne Trimm, staff artist for the New York State Department of Conservation, are an important feature of the book. Each bird illustrated was selected because it presented a problem in field identification or because it had never before been portrayed in color. The illustrations omit such colorful birds as toucans and macaws, as they have been frequently illustrated in the past, and also most migrants, paintings of which are also readily found in the current literature.

Mr. Smithe is to be complimented upon the completion of this important contribution to our knowledge of the natural history of Central America.

> *Dean Amadon*
> Chairman, Department
> of Ornithology,
> The American Museum
> of Natural History

AUTHOR'S PREFACE

This guide to the birds of Tikal has been prepared to aid visitors in identifying the birds they see here and to tell a little about them. Birds are numerous, present in great variety, and many of them are colorful. They attract attention and raise questions: "What do I see over there? What bird is that? How does it live? Where does it nest? What is its voice?" Perhaps this book will help with the answers.

Technically oriented books and papers have been written about the birds of Guatemala, southern Mexico, the Yucatán Peninsula, and Honduras, in short the land of the Maya. They have, in the main, been of a scientific nature, primarily for ornithologists, filed in libraries, and not readily available to the casual birder. One such study (Smithe and Paynter, 1963) listed the birds of Tikal. It reported the scientific names of the birds, as identified by Dr. Raymond A. Paynter, Jr., Curator of Birds at the Museum of Comparative Zoology, Harvard University, and included some data on habitat, breeding activity, and weights of birds as recorded in the field. It was not designed to be a guidebook and therefore did not describe the birds. Two sections, one on "Physiography," p. xvii, and one on "Vegetation," p. xix, have been taken from it and republished here.

This book includes a description of more than two hundred and eighty species of birds presently known within twelve miles of Tikal (see Map B), more than one hundred and seventy original color illustrations (but only one hundred and seven different species), and other information which may add to the pleasure of knowing these birds.

Frank B. Smithe

ABBREVIATIONS

Mid. Am. = Middle America, which includes Mexico, Guatemala, British Honduras, El Salvador, Honduras, Nicaragua, Costa Rica, and Panama.

Trop. = Tropical = Breeding in some part of the tropical lowlands of the Mid. Am. countries, though in many cases the species may also range into the mountains, while in others distribution may be very local.

"Highlands" indicates that in Mid. Am. the species usually breeds above 2500–3000 feet.

Mts. = Mountains, means that the usual breeding range is above 5000 feet.

Carib. = Caribbean   Pen. = Peninsula
S. Am. = South America   Is. or I. = Island
N. Am. = North America   n. = north, s. = south,
U. S. = United States   e. = east, w. = west
Brit. = British   n.e. = northeast,
Fla. = Florida   n.w. = northwest,
Calif. = California   s.e. = southeast,
Pac. = Pacific   s.w. = southwest
Biol. Surv. = United States Biological Survey of 1923
AOU = American Ornithologists' Union
BOU = British Ornithologists' Union
Assn. = association   p. = page   pp. = pages   pl. = plate   no. = number
fpc. = frontispiece   subsp. = subspecie has not been determined
gr. = grams   cms. = centimeters   lb. = pounds
oz. = ounces   in. = inches
Ms. = manuscript
In litt. = in correspondence

ACKNOWLEDGMENTS

Without the aid of many individuals this book would not have been started, much less completed. At the outset, two friends in Guatemala, Carlos Castañeda and Cloyd Smith, made my first visit to Tikal possible. That was a one-man safari, with a *chiclero* as guide, made in February 1948, before the present airstrip existed. My next visit occurred in 1956, and again Carlos Castañeda was of valuable assistance, as he was on subsequent occasions.

Edwin M. Shook, then Director of the archeological work known as *El Proyecto Tikal,* first suggested this bird-study to me, and continued to give me his support and encouragement for it.

Raymond A. Paynter, Jr., accompanied me to Tikal in 1957 and instructed me in the art of collecting. He also trained José Márquez, a resident of the Petén, in the preparation of specimens. Márquez worked closely with me during my later visits. He was a reliable and accurate hunter. Our collecting was checked by binoculars, with the result that often only a single needed specimen was taken.

The specimens collected have been deposited in the Museum of Comparative Zoology at Harvard, where Dr. Paynter, Curator of Birds, rendered valuable assistance in the identification of the more difficult species, and where he wrote most of the technical report referred to on page vii (Smithe and Paynter 1963).

Jorge A. Ibarra, eminent Director of the Museo Nacional de Historia Natural of Guatemala, and Founder of La Asociación Centroamérica de Historia Natural, was a most effective aide. His advice on Spanish and Mayan names is given specifically on page xxvi.

Grateful acknowledgment is made of the wholehearted co-operation of the Government of Guatemala, and of The University Museum, University of Pennsylvania, at whose invitation this study was made.

William R. Coe, a Curator of The University Museum and now Director of the Tikal Project, has been especially helpful, as were members of his staff, some of whom contributed information which is acknowledged within the annotated record.

Antonio Ortiz and his wife Sra. Aura de Ortiz, proprietors of the Jungle Lodge at Tikal, extended welcomed hospitality. Rafael Morales, Administrator of the Tikal Park, and his wife, Vivian Broman, formerly a member of the archeological staff, were helpful in many ways.

Dean Amadon, Curator of Birds at The American Museum of Natural History in New York City, bore the brunt of my efforts to work this book into useful shape. Despite the pressure of his responsibilities, he has given generously of his time, thought, and guidance. His associate, Eugene Eisenmann, gave me critical advice, and a conference with him often resulted in many hours of work by me. Charles O'Brien, Assistant Curator, helped in many friendly ways and other staff members contributed information which I have acknowledged in the references.

To these and to many others not specifically mentioned here, I am deeply grateful.

CONTENTS

LIST OF ILLUSTRATIONS

INTRODUCTION

Location

Tikal, famous site of Maya ruins, is located in the Department of el Petén, the northern section of Guatemala. The Petén is essentially a lowland limestone plateau, lying at the base of the Yucatán Peninsula which reaches north from Central America into the Gulf of Mexico and which, with Cuba, separates the Gulf from the Caribbean Sea (see Map A).

Tikal is 190 miles (306 kilometers) north of Guatemala City, the capital of the Republic of Guatemala and 250 miles south of Mérida, Yucatán, Mexico. Mérida is almost due south across the Gulf from New Orleans. Tikal is reached by air from Guatemala City. The planes usually stop en route at Flores, the capital city of the Petén. In Tikal, good hotel accommodations are available at the Jungle Lodge (Posada de la Selva).

Physiography

The region around Tikal is one of low rolling hills, ranging about 800 feet (250 meters) above sea level, composed of mature, eroded limestones of Oligocene Age (Sapper, 1937). The soil is not as thin as in the northern half of the Yucatán Peninsula, ranging about twelve, often twenty inches deep. Bedrock is exposed on some ridges and where ancient quarries exist. There are no permanent surface streams, but numerous depressions are filled in the rainy season and retain water into the early part of the dry season. These are known locally as aguadas. Larger areas, called bajos, are broadly flooded in the wet months. These may hold water from one year to the next but in the main they shrink considerably during the winter, slowly evaporating, or draining into distant rivers.

Underground streams or pools, which are often found in less matured limestone regions, have not been discovered at Tikal in spite of drilling several wells as deep as 150 meters. The ancient Maya constructed reservoirs to catch the runoff from great plazas and natural drainage valleys. At the archeologist's camp there is such a reservoir which was renovated late in 1957, creating a permanent pond. Aguada Tikal, as it is known, has proven to be attractive to birds and is undoubtedly responsible for the presence of some new arrivals at Tikal. On the other hand, the repair work has obliterated the original wild growth which covered the ancient aguada and caused a few birds to move elsewhere.

Climate

The climate is tropical and relatively dry, although wetter than most of the Yucatán Peninsula. The annual rainfall varies considerably from year to year. For example, at El Paso Caballo, about forty miles west of Tikal, a nine-year record shows an annual average ranging from 990 to 2369 mm. (39 to 93 inches). The average for the entire period there was 1762 mm. (70 inches) (Lundell 1937). A similar variability seems true at Tikal, although as yet there are fewer data from here. Averages based on such varying ranges can be misleading and we therefore believe it best to publish the original data. Completely tabulated daily rainfall and temperature records for Tikal from 1 June 1959 to 31 July 1963 are given in Appendix A. During that time twelve-month averages ranged from 1136 to 1761 mm. (45 to 70 inches), and the twelve-month average for the entire period was 1402 mm. (55.2 inches).

There is a dry period from December through April during which there is considerably less than 60 mm. (2½ inches) of precipitation per month. Early morning fogs are frequent, however, sometimes heavy enough to leave the trees and grasses dripping wet. This offers substantial relief to vegetation during the long dry period. The rains usually begin in May, reaching monthly peaks of 250 to 300 mm. (10 to 12 inches). Even during the rainy season, however, there are many rainless days.

The mean temperature varies little throughout the year. During the heat of the day the temperature ranges between 28° and 35° Centigrade (82° and 95° F). During the invariably cooler nights the temperature drops to between 15° and 22° C (60° and 72° F), with an occasional night in January as low as 10° C (50° F).

Vegetation

Tikal and a vast area of the Petén around it is thickly covered by semideciduous forest. According to Holdridge's broad classification (1956; 1957), this is a "Tropical Dry Forest"—a type of climax forest which occurs in tropical lowland where the annual rainfall is between 1000 and 2000 mm. (40 to 80 inches), and where there is a prolonged dry season. Lundell (1937) calls it a "quasi-rainforest," which is probably a more meaningful term than "Tropical Dry Forest."

Two main types of forest, viz., "high forest" and "low forest," are distinguishable and are of significance in the distribution of the avifauna. The "high forest" is located in the better-drained areas. Here the trees are sometimes as tall as 50 meters (150 feet), the forest floor is dark, and the vegetation of the understory thin. There are local differences in the composition of the high forest; in some sections there is a preponderance of zapote (*Achras zapota,* recently renamed *Manilkara achras*); in other areas mahogany (*Swietenia macrophylla*), ramón (*Brosimum alicastrum*), or Spanish cedar (*Cedrela odorata*) prevail.

A smaller part of Tikal is occupied by "low forest." This occurs in poorly drained bajos. The trees rarely exceed 15 meters (50 feet) in height, considerable light reaches the ground, and the understory is choked with small trees, thorny shrubs, and vines. There are two principal types of low forest at Tikal, the escobal and the tintal.

In the former the escoba palm (*Cryosophila argentea*) and the botán palm (*Sabal morrisiana*) are common. In the tintal, which is the more extensive type at Tikal, the logwood tree (*Haematoxylum campechianum*) is predominant.

In the tintal I was especially impressed by the way some birds favor chosen habitats. The hummingbird *Amazilia yucatanensis,* the jay *Cissilopha sanblasiana,* and the chat *Granatellus sallaei* are found only in the tintal. The local subspecies of White-eyed Vireo (*Vireo griseus semiflavus*) is particularly common there, but also occurs in sunny, low growth near the airfield. A far greater number of species avoid the tintal entirely.

The forest has been cleared around the archeologists' camp, the airfield, and some of the ruins, its place taken by grasses and shrubs. This type of vegetation rarely occurred prior to the current project. Consequently, many changes in the avifauna are already evident.

The Maya at Tikal

The Maya civilization was one of the earliest in ancient Mesoamerica, and in many ways it was the most advanced. Tikal (*tee-káhl*) was the largest and the oldest of the many ceremonial (and possibly urban) centers of the Maya.

The earliest traces of occupation at Tikal go back to at least 600 B.C. By 100 B.C., if not earlier, the Maya of Tikal had developed many of the attributes of their high civilization. In time, they perfected a system of recording dates and other matters by means of hieroglyphs, which were often carved on pillar-like slabs of stone, called stelae. Experts have come to interpret Maya dates in terms of our calendar system. The earliest known stela with a preserved calendric inscription in the lowland Mayan area is here at Tikal, dated the equivalent of A.D. 292; the latest stela is read as A.D. 869. These two dates encompass almost the whole of what is called the Classic Period (A.D. 250 to 900), the era of the finest Maya work.

The use of limestone at Tikal for pyramids, temples, and other structures was common long before the beginning of the Classic Period. Evidence of such early use is not readily apparent, because of the predilection of the Maya to largely destroy and level off the earlier buildings, then bury them under new construction. However, the *Classic* stone structures have lasted well and, when carefully excavated, are visible today. Some three thousand lesser works, largely habitations, spread out for miles beyond the central pyramid-temples. Archeologists, after years of investigation of these small, ancient houses, estimate that *at least* ten thousand persons were resident in Late Classic times, within the 6.7 square miles of mapped Tikal.

There are many other Maya sites, each with its own fascinating architecture, but none with so many, so high, and such very steep pyramids. Six magnificent pyramids may be seen here; the tallest, including the temple at its top, is 212 feet (64.6 meters) high!

About A.D. 900 the priestly control and direction collapsed mysteriously. Reasons for the collapse, which was quite sudden at Tikal, are unknown, although a number of theoretical possibilities have been advanced. No new pyramids, no new temples, no new stelae were again erected here. Equally perplexing was the almost simultaneous death of all other lowland Maya cities of the Classic Period; all gradually reverted to the jungle, forgotten by time.

Tikal Today

The Government of the Republic of Guatemala and The University Museum of the University of Pennsylvania recognized the importance of this famous site. With the permission and cooperation of the Government the archeologists of the Museum began in 1956 an eleven-year project, *El Proyecto Tikal,* to study the site and preserve some of the buildings. The Government took an additional forward-looking step. It declared five hundred and seventy-six square kilometers (about fifteen miles on a side) The Tikal National Park, the first such park in Central America.

Biological Field Work

It was realized from the beginning that biological research should go hand in hand with archeology, that the flora and fauna should be surveyed promptly while the area and park were still undisturbed by modern man, and that such studies would be useful not only to the project but also to the economic development of the Petén. Accordingly scientists, eager to work in the little-known jungles of the Petén, were encouraged to offer their services.

Early in 1957 Raymond A. Paynter, Jr., and the author, an engineer and amateur ornithologist, initiated a study of the birdlife. This continued through 1963, resulting in two preliminary publications and finally in the publication of this book. The time spent in the field is listed in the following table, which indicates that good annual coverage was obtained, except for the months of November, December, and January.

1956 from	28 March	to	4 April
1957 "	8 March	to	9 April
1958 "	5 February	to	12 March
1959 "	22 April	to	14 August
1962 "	17 August	to	27 October

During 1957 the author was accompanied by Paynter from 8 to 20 March; during 1958 he was accompanied from 5 to 27 February by Jorge A. Ibarra, Director of the Museo Nacional de Historia Natural. Visitors and residents cooperated with reports of value to the study.

Twelve miles (about 19 kilometers) north of Tikal is another ancient Maya center known as Uaxactún (*wah-shac-toón*). A small village has existed there for years, primarily a station for the collection and distribution of chicle. The well-known ornithologist, the late Josselyn Van Tyne, studied the birdlife there from 26 March to 15 May 1931, during which short period he found one hundred and twenty-seven species (Van Tyne 1935). The country surrounding Uaxactún is identical with that of Tikal, and the flora and fauna are substantially the same. Because of this close similarity and proximity, these two sites are treated as one in this publication. Only five birds found by Van Tyne at Uaxactún have not yet been found at Tikal: Rufescent Tinamou (*Crypturellus cinnamomeus goldmani*), Great Black Hawk (*Buteogallus urubitinga ridgwayi*), Common Potoo (*Nyctibius griseus mexicanus*), Streak-headed Woodcreeper (*Lepidocolaptes souleyetii insignis*), and Chipping Sparrow (*Spizella passerina pinetorum*).

Three other birds have been included on the evidence of bones collected by the archeologists from ancient Tikal burials, from caches, and from the dust and debris in temples and other structures, although none of the three are believed to be present here today. They are:

Black-throated Bobwhite (*Colinus nigrogularis*), Barn Owl (*Tyto alba*), Ferruginous Pygmy-Owl (*Glaucidium brasilianum*).

With these additions included, we can say that two hundred and eighty-one species of birds have been found at Tikal, of which some one hundred and eighty are probably permanent residents, four are summer residents, three "former" residents, twenty-one are visitors, and seventy-three are migrants.

Petén Records (*beyond Tikal*)

Reference is made in Appendix B to the work done by others, outside of the Tikal-Uaxactún area, but within the Petén. This is divided into three sections. Section 1, taken from the collections made in 1932 by Alulah M. Taibel (Taibel 1955), plus one individual collected by Ibarra at La Libertad in 1956, adds eighteen species to the Tikal listing; Section 2, from the collections made in 1923 by Harry Malleis (Van Tyne 1935), adds another eighteen species; Section 3, from very early collections made in the Petén during the mid-nineteenth century (Salvin and Godman 1879–1904), adds a final sixteen species. Taken all together we have three hundred and thirty-three birds known for the Petén.

SPECIAL NOTE

Recent reports received from members of the Florida Audubon Society, courtesy of Miss Margaret Hundley, indicate the possible presence at Tikal of the following species, not previously found and not included elsewhere in this publication.

17 March 1965.

Common Ground-Dove (*Columbigallina passerina*)
Solitary Vireo (*Vireo solitarius*). A migrant.
Golden-cheeked Warbler (*Dendroica chrysoparia*). A migrant.
Bronzed Cowbird (*Tangavius aeneus*), questionably reported earlier by others.

10, 11, 12 April 1965.

Fork-tailed Flycatcher (*Muscivora tyrannus*)
Tropical Parula Warbler (*Parula pitiayumi*)
Grayish Saltator (*Saltator coerulescens*)

PLAN OF THE BOOK

Scientific Names

In this publication the scientific names are those used in Smithe and Paynter (1963). Only where specimens have been collected at Tikal or at nearby Uaxactún (Van Tyne 1935), and where the specimens have been carefully identified, have trinomials (subspecific designations) been retained. Where sight records are relied upon, an asterisk (*) precedes the scientific name, which is then noted only to species. In the rare instances where a bird is described which has not been found at either Tikal or Uaxactún, two asterisks (**) precede the name. Three asterisks (***) precede those known only from their bones. In the few instances where the names do not agree with the nomenclature of the AOU. Check List of North American Birds (1957), a second line is added, giving the AOU equivalent, and this line is enclosed in brackets.

Outline of Plan

Scientific Name

English Name   Spanish Name

Maya Name

Range—from Eisenmann (for species only, not for races)

Status   Length, inches   Weight, grams (some in lbs.)

Description

   Common, Fairly common, Not uncommon, Uncommon,
   Rare

Habitat
Behavior
Plumage and soft parts
Voice
Nest and Eggs

REFERENCES:
(a) Illustrations, color mainly.
(b) Life histories.
(c) Sources of data on voice and nests.

Common Names

Following the scientific nomenclature are the vernacular
names: English, local Spanish, and Maya. The local Spanish
names were chosen with the help of Jorge A. Ibarra; primarily
names familiar to Central Americans have been used, sup-
plemented by selections from Alvarez del Toro (1964). There
were occasionally a half-dozen to choose from, while at other
times none were available. In some instances two choices have
been listed in the hope that we might encourage a meeting of
minds among Spanish-speaking Central American ornithologists to agree on a single name for most species. I have arbi-
trarily capitalized them.

English names follow Eisenmann 1955 almost entirely.

Maya Names

The Maya names, when available, derive from Van Tyne
(1935), from Ibarra (in litt.), from Cruz (1939), and from
Paynter (1955). To quote from Paynter (p. 3) ". . . with
the aid of Mr. D. Brainerd Legters of Mérida, Yucatán,
many Maya names are presented. It is notoriously difficult
to record words from an unwritten language, and one will
find many variants of spelling and accent (vide, Boucard
1883, Cole 1906, Van Tyne 1935). The system which Mr.
Legters employs is superior, I believe, in that the Spanish
alphabet is used and no special symbols are required, except
for the apostrophe ('), which indicates glottalization." The

Maya names have been capitalized by me to make them conform with Legters' system.

Range

Following the vernacular names is a line which gives the general range of each species, but not the subspecies (taken from Eisenmann 1955), an item of information which may extend the usefulness of this guide beyond the environs of Tikal. The species breeding range runs to the first semicolon, or to the end if there is no semicolon. The data have been brought more up-to-date from the notes and with the permission of Eugene Eisenmann.

Status

Following the range is a classification of each species as Resident, Summer Resident, Visitor, Winter Resident, or Transient.

"Resident" is used for nonmigratory birds known to breed at Tikal, or for birds assumed to breed in the area because of their sedentary nature. (Three "former" residents are included.)

"Summer Resident" is a species which breeds in Tikal but migrates from the Petén, probably southward; only four such have been found at Tikal.

"Visitor" is a nonmigratory bird which breeds in northern Central America and southern Mexico, wanders from its breeding ground, appears at Tikal, sometimes for long periods, but is believed *not* to breed here.

"Winter Resident" is a migrant which arrives from the North in the late summer or fall and remains through the winter until the following spring. Some or many individuals of the species in this group are also transients. Some, usually immatures among herons and shore-birds, may remain through the summer.

"Transient" is used for migrants that appear for a day or more (sometimes weeks), passing through in the fall to more southerly climes, or in the spring to northerly breeding grounds, or sometimes passing through in both seasons but believed *not* to winter over. The distinction between a transient and a winter resident is difficult to determine because of the limited observations which have been made at Tikal.

Measurements

The length of the bird is given in inches. For readers who prefer to think in metric terms, one inch equals 2.54 centimeters. The weight is given in grams. A four-ounce or quarter-pound bird equals 113.4 grams; one pound is 453.6 grams. Both of these figures of length and weight are approximate. They often vary from place to place and individually, and weights are likely to vary depending on the season and other factors. Frequently there is a wide difference in size between the sexes of the same species, a phenomenon which is shown by some of the hawks where the male may be little more than half the size and weight of the female. The figures represent an average which is most useful to observers. Detailed weights of specimens taken at Tikal were published in Smithe and Paynter (1963); additional weights have been obtained more recently.

Illustrations and References

When an illustration is included, its plate number in the book is given. Additional references will be found at the end of the description of each species, limited to the following categories: illustrations of special value; life histories; sources of data on voice, nests, and eggs.

Descriptions

It seemed unnecessary to repeat in this publication the descriptions of North American migrants which are well described and pictured by Roger Tory Peterson in his *A Field Guide to the Birds of Texas* (Peterson 1960). Peterson's two well-known guides, one for Eastern and one for Western birds, are also useful, but they omit, even when combined, more of the birds of Tikal than does the Texas guide.

It seemed equally unnecessary to repeat the detailed descriptions of those nonmigrants given in Emmet Reid Blake's *Birds of Mexico* (1953). These two guides *combined,* describe all but the following three Tikal birds: Scaly-breasted Hummingbird (*Phaeochroa cuvierii*), Purple-crowned Fairy (*Heliothryx barroti*), and Ruddy-tailed Flycatcher (*Terenotriccus erythrurus*).

Descriptions, therefore, have been reduced to a minimum, but a minimum which it is hoped will still make recognition possible, bearing in mind that reference to Peterson (1960) and Blake (1953) is inferred throughout. It is not essential to carry them into the field, as they are available for reference in the library of the Sylvanus G. Morley Museum in Tikal, together with other pertinent literature and recordings of bird songs.

Included with the descriptions are brief notations on voice, nests, and eggs of *resident* birds. This information has been culled almost entirely from localities other than Tikal. Description of voice is often of little value until one has tied it in with his own field experience, but it will at least help to separate broad differences. Similarly for nests; the descriptions will inform the reader of the birds that burrow into the ground (a surprising number in Middle America), or those that nest in holes in trees; they will help to allocate broad differences, such as birds that use pensile, retort-shaped enclosures from those that use oven-shaped types which are not suspended. Now and then a more complete description has been attempted, as with the hermit hummingbirds, some of which build in a very specialized manner. Wherever clutch sizes are given every effort has been made to use mainly data from Middle America and to avoid the wide variances and errors which would occur if data from areas substantially to the North were included (see Lack 1947, Ibis 89, p. 303). The sources relied on are indicated in the text "references" for each bird.

ANNOTATED LIST

TINAMIDAE

Tinamus major percautus Van Tyne

Great Tinamou   Mancolola Grande
                                     Perdiz Grande

Nom
Ix Mancolol

Trop. Mid. Am. (except El Salvador) and n. S. Am.
Resident   15 in.   1100 gr. (2½ lbs.)   Plate 1

Tinamous, although not closely related to fowl-like birds, are very much like short-tailed chickens in appearance. They are eminently edible and are therefore severely hunted. As population pressures increase in the Petén, there will be a need to establish sound wildlife management practices to protect them.

The Great Tinamou, a common bird close to camp before hunting reduced its numbers, is the largest by far of the local tinamous, about the size of a two-pound chicken; a dark gray-brown bird with sturdy gray legs (with rough scutes); more prevalent in the drier high-forest hills with fairly open forest floor rather than in the moist bajos; almost entirely terrestrial, but has been known to roost at night in trees (1).

The song or call is a sequence of full, long-drawn, penetrating, flute-like whistles, all on the same pitch, and in a minor key which gives a plaintive effect. First two, then two more, then another two notes are repeated to make a complete sequence, after which there is a period of silence before the call is again given. Meanwhile there may be answering calls from other tinamous.

The eggs have a highly glossed porcelain-like surface, colored a beautiful blue-green, about four to a clutch (1), varying from two to eight in some areas (2). They are laid on the ground, often between the buttresses of a tree, where leaves and other organic material may chance to be, rather than in a nest, but are well concealed by surrounding vegetation.

REFERENCES: Aveledo 1958, p. 40, picture in color. Austin 1961, end papers, egg in color.
(1) Animal Kingdom, 62:6:179–183, life history (Skutch), and picture in black and white.
(2) Eisenmann 1952.

** Crypturellus soui

Little Tinamou   Mancolola Enana
                                            Perdiz Chica

                          Nom
                          Kel Nom

Trop. Mid. Am. (except El Salvador) and n.w. S. Am.
Resident in Petén   9 in.   Plate 1

Not yet found at Tikal or Uaxactún, but reported by Malleis' Biological Survey of 1923 (Van Tyne 1935) for Chuntuqui, Sacchich, and Remate. This is the smallest of the four tinamous of the Petén, about the size of a Bobwhite; a rich ruddy brown in color, and with smooth yellow-green legs. It is found in dense brushy cover, abandoned milpas, second growth, and forest edges; probably sleeps on the ground.

The song is described as so varied as to be in reality a number of different songs. One is a long series of drawn-out, trilling whistles, very slowly given; first a minor key whistle low in the scale followed after a pause by one higher in pitch, the two repeated after a still longer pause, and so on, sometimes higher, sometimes lower in the scale; another tinamou may respond, seemingly during the pauses (3). Another is simply a single tremulous whistle, long continued (1).

Eggs are laid on the ground, concealed by the surrounding vegetation; probably no more than two to a clutch; highly glossed purplish drab in color (1), (2).

REFERENCES: Aveledo 1958, p. 52, picture in color.
(1) Condor 65:3:224–233, life history (Skutch).
(2) Eisenmann 1952.
(3) Bird Songs, recordings by Paul Schwartz.

Crypturellus boucardi boucardi (P. L. Sclater)

Slaty-breasted Tinamou   Mancolola Morena
                                           Perdiz

                        Nom
                        Balih

Carib. slope trop. Mid. Am. to n. Costa Rica (both slopes)
Resident   10 in.   440 gr. (1 lb.)   Plate 1

More common and about half as large as the Great Tinamou. A dark gray and brown bird, with smooth reddish legs. It is found in the forest cover adjacent to open areas such as cleared pyramids and plazas, roads and trails, the camp and village; seems to prefer the lower altitudes and the proximity of moist bajos more than the drier areas frequented by the Great Tinamou.

The voice is described in detail—see reference below—as sufficiently variable in pitch between one male and another as often to permit individual identification; also, the typical call rendered by the female is quite unlike the male's call. My notes give a generalized description: one short but deliberate whistle followed by one long-drawn clear plaintive whistle, then a few moments (sometimes minutes) of silence before the call is repeated. Meanwhile there may be answering calls from other tinamous (1), (2).

Females about to lay were found as early as March and chicks as late as 23 July. Eggs are laid directly on the ground-cover, much as with other tinamous, as many as ten to the clutch, of a glossy purplish pink color.

REFERENCES:

(1) Condor 66:3:165–181 and 66:4:253–276, life history (Lancaster).

(2) Mexican Bird Songs, recordings by L. Irby Davis.

Crypturellus cinnamomeus goldmani (Nelson)

Rufescent Tinamou   Mancolola de Garganta Blanca
                               Perdiz Canela

                    Nom

Trop. Mid. Am. to n.w. Costa Rica; also n.e. Colombia and
Venezuela

Resident   11 in.   440 gr. (1 lb.)   Plate 1

Not yet found at Tikal but breeding birds were taken at
nearby Uaxactún (Van Tyne 1935). Perhaps this was the
species heard by me in sunny, brushy cover beyond the airstrip at Tikal in 1962.

Another smallish tinamou, slightly larger than the Slaty-
breasted Tinamou and with similar smooth, reddish legs;
identified by its brighter cinnamon brown color, well-defined
ear-coverts, and decidedly barred effect. Some Slaty-breasted
Tinamous are browner and brighter-colored than the one illustrated, in which case the conspicuous barring of the
Rufescent may be the deciding factor.

The call is a long, mellow, tremulous whistle, rising only
slightly at the end; repeated after equally deliberate pauses
(1), (2), (4).

Eggs are a lustrous but not highly glossed, faintly purplish
pale tan, two or three, sometimes four or five to a clutch, laid
on the ground, often at the foot of a tree, and concealed by
surrounding tangle of vegetation (1), (2), (3).

REFERENCES: Blake 1953, p. 3, picture in black and white.
Wilson Bull. 63:2:fpc., picture in color.

(1) Ibid. pp. 67, 68, partial description (Sutton).

(2) Auk 59:1:6–7, partial description (Sutton and Pettingill).

(3) Wildlife Survey No. 5, p. 23.

(4) Mexican Bird Songs, recordings by L. Irby Davis.

PODICIPEDIDAE

Podiceps dominicus brachypterus (Chapman)

Least Grebe   Zambullidorcito
                                                   Pato Chico

Ah Bich or Xpatux Já

S.e. Texas, Mid. Am., Greater Antilles, Bahamas, and trop.
   S. Am.
Resident   9 in.   135 gr.

Not uncommon but localized; found in the more persistent
aguadas.

A diminutive, chunky, dark grayish brown grebe, half the
size of the Pied-billed Grebe. The small black bill is slender
and pointed, the eyes are golden, and the wings show a white
patch in flight (which seldom occurs).

The voice, as heard here, is a nervous, rapidly uttered
chatter.

Nest is raft-like, over shallow water, with a clutch of about
four pale greenish buff eggs (1).

REFERENCES:
(1) Auk 66:1:42–52, life history (Gross). Gilliard 1958, plate
2, color photograph.

* Podilymbus podiceps subsp.

Pied-billed Grebe   Zambullidor

Ah   Bich

N. Am., Mid. Am., West Indies, and S. Am.
Winter Resident   13 in.   440 gr.

Not common, but a couple regularly arrive at the Aguada
Tikal since fish were introduced there, appearing in late
October and remaining until mid-February. One individual
was reported as late as 17 March.

This chunky, thick-billed, water bird is seen at Tikal in winter or immature plumage, when the distinctive vertical band on the bill is lacking. The bill may be yellow or a dusky color. These birds may breed in the Petén and it is possible that they are wanderers within the Petén, rather than visitants from the North.

Its call is a long series of resonant, cuckoo-like *cow-cow-cow-cow* notes; or *koo-koo-kuk-kukukuk-kuk–kuk–kuk,* first accelerating, then slowing down (1).

REFERENCES: Condor 50:2:fpc., picture in color. Austin 1961, p. 23, picture in color.
(1) Slud 1964.

PHALACROCORACIDAE

* Phalacrocorax brasilianus subsp.
[*Phalacrocorax olivaceus*–AOU 1957]

Olivaceous Cormorant   Malache
Neotropic Cormorant   Cormorán

Louisiana, Texas, Bahamas, Cuba, Mid. Am., and S. Am.
Visitor   25 in.   1500 gr.

Fairly common since the Aguada Tikal was stocked with small fish; first seen in September 1959 and thereafter two to eight have been seen practically all year round. Sporadic absences in December through March have been noted. It is doubtful that they nest here. Probably they are wanderers from large breeding colonies known to exist at Lake Petén-Itzá (Taibel 1955), some twenty-five miles to the south. Their eggs, about 4 to a clutch, are a chalky pale blue.

The heavier bill, hooked at the tip, and the less conspicuous tail distinguish it from the Anhinga. Tikal birds, perhaps immatures, are mainly dark brown rather than black, the throat-patch is small and dingy yellow in color. They perch and spread their wings to dry in typical cormorant fashion.

The method of fishing is occasionally unusual. While remaining in one spot on the water, a bird will slap the surface hard for eight or ten seconds, flapping both wings rapidly in unison against the water. Following a sudden stop, the cormorant will dive and continue fishing under water in the customary manner.

They voice guttural, somewhat pig-like grunts.

REFERENCES: Sutton 1951, p. 16, picture in color. Wilson Bull. 64:1:fpc., picture in color.

ANHINGIDAE

Anhinga anhinga subsp.

Anhinga   Pato Aguja

S. U. S., Cuba, Mid. Am., and S. Am.
Visitor   34 in.   1350 gr.

While a fairly common nesting resident at Lake Petén-Itzá (Taibel 1955) and at other ponds, lakes, and streams of the Petén where there are fish, Anhingas are uncommon, erratic visitors at Tikal. One individual at a time was seen in September 1959, May 1961, and in the spring of 1962; two in April and again in June 1964.

This glossy black or very dark brown water bird is readily distinguished from the cormorant by broad white wing coverts, a very long, thin, snake-like neck, a long slender pointed bill, and a longer tail. The female differs additionally by the golden buff color of the upper part of its body, neck, and head.

Aubrey Trik, Field Director of the Tikal Project, tells the following story of a brown-breasted female (possibly an immature) which arrived in May 1961 in a molting condition, almost flightless, with only one feather left in the tail. Perhaps the crocodile in the Aguada Tikal had played a part here. Trik slowly backed the bird onto the ground. When very close he feinted with one hand and, as she turned in that direction, he grabbed her around the neck with the other hand. After a period of time spent in quieting her, he fed her small fish, which she accepted readily. Trik regularly whistled to her along with each feeding and by the third day she responded to his whistle-call by leaving the water, walking up the bank to him, and taking the offered fish directly from his hand. Shortly thereafter Trik had to leave the Camp for Guatemala City and during his absence the bird disappeared. The crocodile was again suspected.

They sometimes utter low guttural grunts but are usually silent. When soaring about, they may voice hawk-like whistles.

Anhingas congregate in rookeries to nest, often mingling with herons (and ibises if present). The nest is built near or over water, in bushes or small trees. It is a bulky affair of sticks, lined with twigs and softer material. The twigs still carry green foliage, and fresh leaves are also added, behavior which is not followed by herons. Eggs, about four to a clutch, are pale blue, with chalky-rough surface (1).

REFERENCES: Allen 1961, plate 4, color photograph. Rand 1956, plate 22, color photograph. Austin 1961, end papers, picture of egg in color.

(1) Bent, No. 121.

ARDEIDAE

* Ardea herodias subsp.

Great Blue Heron Garzón Azulado

N. Am., West Indies, Mexico, Galápagos Is.; regular throughout the year in Mid. Am., though breeding uncertain; winters to n. S. Am.

Winter Resident   46 in. (6 ft. wingspread)   3000 gr. (7 lbs.)

Uncommon; only three sight records have been noted. Aubrey Trik reported that one arrived 2 November 1960 and remained a few days. Another arrived 20 January 1961 and was captured and eaten by a crocodile six days later. A third was seen flying over the airstrip 17 October 1962. An immature was taken early November 1964.

The largest of the herons at Tikal. A blue-gray bird, with whitish gray head and throat, long brownish black legs, and a long pointed bill which is yellow below and dingy brownish yellow above.

When startled they voice harsh croaks or deep throaty squawks; when flying they utter harsh, but more goose-like *honks*.

REFERENCES: Austin 1961, p. 50, picture in color. Peterson 1960, p. 28, picture in color. Rand 1956, plate 34, picture in color. Gilliard 1958, plate 16, color photograph.

Butorides virescens virescens (Linnaeus)

Green Heron   Garcita Verde

N. Am., West Indies, Mid. Am.; winters to n. S. Am.
Winter Resident   18 in.   190 gr.

Rather common, with one or two to be found wherever there is water. They never tolerate more than one other Green Heron in the same pond; sometimes not even one more is tolerated, the dominant bird chasing after the other every time he lands until the harried visitor gives up and flies away.

When hunched up, quietly watching the water for evidence of a meal, this smallest of the local herons is a chunky, sharp-billed bird, gray-green above and brown below. When alarmed it stretches its neck, raises a handsome crest, and then looks entirely different, still gray-green and brown, but with a long streak of white down the brown throat.

In Aguada Tikal the Green Heron very often fishes close by the crocodile, but there has been no indication that it has ever been victimized, as were other species of herons, "puddle ducks" which were introduced, and even chickens which were feeding close to the water.

The voice most commonly heard is a very penetrating, strident *kyow;* it also utters subdued clucks and grunts.

There is some question whether all the Green Herons present are migrants from the North. Although not found breeding at Tikal and absent steadily from 14 May to 23 August 1959 (and irregularly absent other months), some may be visitors from known breeding areas on the Yucatán Peninsula.

Nests are to be found in low bushes and in high trees,

mostly singly, sometimes in small groups. They are made of loosely woven sticks. The two or three eggs are a pale blue-green, with a rather dull chalky surface.

REFERENCES: Austin 1961, p. 50, picture in color. Peterson 1960, p. 21, picture in color. Allen 1961, plate 7, color photograph.

Hydranassa caerulea (Linnaeus)
[*Florida caerulea*—AOU 1957]

Little Blue Heron
Garza Gris
Garcita Azul

S. U. S., West Indies, Mid. Am., and S. Am.
Winter Resident   24 in.   300 gr.

The commonest heron at Tikal; present throughout the year. Flocks as large as twelve sometimes settle for an hour or so in the trees at Aguada Tikal. White, immature birds then predominate in a ratio of six or even twelve to one adult.

In 1959 two immatures in almost pure white plumage were present in Aguada Tikal from about mid-April to mid-August. During this time they gradually changed, becoming steadily bluer, until in my last record, made on 14 August, I estimated that both birds were in 90 percent blue plumage.

Feeding territory is aggressively defended. In 1962 I arrived on 17 August to find one adult and one white plumaged immature present, the adult harassing the immature with only partial success, as the latter would feed awhile on the nearby airstrip and later return to the pond. On 19 September seven new herons flew in, one an adult Little Blue, one a Snowy Egret, the others immature white plumaged Little Blues. Before the morning was over, only the dominant adult and one immature remained. At 6:30 A.M. on 4 October, eleven immature white plumaged Little Blues again flew into the trees. An hour later only the dominant adult and two immatures remained and the latter were chased out later in the morning. By 22 October the adult was compelled to accept the steady presence of one other adult and the occasional presence of one immature.

One Little Blue used a unique method of fishing. Standing

in the water on one foot, he raised the other just barely to the surface of the water, which he then agitated considerably by shaking the elevated foot back and forth in a very rapid tremor, followed by a sudden swift "strike" with his bill. I could not determine whether or not the procedure was productive.

The usual alarm note is a long hoarse croak or *kraaak;* when quarreling, they may use parrot-like screams; sometimes merely low clucking notes are heard (1), (2).

REFERENCES: Peterson 1960, p. 28, pictures in color. Rand 1956, plate 31, color photograph.
(1) Pough 1953.   (2) Slud 1964.

Ardeola ibis ibis (Linnaeus)
[*Bubulcus ibis*–AOU 1957]

Cattle Egret   Garcita Bueyera
                                                    Garza del Ganado

Warmer parts of Old World, recently breeding in n. S. Am., e.
  U. S., Mid. Am. (exact status still in flux)
Visitor   20 in.   320 gr.

Uncommon, but no one can say they will continue to be so. The first record of one in the Petén was made at Aguada Tikal, 25 April 1959 (Smithe and Land 1960). In March 1963 three were reported by visiting members of the Florida Audubon Society, who saw them feeding along the edges of the airstrip, a favorite feeding place for the Little Blue Herons also. On 22 February 1964 I counted over thirty-five among a large herd of cattle at Fallabón, el Petén. These records reflect the great adaptability of Cattle Egrets; though found in largest numbers where cattle stir up insects, at Tikal they are not dependent on cattle, but search for their food in much the same manner as other herons.

The Cattle Egret is readily distinguished among Snowy Egrets and immature white plumaged Little Blues. It is smaller, shorter-necked, and stockier in appearance. Its bill is shorter, thicker, and clear yellow. When in breeding plumage adults add a buff color to their crowns, napes, backs, and breasts.

They voice a variety of croaking notes (1).

Birds of very social habits, they congregate in colonies for nesting. Nests are placed in shrubs and small trees and are made of large and small twigs. Eggs, about four to a clutch, are light blue (1).

REFERENCES:
(1) Peterson 1960, p. 28, picture in color. Gilliard 1958, plate 15, color photograph (with nest).

Hydranassa rufescens
[*Dichromanassa rufescens*—AOU 1957]

Reddish Egret   Garza Rojiza

S. U. S., Bahamas, Greater Antilles, and Mexico (both coasts); winters to Pac. coast Guatemala and El Salvador. Transient?   29 in.   450 gr.

On only one occasion have Reddish Egrets been noted here, so we must consider the species as an accidental or very casual visitor. At 10 A.M., 12 March 1958, three flew in at Aguada Tikal along with one Common Egret. Two remained until late that afternoon. At no time did they come down to the water.

It is probable that they were still in somewhat immature or nonbreeding plumage as their bills, though black-tipped, were mainly dusky gray, and their legs a dark greenish shade. Otherwise they were typical long-legged, medium- or slightly larger-sized, gray-colored egrets with rust red heads and necks. The neck feathers were loose and shaggy. The irides were white.

They voice a guttural squawk, lower in tone and less harsh than most herons (1).

REFERENCES: Peterson 1960, p. 28, picture in color. Rand 1956, plate 23, color photograph.
(1) Pough 1953.

Egretta alba subsp.
[*Casmerodius albus*—AOU 1957]

Common Egret   Garza Real
Great Egret

Bach Ha

Old World, U. S., West Indies, Mid. Am., and S. Am.
Winter Resident   40 in.   1000 gr.

Not uncommon, but not nearly as numerous as the Little
Blue Heron. This large pure white wading bird, with its long
all-black legs and long yellow bill, has been seen at Tikal
every month of the year, except April, May, June, and July.
In February and March of 1958 the water level of the Aguada
Tikal was very low and many crawfish became available to
the herons. During this period a solitary Common Egret
worked over the pond day after day until the supply of crawfish was practically exhausted, after which he disappeared. In
early August 1959, Field Director Aubrey Trik reported, "One
beautiful Common Egret came in. He seems to be pretty
'tame' and constantly circles the Aguada, spearing tadpoles.
It is easy to get rather close to him before he glides off a few
yards and resumes fishing." At other times, instead of such
steady attendance, the Common Egret has been a much more
temporary and infrequent visitor. In 1962 I was at Tikal from
17 August to 27 October and noted only two short visits, one
on 23 August, the other on 22 October.

Its voice is a long, deep rattle-like croak (1).

REFERENCES: Peterson 1960, p. 28, picture in color. Rand
1956, plate 18, color photograph. Gilliard 1958, plate 2, color
photograph (bird on nest).
(1) Pough 1953.

* *Egretta thula* subsp.
[*Leucophoyx thula*—AOU 1957]

Snowy Egret   Garcita Blanca

Bach Ah

U. S., West Indies, Mid. Am., and S. Am.
Winter Resident   25 in.   340 gr.

Uncommon at Tikal, this beautiful and most graceful of the herons has been recorded as early as 19 September and as late as 14 May. Other than these two months our only records are for February and March. Of medium size, pure white at all times, it may be identified among other white-plumaged birds by the fact that both bill and legs are black, and the legs conspicuously ornamented by yellow feet. In addition, if feeding, they usually shuffle about a great deal to stir up food.

It is possible that some individuals are really visitors from breeding colonies along the coasts or keys of the Yucatán Peninsula.

It may utter a low hoarse croak occasionally, but is usually silent when not on its nesting grounds.

REFERENCES: Peterson 1960, p. 28, picture in color. Allen 1961, plate 10, color photograph. Rand 1956, plate 19, color photograph. Austin 1961, end papers, picture of egg in color.

Nycticorax violaceus violaceus (Linnaeus)
[*Nyctanassa violacea*—AOU 1957]

Yellow-crowned Night-Heron   Garza de Noche de
                                          Corona Amarilla

U. S., West Indies, Mid. Am., and S. Am.
Visitor   24 in.   660 gr.

Fairly common at Aguada Tikal since the first solitary bird arrived on 13 July 1959. Prior to that time they had not been reported for any part of the Petén. By September of that year more than twelve were present. Since then they have been reported yearly, but somewhat irregularly for every month except April, May, and June. From early August through October 1962, only four birds were present. Efforts to find nests have been unsuccessful. It would be interesting to learn where they come from.

They are medium-sized, stocky, uniformly gray-bodied herons, with strongly marked black and white heads. (The yellow color of the crowns does not show clearly.) When flying, their feet and a portion of their legs extend beyond their tails.

The voice is a short *kwock* or *quak,* higher pitched and less harsh than that of the Black-crowned (*Nycticorax nycticorax*) (1), (3).

Nests are bulky platforms of sticks, lined with soft materials, and located both high and low. Eggs, about four in number, are pale blue-green (1), (2); clutches of two or three are reported in Trinidad (4).

REFERENCES:
(1) Peterson 1960, p. 21, picture in color. Rand 1956, plate 27, color photograph.
(2) Pough 1953.   (3) Slud 1964.   (4) Herklotz 1961.

Tigrisoma mexicanum mexicanum Swainson
[*Heterocnus mexicanus*]

Bare-throated Tiger-Heron   Garza Tigre

Trop. Mid. Am.
Resident   30 in.   1150 gr.   Plate 2

If allowance is made for their solitary habits (only one or two are present at any one wooded swamp), these herons may be called common but not numerous. In 1956 I watched an immature feeding within twenty feet of me, at Aguada Tikal. At that time the aguada was almost hidden by grasses, vines, shrubs, and small trees, with only scattered patches of open water. After the aguada was cleaned out Tiger Herons, along with many other water birds, became rare visitors, although they are found regularly at other nearby aguadas.

The adult has a black cap and gray cheeks; the neck and

mantle brownish, narrowly barred with black; underparts are shades of reddish brown and cinnamon, except for the diagnostic upper throat which is greenish yellow and devoid of feathers. The long bill is largely black shading to a delicate apple green at the base; the legs greenish gray; the eyes pale yellow, surrounded by greenish yellow bare skin.

The immature differs materially from the adult and reminds one of an American Bittern, except that it is barred instead of streaked. It is dark brown above, coarsely barred with tawny; below a light brown or buff ground color, boldly barred with dark brown. The throat is bare and a conspicuously light greenish yellow as in the adult. It is in this plumage that we almost always find them.

Because it is so distinctive there would be no possibility of mistaking it for any other heron at Tikal, were it not for the extremely rare chance of seeing a close relative, the Rufescent or Banded Tiger-Heron (*Tigrisoma lineatum*). The immatures of both species closely resemble each other; the adults do not. The throat of both adult and immature *T. lineatum* is not bare, but is mainly feathered with white; the adult has unmistakable rich rufous chestnut on the head and neck (see plate 2). Anyone finding *T. lineatum* north of Honduras should note it carefully.

T. mexicanum nests close to or above water in shrubs or trees, from three to fifteen (even fifty) feet up. Breeding is solitary, as a rule, but sometimes occurs on the periphery of colonies of other species of herons. The nest is a loosely constructed, shallowly concave platform of coarse sticks and twigs, containing three eggs (1), (2), dull, unspotted white, with a greenish tinge (3).

The eggs of *T. lineatum* are *spotted* with brown or pale purple (1), (4), (5).

On 26 June 1959 I was awakened at 2:30 A.M. by the "terrific screeching combined with pig-like grunting" of two birds in the top of a tall tree by my cottage. After four or five minutes of this activity the birds flew off, but I was unable to identify them, except in general as herons. A native Indian who also heard them said they were the Garza Tigre.

REFERENCES: Sutton 1951, p. 128, picture in color. Austin 1961, p. 52, picture in color (adult *T. lineatum*).

(1) Auk 81:2:230–231, picture in black and white (with nest and eggs), and nest described (Walter Dawn).

(2) Auk 59:1:7, nest described (Sutton and Pettingill).

(3) Field Mus., Zool. Ser. 23, 1938 (Dickey and van Rossem).

(4) Ardea 50:3:173 (Haverschmidt).

(5) Handbuch der Oölogie, part 2, pp. 84, 85.

Cochlearius cochlearius subsp.

Boat-billed Heron   Garza Pico de Zapato
Chucharón

Kuka'

Trop. Mid. Am. and S. Am.
Visitor   20 in.   580 gr.

One individual was found on 11 April 1961 at the edge of Aguada Tikal. It roosted that night in a tree, and about midnight was captured by hand. The next day a color photograph was taken and the bird was released (Dennis E. Puleston, in litt.); not reported by Van Tyne (1935) for nearby Uaxactún but one specimen was reported for Dos Arroyos 22 May 1931, and another for Lake Petén-Itzá by Taibel in 1932. Probably not as rare as these scanty records indicate, as the Boat-bill is rather shy and feeds chiefly at night. It nests singly or in small colonies, sometimes along with night-herons. The nest is a shallow platform of sticks, in which two to four blue-white, brown-speckled eggs are laid (1).

At a distance it resembles a Black-crowned Night Heron (*Nycticorax nycticorax*), black above and white below. Closer examination reveals a more complicated pattern of black and blue-gray above, a white forehead, broad black crest, and very large eyes; below brownish with black under wing coverts. The bill is outstandingly broad and flat, some three inches long and two inches wide.

In general, chicken-like terrestrial birds, with chunky bodies, stubby tails, slender necks, small heads, sturdy legs.

GREAT TINAMOU

p. 1.

15 inches, chicken size; dark brown with darker bars; legs dark gray and *coarse*.

LITTLE TINAMOU

p. 2.

9 inches, Bob-white size; brown above, ruddy below; legs greenish, smooth.

SLATY-BREASTED TINAMOU

p. 3.

10 inches, squab size; grayish effect (some browner than others); belly barred strongly; legs reddish, *smooth*.

RUFESCENT TINAMOU

p. 4.

10 inches, squab size; bright ruddy effect; clearly barred; cheeks pale; legs "peach" red, smooth.

PLATE 1

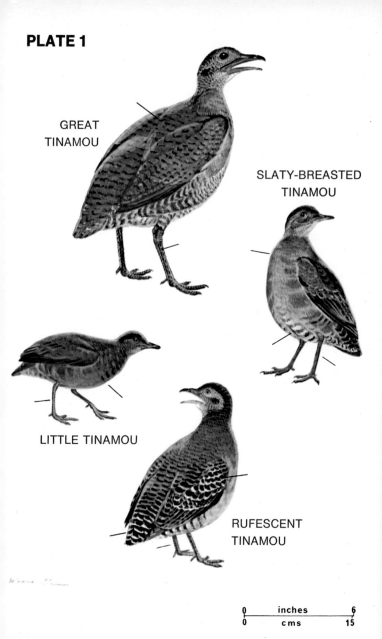

GREAT
TINAMOU

SLATY-BREASTED
TINAMOU

LITTLE TINAMOU

RUFESCENT
TINAMOU

| 0 | inches | 6 |
| 0 | c m s | 15 |

Adults are distinctively different and readily identified. Immatures differ greatly from adults and the two species are very similar to each other.

BARE-THROATED TIGER-HERON *p. 15*

ADULT: 31 inches; throat bare, green-yellow; bill long, heavy, apple green at base; head with black cap, gray cheeks; back and neck finely barred with black and brown; underparts brownish.

IMMATURE: throat bare, green-yellow; bill (shorter than adult) lacks upturned effect of the other species; brown and tawny barring very coarse; tail black with narrow white bars.

BANDED TIGER-HERON *p. 16*

ADULT: 24 inches; throat feathered, whitish (yellow bare skin sides of chin); bill more slender and shorter than the other species, has effect of being upturned; head bright rufous continuing down nape and sides of neck; neck streaked rufous and whitish; back finely barred black and gray-brown.

IMMATURE: throat feathered, white (yellowish at base of bill); bill with slender, upturned effect; coarse barring above becoming black on tail; below spotted rather than barred, the breast and belly whitish.

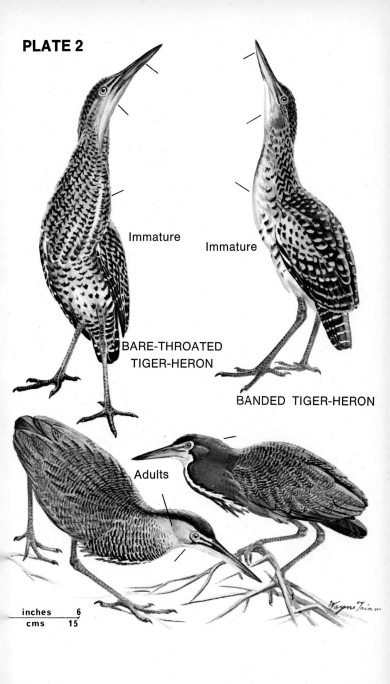

PLATE 2

Immature

Immature

BARE-THROATED
TIGER-HERON

BANDED TIGER-HERON

Adults

inches 6
cms 15

PLATE 3

HOOK-BILLED KITE

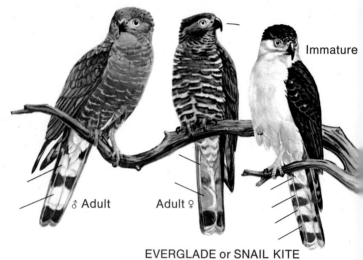

Immature

♂ Adult

Adult ♀

EVERGLADE or SNAIL KITE

♂

♀

| 0 | inches | 6 |
| 0 | cms | 15 |

The Hook-billed Kite has four distinctly different plumages; three gray and brown phase examples shown here; black phase shown on Plate 4 (note different scale). All have whitish or pale yellow eyes, and massive, strongly hooked bills.

HOOK-BILLED KITES   p. 25.

ADULT MALE: 16 inches; dark slate gray above; medium gray below; tail has two broad white bands; bill strongly hooked; cere and bare facial skin conspicuously green (with some yellow).

ADULT FEMALE: dark brown above with bright rufous collar; boldly barred below with rufous and white; tail has two indistinct grayish white bands; bare facial skin and cere as for male.

IMMATURE: dark brown above with creamy white collar; creamy white underparts (some slight barring); tail has three (or four) narrower white bands.

EVERGLADE (SNAIL) KITE   p. 29.

ADULT MALE: 18 inches; black; basal half of tail (not rump) white; bill slender and hooked more than other kite; eyes, facial skin, cere, and legs, red.

ADULT FEMALE: dark brown above; streaked below with brown and buff; base of tail whitish; facial skin, cere, and legs, orange; pale line above eye. (Immature similar.)

The voice is a harsh deep-throated frog-like quawking; sometimes also a stork-like rattling of the bill (1).

REFERENCES: Blake 1953, p. 37, picture in black and white. Austin 1961, p. 55, picture in color.
(1) Van Tyne and Berger 1959.

CICONIIDAE

* *Mycteria americana* Linnaeus

Wood Stork   Garzón Pulido
Wood Ibis   Cigüeñon

S. U. S., Greater Antilles, Mid. Am., and S. Am.
Visitor   40 in. (5½ ft. wingspread)   3200 gr. (7 lbs.)

An extremely rare visitor. One was identified at Aguada Tikal 24 November 1959, by Trik (in litt.); it had not previously been recorded from the Petén; four were seen on 17 March 1965 (Hundley, in litt.).

Almost as large as a Great Blue Heron, it is largely white in appearance when not in flight, with a dark bare-skinned head and upper neck, dusky down-drooping bill, and black legs; when flying it conspicuously displays its black tail and black wing tips. They often soar in groups.

Usually a silent bird, it utters a hoarse croak when disturbed. The young in a nesting colony, usually a large congregation, produce a bedlam of sounds.

Nests are bulky, flat platforms of sticks lined with mosses, located in trees in marshes. Three dull white, chalky eggs are usual (1).

REFERENCES: Peterson 1960, pp. 21 and 23, picture in color. Rand 1956, plate 37, color photograph.
(1) Pough 1953.

ANATIDAE

Ducks have been seen in Aguada Tikal, but only the Blue-winged Teal has been identified.

* *Anas discors*

Blue-winged Teal   Pato Careto

Cutz-Ha

N. Am. and possibly Mexico; winters Mid. Am. and S. Am.
Transient   15½ in.   400 gr.

Uncommon. On 3 October 1962 a pair flew into the Aguada Tikal and were noted as "fast flying ducks, smallish, teal?, with dull crescent over bill, bluish gray in wings even when at rest (but not a speculum), tails held low near water."

In late January 1964 Trik saw six ducks at the Aguada Tikal and made a positive identification of Blue-winged Teal, mostly males. They occur in flocks of hundreds farther south at Sayaxché, on Río de la Pasión (two reports for the month of March).

The male voice is a peep-like note, the female's a weak quack.

CATHARTIDAE

* *Sarcoramphus papa* (Linnaeus)

King Vulture   Rey Zope
                                                          Zopilote Rey

Oc

Trop. Mid. Am. and S. Am.
Resident   32 in. (6½ ft. wingspread)   3400 gr. (7½ lbs.)

Uncommon, but present irregularly throughout the year. We have never seen more than one at a time, all adults. Occasionally one has been seen soaring with a large aggregation of other vultures although it remained aloof and on the edges of the flock. It has little fear of man and can be approached to within thirty feet, when its white iris and the brilliant colors of its naked head and upper neck, shades of orange, yellow, bright red, blue, and purple, are bewilderingly beautiful. A caruncle of orange ornaments the large orange and black bill. Below the bare neck is a dark gray ruff-like collar; the remainder of the large body is mainly creamy white, with black rump and tail, and more than half the wings also black. Immatures are blackish.

Nests were unknown until one was found in March 1965, in the heavy wet forests of Panama, about three hundred feet above sea level. It was little more than the rotted surface of an old stump, only a foot above ground, where a single egg was deposited. The King Vulture's egg is said to be white (1).

REFERENCES: Blake 1953, p. 63, picture in black and white. Austin 1961, p. 72, picture in color. Allen 1961, plate 19, color photograph.

(1) Amadon Ms. (including recent report of find by Neal Smith).

* *Coragyps atratus* (Bechstein)

Black Vulture   Zopilote Negro
                                               Zopilote

Ch'om

S. U. S., Mid. Am., S. Am.
Resident   24 in. (less than 5 ft. spread)   2000 gr. (4½ lbs.)

Common. Their number increased from about five in 1956 to over thirty in 1959, after which they decreased to about five in 1962. The decrease was accompanied by a corresponding increase in the number of Turkey Vultures. Two comparative records are:

19 July 1959, 1 King, 5 Turkey, 30 Black Vultures soaring over camp; 17 August 1962, 25 Turkey, 5 Black Vultures soaring over camp.

However, from 14 to 22 February 1964, no Turkey Vultures at all were present, and only six Black Vultures were seen by me.

The name itself describes the Black Vulture, even the naked head being black, the legs gray. Though slightly shorter in length than the Turkey Vulture, with a smaller wingspread and shorter wings, it is stockier in appearance and somewhat heavier in fact. In flight it discloses a large conspicuous white area on both the upper and under side of the wings, near their tips; the tail is short enough to expose the extended legs.

Usually silent, it is occasionally heard hissing, grunting, or blowing (1), (2).

Two eggs, pale gray-green and blotched with brown, are laid on the ground in some sheltered spot (1), (2).

REFERENCES: Austin 1961, p. 72, picture in color. Peterson 1960, p. 81, picture in black and white. Wilson Bull. 75:3:244–249, migration discussed (Eisenmann).

(1) Bent, No. 167.
(2) Auk 59:1:12, picture of bird on nest (Sutton and Pettingill).

Cathartes aura

Turkey Vulture   Viuda
                                                     Aura

                        Ah Chom
                        Ch'om

N. Am., West Indies, Mid. Am., S. Am.
Resident   29 in. (6 ft. spread)   1600 gr. (3½ lbs.)

Common. The numbers of these scavengers, especially when other species are included, seem greater than the food supply can support. One might conclude that mortality among wildlife at Tikal is greater than meets the eye.

Which race is present has not been determined; no specimens have been taken. Their sedentary actions however seem to reduce to a minimum the possibility that some are migrants.

In color they are dark brown, with a small naked red head (blackish in young birds). They have a much greater wingspread and longer tail than the Black Vulture, and soar high in the air a great deal, at which time the lighter-colored trailing wing feathers contrast with the much darker fore wings. They seem to prefer the drier places, while the Black Vultures tend to prefer wetter, swampy areas.

It is usually a silent bird, but utters hisses and raucous grunts if cornered, or feeding (1).

Two cream-colored eggs, blotched with brown, are laid on the ground, preferably using large cavities where available, or other sheltered and secluded spots (1).

REFERENCES: Austin 1961, p. 72, picture in color; end papers, egg in color. Peterson 1960, p. 81, picture in black and white.
(1) Bent, No. 167.

ACCIPITRIDAE

Elanoides forficatus subsp.

Swallow-tailed Kite   Gavilán Tijereta

S. U. S., Mid. Am. (not reported El Salvador), and S. Am. Resident   24 in. (almost half is tail)   450 gr.

Not uncommon at times, as indicated by numerous sight records from mid-March to mid-August. We lack information for other months except that none were seen during my visit from 17 August to 27 October 1962. I assume they are residents, perhaps Summer Resident (3), rather than migrants partly because Van Tyne (1935) reported a female with an egg ready to be laid, on 3 April 1931, at nearby Uaxactún. Their normal habitat includes tall trees in swampy forests or along sluggish streams and Tikal appears too dry to attract them as residents. However, there are large swampy areas available to them within the twelve-mile radius of this report. More data are needed to determine their status.

With pure white head, neck, and under parts sharply contrasted against black upper body and wings, and a long black, forked tail, this kite is not likely to be mistaken for any other bird.

They are almost always seen flying high or skirting tree-tops, but on one occasion, 10 August, we saw three perched in the top of a tall leafless tree, north of the airstrip. On another occasion, also early in August, four flew in low over Aguada Tikal where, despite the large trees which blocked two sides of the pond, they gracefully glided down to the very surface of the water, to skim, with open mouths dipped into it, for ten feet or more before rising to swing around in a tight circle for another dip. At first they appeared to drink with each dive. Later they dipped the body also, as though bathing. The performance continued for close to ten minutes before they flew off and high into the air.

Nests of loosely woven twigs lined with soft material are built in the tops of tall trees, often well out on a branch. Eggs are buffy white, blotched with brown, usually two in number (1), (2).

They voice a series of shrill, keen squeals or whistles (sometimes given softly and plaintively).

REFERENCES: Peterson 1960, p. 80, picture in black and white. Austin 1961, end papers, picture of egg in color.
(1) Bent, No. 167.   (2) Pough 1953.
(3) Condor 67:3:235–246, life history (Skutch).

Chondrohierax uncinatus subsp.

Hook-billed Kite   Gavilán Pico Ganchudo

Ah Chuy (in general)
Balumil Chich

Trop. Mid. Am., S. Am., Grenada
Resident   16 in.   260 gr.   Plates 3, 4

Fairly common at Aguada Tikal and at other aguadas where snails (*Pomacea flagellata*) (3), frogs, and lizards are numerous. Van Tyne 1935, p. 17, found them at nearby Uaxactún; Taibel 1955, found none at Lake Petén-Itzá, some twenty-five miles to the south, but instead he noted the larger Snail Kites (*Rostrhamus sociabilis*).

It is about the same size as a Broad-winged Hawk (*Buteo platypterus*). The plumage is extremely variable. In the more usual, lighter color phase, the adult female is dark brown above, with a rufous collar; from below, the body is very boldly barred with rufous and dull white, and the tail has two broad whitish gray bands. The adult male is dark gray and lacks the rufous collar; below it is a lighter gray, the body and wings both barred with white and the tail crossed by two white bands, the trailing band being the larger and clearer of the two. Immature birds are dark brown above but with a white collar; below they are creamy white, the dusky wings barred conspicuously with gray or with white, and the tail showing three or four pairs of alternately dark and light bands.

The heavy bill is strongly hooked, the eyes are white or very pale yellow, the cere and the bare skin about the eyes have a decidedly green color which was very conspicuous on the Tikal birds.

In the black phase both sexes are plumbeous black all over except the tail which has a *single* broad white band. Collars and barring of underparts and wings are lacking (Van Tyne 1935). Immature birds show two or three grayish tail bands.

The race at Tikal is probably *C. u. aquilonis,* but male specimens are needed to determine the subspecie. See Paynter 1955, p. 55, for discussion of this question.

The shallow-cupped nest, about the size of a crow's nest, made of dried sticks and twigs, is located about thirty feet up and often far out on the branch of a tall tree. Eggs, two in number, are of a white ground color overlaid with dots and irregular spots of chocolate brown (1).

The voice is a musical oriole-like whistle; also loud shrill screams when defending against other hawks (2).

REFERENCES: Sutton 1951, p. 194, pictures in black and white.

(1) Jour. für Ornith., 105:1:64–66, nesting data (Haverschmidt).

(2) Amadon Ms.   (3) Basch 1959.

Harpagus bidentatus fasciatus Lawrence

Double-toothed Kite   Gavilán de Dos Dientes
                                         Gavilán Bidentado

Ah Chuy

Trop. Mid. Am. (not reported Brit. Honduras) and S. Am.
Resident   13 in.   200 gr.   Plate 8

Uncommon but not rare. This small forest kite is a short-winged bird of accipiter-like proportions. It has, in all plumages, a white throat distinctly divided by a dusky midline; its double-notched bill is a positive mark of identity, if visible. Adults are blue-gray and dark brown above; below marked with a series of narrow alternately white, rufous and gray bars, blending on sides of the breast to more uniform rufous; the tail has three dusky white bars; the dark brown wings from below are barred with white and dark gray. Eyes are yellow-orange, cere yellow-green, legs yellow. Immatures are dark brown above, streaked and mottled with white; creamy white below streaked with brown; the throat with a single dark streak.

The voice is a thin *tsip-tsip-tsip-tsip-wheeeoooip,* and a long-drawn *wheeeooo,* like that produced by some small flycatchers; quite vocal, at least when nesting (1).

The nest is a shallow saucer of twigs, largely concealed by leaves, and located high in tall trees. An egg was reported as "speckled" (1), (2).

REFERENCES: Sutton 1951, p. 195, pictures in black and white.
(1) Amadon Ms.
(2) Condor 67:3:235–246, life history (Skutch).

* *Ictinia plumbea* subsp.

Plumbeous Kite   Gavilán Plomizo

Trop. Mid. Am. and S. Am.
Visitor?   14 in.   250 gr.

Uncommon. This small kite was reported by Margaret

Hundley as a sight record on 19 March 1964, also witnessed by other members of the Florida Audubon Society, an immature bird which soared above the Jungle Lodge area for about fifteen minutes, the rufous color in the wings clearly visible. In February 1958, one was seen by Jorge Ibarra. Van Tyne (1935) did not report it for Uaxactún, but he quoted records made by Malleis in June 1923, at Flores, Ixtinta, and Pacomón. Taibel (1955) reported taking one at Lake Petén-Itzá, July 1932. Salvin and Godman (Biol. Cent. Amer., III, 1901) reported them for the Petén.

Adults are dark gray above, lighter gray below, with conspicuous rufous areas visible on the extended wings. The long falcon-like wings extend beyond the very square tail, the latter crossed by two (and part of a third) white bands. Eyes are reddish. Immatures are blackish above, streaked and barred with white; below white or buff heavily marked with black; the wings show rufous areas and the square tail three whitish bands (1), (3).

It feeds mainly on large insects which are often hunted while it soars about, striking out with one foot or the other to catch its prey, which is then leisurely eaten while on the wing. These habits are not shared by other birds of prey except the very similar Mississippi Kite (*Ictinia misisippiensis*).

Nests are built of coarse sticks, the shallow saucer lined with twigs and leaves, and located from thirty feet up to very high in trees, usually far out on a limb. Eggs, possibly only one to a clutch, are white with a faint bluish tinge (2).

This kite is usually silent. The only notes heard by Skutch were "thin, high-pitched, weak monosyllables, sometimes repeated twice or thrice and uttered usually at the nest tree" (2).

REFERENCES:

(1) Wilson Bull. 56:1:fpc., picture in color; pp. 3–8, discussion, similar kites (Sutton).

(2) Condor 49:1:25–31, life history (Skutch).

(3) Auk 80:1:74–76, distinguishing I. plumbea from I. misisippiensis (Eisenmann).

** *Rostrhamus sociabilis* subsp.

Everglade Kite   Gavilán Caracolero
Snail Kite

Local in marshes: Fla., Cuba, Mid. Am. (except El Salvador),
    and S. Am.
Resident at Lake Petén-Itzá   18 in.   ♂ 350 gr. ♀ 400 gr.
                                                    Plate 3

None have been seen at Tikal and none were noted by Van
Tyne (1935, p. 17) for nearby Uaxactún, but he reported two
immature males for Lake Petén-Itzá, and Taibel (1955, p.
29) reported one immature female at the same lake. Large
snails (*Pomacea flagellata*) (2) are present in quantity at
three or more aguadas at Tikal and they should prove attractive to the Snail Kite, but in its stead we have the Hook-billed
Kite (*Chondrohierax uncinatus*) which enjoys a more varied
diet.

Adult males are black, with white at the base of the tail.
The black, sharply hooked bill is conspicuously slender, the
cere, the bare area about the eyes, the eyes themselves, and
the legs are red. Adult females and immatures are dark brown,
streaked below with shades of buff, with a broad line of conspicuous white above the eyes, and with white at the base of
the tail. Cere and legs are orange.

Their voices are variously described as low, chuckling,
rattling-like notes; a rapid series of high-pitched squeaks
which sound like a weak chatter; a bleating cry much like a
sheep, when the kite is turning somersaults in the air (1).

They nest in small colonies; the compact structure of twigs,
moss, and leaves is located only a few feet above marsh-
waters. Eggs, about three per set, are white, profusely covered
with brown markings (1).

REFERENCES: Austin 1961, p. 76, picture in color.
(1) Bent, No. 167.   (2) Basch 1959.

Accipiter bicolor bicolor (Vieillot)

Bicolored Hawk   Gavilán Bicolor

Trop. Mid. Am. (except El Salvador) and S. Am.
Resident   ♂ 14 in. ♀ 18 in.   ♂ 240 gr. ♀ 425 gr.
                                                         Plate 7

    This forest bird-hawk, bold and rapacious, is uncommon
but not rare, having been seen regularly at Tikal. About the
size of Cooper's Hawk (*Accipiter cooperii*), it is dark brownish black above; from below the body is a uniformly smooth
color, varying widely in adults through shades of gray which
contrast sharply with ruddy thighs; for immatures from tawny
buff to nearly white. Tails (seen from below) have three white
or brownish bars for adults, four on immatures, and wings
are also barred accipiter-like, with white. Immatures may
have a buff nuchal collar. Among adults the rufous thighs
are definitive field marks. Males are much smaller than females, some only half as large.
    In the vicinity of their nests, the males utter a soft, clear
whistle, the females a loud *cac-cac-cac* (1).
    Nests are well constructed of sticks and twigs, both green
and dry, with softer material for a lining, and are placed high
in trees. Eggs are whitish with some light brown spotting, and
number about two per set (1).

REFERENCES:
(1) Amadon Ms.

Buteo platypterus platypterus (Vieillot)

Broad-winged Hawk   Gavilán Aludo

N. Am., West Indies; migrates and winters through Mid. Am.
   and S. Am.
Transient   ♂ 15 in.   ♀ 17 in.   ♂ 400 gr.   ♀ 500 gr.
                                                          Plate 5

An uncommon but probably regular visitant during migrations, this small crow-sized buteo has been found in Tikal 8
October, 4 December, and 28 March. Autumn birds were in
immature plumage and all three were solitary. We never
witnessed any mass migrations such as Skutch described for
Costa Rica (1).

Adults are dark brown above, and a rusty light brown
mottling below, darker and more uniform on the upper breast;
the tail has two conspicuous white bars (a third near base is
obscure); the wings from below are mainly dull white.

Immatures are also dark brown above but heavily streaked
with white, and are a dingy white below, streaked with dark
rusty spots; the tail is obscurely crossed with four or five
pale gray bars.

The distinctive call is a shrill, long-drawn-out whistle, as
kwee-e-e-e-e, diminishing in volume (2).

REFERENCES: Murphy and Amadon 1953, plate 9, color photograph. Peterson 1960, p. 60, pictures in color.

(1) Northwest Science 9:4:80–88, paper on migrations
(Skutch).

(2) Bent, No. 167.

Buteo magnirostris direptor (Peters and Griscom)

Roadside Hawk   Gavilán de los Caminos
                                     Gavilán Chapulinero

Ch'uy

Trop. Mid. Am. and S. Am.
Resident   ♂ 14 in. ♀ 16 in.   ♂ 275 gr. ♀ 320 gr.
                                              Plate 5

This is the most common hawk at Tikal. The immature
bird is rather similar to the immature Broad-winged Hawk
(*B. platypterus*), but smaller. It has very little fear of man and
is often seen perched low in thinned forest, forest edges, and
clearings. A young bird was captured by slowly stalking it and
covering it with a piece of cloth. Another, perched in a bare
tree, was being annoyed by a youngster who threw stones at
it; it merely jumped up an inch or two with slightly raised
wings whenever a stone came close or hit its perch; only after
half a dozen such reactions did it fly off sluggishly to another
part of the field.

Adults are gray-brown above, the open wings disclosing a
rufous area; the underparts are also gray-brown across the
breast, blending downward into the dull brown and white,
coarsely barred belly; the tail has a conspicuous series of
about four bands, light gray against dark brown. Eyes are
yellow.

Immatures are browner above than adults, the heads
streaked with buff; below they are a pale tawny color, the
breast streaked with dark brown, the belly with triangular
wedges of brown, the tail showing a conspicuous series of
bands, usually more numerous than on adults. Some immatures approach the gray breasts and the barred abdominal
areas of adults.

Although they may eat small birds now and then, their diet
is more likely to include lizards, large insects, scorpions, and
the like, so much so that they are often called Insect Hawk.

Its more usual voice, often used on the approach of a per-
son to its perch, is a high-pitched, whining whistle, diminishing

in pitch and repeated with slow deliberation; also used when on the wing. Less frequently it utters a loud cackling *kek-kek-kek-kek* (1).

Nests are built in trees, not very high up, and are made of interwoven sticks, the shallow cup lined with leaves. Two eggs are usual, white in color with rust brown spots (1).

REFERENCES: Sutton 1951, p. 100, picture in black and white. (1) Amadon Ms.

* *Buteo nitidus* subsp.

Gray Hawk   Gavilán Gris

S.w. U. S., Mid. Am., and S. Am.
Resident?   15 to 18 in.   ♂ 400 gr. ♀ 600 gr.
                                                    Plate 5

Very uncommon, although it has much the same preferences for food and habitat as the common Roadside Hawk (*B. magnirostris*). Van Tyne (1935) did not find it at nearby Uaxactún; Taibel (1955) did not report it from Lake Petén-Itzá, twenty-five miles to the south; but it was reported for Chuntuqui, some fifty miles to the northwest, and elsewhere in the Yucatán Peninsula (Paynter 1955, p. 63).

Eight sight records noted at Tikal all occurred between 16 March and 4 April or 17 to 27 August.

Adults are light gray, coarsely barred with darker gray above, and a white rump. Underparts are finely barred with white and gray; tails have two conspicuous white bands. Immatures are difficult to separate from immatures of other similarly sized buteos; they are very dark brown above, mottled with white and buff; below, the breast is white streaked with tear-shaped spots of dark brown, belly and thighs spotted with wedge-shaped brown; the tail is crossed by several obscure bands.

Its usual cry is a loud, high-pitched, plaintively whistled *cree-eeeeeee,* the second half long-drawn-out and decreasing in pitch. In courtship flights it utters musical, flute-like, piping notes (1). Less frequent is a *ker-ker-ker-ker* series of notes (2).

Nests are small, well-built, compact structures, fairly high up in trees, and lined with softer materials. Two eggs are usually deposited, white or very pale blue, unmarked or only very obscurely spotted (1).

REFERENCES: Sutton 1951, p. 80, picture in color. Peterson 1960, p. 65, picture in black and white.
(1) Amadon Ms.   (2) Slud 1964.

Leucopternis albicollis ghiesbreghti (Du Bus)

White Hawk   Gavilán Blanco

Cot

Trop. Mid. Am. (except El Salvador) and S. Am.
Resident   19 to 22 in.   650 gr.

Not numerous but widespread, this large hawk was regularly seen and is probably present throughout the year. It has very little fear of man. On one occasion the author and three companions saw a pair perched about forty feet high in a tree overhanging our trail. The pair slowly turned their heads, eyeing us intently, but remained otherwise motionless while we slowly but steadily continued on, walked beneath them and past them. Many hawks here display a lack of fear but none were quite as trusting as were these.

Adult birds are almost entirely immaculate white, with a narrow black band near the end of the tail and a broad area of black across the wing tips. Immatures are much the same except that the black areas are larger.

Usually it is silent and does not react to one's approach as does the Roadside Hawk, but when it does call it screams a harsh *shee-ee-er,* uttered either when perched or flying (1); or a shrill, plaintive *ker-wee,* typically buteonine, but ending in a queer buzzing note (2).

The nest, located high in trees, is made of twigs, lined with dead leaves and a few green leaves. The egg is bluish white with brown smears (1).

REFERENCES: Blake 1953, p. 85, picture in black and white.
(1) Amadon Ms.   (2) Van Tyne 1950.

* *Buteogallus anthracinus* subsp.

Common Black Hawk   Gavilán Cangrejero

S.w. U. S., Mid. Am., S. Am., Lesser Antilles (St. Vincent)
Visitor   18 to 22 in.   ♀ 650 gr.   Plate 4

Rare, even accidental, breeding along the distant coastal
areas of the Yucatán Peninsula. The adult is separable from
the Great Black Hawk (*B. urubitinga*) by the lack of a white
rump, yellow instead of dark lores, shorter legs and unbarred
thighs, and shorter tail with only one conspicuous white bar
across the middle.

Immatures are very dark brown above, with broad, pale
buff streaks; underparts are a light buff color streaked with
dark brown; the tail has perhaps six very light tawny bands
sharply contrasting with somewhat wider bands of very dark
brown.

We have only a single sight report of an adult, 16 March
1963, made by C. Russell Mason, Director of the Florida
Audubon Society, who, along with others, watched it soaring
above the camp grounds. We have illustrated it along with
other black hawks to aid future efforts to identify it. If the
observation is confirmed, this will be a new record for the
Petén.

The voice is as a long whistling scream, nasal, and high-
pitched; during courtship (in Cuba), a three-syllabled whistle
is uttered while soaring (1).

Nests are placed both high and low in trees. The base is
made of heavy sticks mixed with smaller ones and coarse
stems. It is lined with twigs and always contains green leaves.
Eggs, usually one, sometimes two per set, are coarse-grained
grayish white (1).

REFERENCES: Peterson 1960, p. 64, picture in black and white.
(1) Amadon Ms.

Buteogallus urubitinga ridgwayi (Gurney)

Great Black Hawk   Gavilán Negro

Trop. Mid. Am. and S. Am.
Visitor   20–24 in.   ♂ 1000 gr.   Plate 4

Very uncommon; noted by sight records at Tikal, and confirmed by a specimen taken at nearby Uaxactún (Van Tyne 1935), in habitat identical with that of Tikal.

This large hawk is black except for a distinctive white rump (lacking on *B. anthracinus*), two white bands across the tail with the lower band somewhat the wider, and thighs lightly barred with white. Its legs are decidedly longer, heavier and much coarser than the legs of *B. anthracinus*, and a deeper orange-yellow instead of straw yellow; the yellow cere contrasts with dark slaty, bare facial skin. Immatures are very dark brown above, spotted with buff about the head and nape. Underparts are a light buff color streaked with dark brown, and brown-barred thighs. The tail is very light tawny below, crossed by numerous narrow dark brown bands.

Both species have similar feeding habits and both soar readily, but *B. urubitinga* seems to be more partial to inland habitat and less confined to the vicinity of coastal swamps.

Its voice is a prolonged, rather even, screaming whistle, like *oo-ée-eeeee,* sometimes interrupted by a break, continuing at a higher pitch (1); and hear (3).

It is doubtful that it nests anywhere near Tikal. Nests are located in trees, both high and low. They are made of sticks, deeply cupped and lined with dead leaves. A clutch is usually one egg, pale blue, heavily spotted with red-brown (2).

REFERENCES: Sutton 1951, p. 196, pictures in black and white (tails only).
(1) Slud 1964.   (2) Amadon Ms.
(3) Mexican Bird Songs, recordings by L. Irby Davis.

Spizaëtus ornatus vicarius Friedmann

Ornate Hawk-Eagle   Aguilucho de Penacho
                                         Águila Penachuda

Trop. Mid. Am. and S. Am.
Resident   25 in.   ♂ 1000 gr. ♀ 1450 gr.

Uncommon but not rare, this large, long-tailed, most colorful of hawks, was found at various aguadas, over a wide territory. Unless suddenly surprised, it may be closely approached.

In all plumages it displays a conspicuous crest, black for an adult (brown for immatures). Below the crest the adult has a rich rufous head and nape (white for immatures), this color continuing down into the sides of the breast. The bill is black, the cere yellow, the bare eye skin greenish yellow, the eyes orange-yellow; the chin and throat pure white, partly outlined by a black border. Upperparts are mainly shades of deep brown; underparts are largely white, boldly barred with blackish brown. The long dark tail has three conspicuous bands, light brown when seen from above, white from below.

It preys on birds as large as chickens and on medium-sized mammals of similar proportions.

Its calls are more varied and complicated than any other of our hawks and defy concise description. When flying through the forest it may utter clear, thin, high-pitched screams; when near the nest a high-pitched, but not loud, *wheeoo—whee-pee-pee* (1), perhaps a faint version of its normal call; or when hunting from a tree-perch it may utter a cry that sounds like the snarling of a hundred-pound cat, enough to drive the hunted birds on the ground below it screamingly frantic (2).

The nest, located high in a tree, is large and bulky; the sticks of which it is built range between one and four inches in diameter (1). I have found no description of the eggs.

REFERENCES: Austin 1961, p. 80, picture in color. Allen 1961, plate 22, color photograph.
(1) Amadon Ms.   (2) Slud 1964.

Spizaëtus tyrannus serus Friedmann

Black Hawk-Eagle   Aguilucho Negro

Trop. Mid. Am. (except El Salvador) and S. Am.
Resident   25–28 in.   ♂ 800 gr.   Plate 6

A rare bird at Tikal, this large hawk was first found 23 September 1962, perched high in a tree. It was an immature male and weighed 778 grams.

Adults are mainly black. A short but conspicuous black crest has much partly concealed pure white. The thighs and fully feathered legs are strongly barred with white and the wings also display considerable white barring from below. The long rounded tail has three wide bands (a fourth partly visible), white from below, light brown above. Immatures display much white on the head, throat, and breast, a white crest tipped with brown, the cheek blackish, the breast streaked with black. Underparts are otherwise prominently barred black and white, even over the flanks and tail coverts. The long tail is much like that of adults, but with four clear bands instead of three.

This hawk-eagle soars slowly about, when its field marks are readily seen. It chooses more open situations than does the Ornate Hawk-Eagle, although their feeding habits are similar.

It is vociferous, especially when soaring, voicing a loud, resounding, characteristic *wheet, wheet, wheet-eeeeer, wheet-eeeeer,* over and over again. The stressed long-drawn note comes late in the series: the reverse is true of the Ornate Hawk-Eagle (1).

A nest was found in Panama, March 1965, about forty-five feet up in a group of palms. It was about four and a half feet across, and held one or more young birds (2).

REFERENCES: P.C.A. 34:444, feeding behavior (Skutch).
(1) Amadon Ms.
(2) Amadon Ms. (report of find by Neal Smith).

Geranospiza caerulescens nigra (Du Bus)

Crane Hawk Gavilán Ranero

Trop. Mid. Am. and n.w. S. Am.
Resident 18 to 20 in. 350 gr. Plate 4

Not uncommon at Tikal, where we saw them more frequently than the White Hawk (*Leucopternis albicollis*), apparently a local condition, as they had not been found in the Petén previously and have been considered a rare bird in Mexico and Central America.

Adults are a dull black except for two conspicuous white bands on the long tail, brilliant red eyes, and a white band across the under surface of the spread wings. The eyes of the Tikal birds were recorded as orange-red and orange, rather than brilliant red. Bright orange legs, long and slender, help to give this light-bodied hawk a "lanky" appearance. Immatures, much like the adults, have grayish white on the forehead, chin and upper throat, gray barring on the lower belly and thighs, and some buff about the lower tail coverts.

They search for food in cavities in trees and among tree foliage and clumps of bromeliads, for insects, lizards, nestlings; one bird at Tikal had eaten a mouse which we found almost intact in its stomach.

Although usually silent, it utters a nasal, whining, whistling call, similar to that of the Roadside Hawk. Another call, very different from what is expected from a hawk, is given in the dusk of early morning and late evening. It is described as a loud, hollow *how* uttered singly and repeated at about one- or two-minute intervals (1).

Nests of twigs and vine stalks, their well-cupped recesses lined with grass and leaves, are located fairly high up in trees. Two eggs are usual, white, rarely spotted with sepia (1).

REFERENCES: Wilson Bull. 66:4:fpc., picture of head in color; pp. 237–242, descriptive details (Sutton).

(1) Amadon Ms.

FALCONIDAE

Herpetotheres cachinnans cachinnans (Linnaeus)

Laughing Falcon

Vaquero
Guaco
Güance

Kos

Trop. Mid. Am. and S. Am.
Resident   18 to 22 in.   ♂ 400 to 600, ♀ to 650 gr.

Not uncommon but still not numerous, the Laughing Falcon was heard more often than it was seen, despite the fact that it is conspicuously marked. It is largely buff or creamy white with a dark brown back and wings, and a conspicuous black, mask-like patch on the side of the face which continues on around the nape as a narrow black band. The black tail has four or more buffy white bands crossing it. The bill is black, yellowish at its base, the cere is lemon yellow, the eyes brown, the legs light yellow, almost white.

It feeds almost entirely on snakes, including venomous ones.

One individual would come in from the forest now and then and perch boldly in a bare tree in the middle of the semi-cleared camp. On one such occasion, on the early morning of 20 May, its loud calls greatly excited a Melodious Blackbird (*Dives dives*), which perched on another and higher branch of the same tree. There the blackbird performed a dance in perfect unison with the Laughing Falcon's music, jumping nearly a foot into the air and back on its perch to match each syllable of a laughing series. When the series stopped the blackbird stopped; when a new series began the blackbird again danced to it, and seemed to be calling raucously at the same time. This continued for more than ten minutes, with short intervals of quiet, ending only when the falcon flew off to a distant point.

The call which so excited the blackbird begins with a slow laugh-like *ha-ha-ha-ha-ha,* gradually increasing in tempo and crescendo to become a truly mad, short *hahahahaha* at the end. Another call which is characteristic enough to give the bird its name of Guaco is not unrelated in quality and tone to the laughing call. It begins with a series of deliberate *gwa*'s which gradually become more intense and transform into a new series of two syllabled GẂA-*co*'s, with the first syllable higher in pitch and intensity (1), (2), (3).

The Laughing Falcon makes little or no effort at building a nest, sometimes using one abandoned by another hawk, usually using a cavity in a tree which has lost its top or a large limb, perhaps as high up as a hundred feet. The single egg, white with a brownish wash, is heavily marked with chocolate brown.

REFERENCES: Sutton 1951, p. 198, picture in black and white.
(1) Slud 1964.
(2) Mexican Bird Songs, recordings by L. Irby Davis.
(3) Bird Songs, recordings by Paul Schwartz.

Micrastur semitorquatus naso (Lesson)

Collared Forest-Falcon   Gavilán de Collar

Trop. Mid. Am. and S. Am.
Resident   18 to 24 in.   ♂ 550 to 650, ♀ to 750 gr.
                                                    Plate 7

Uncommon but not rare, this falcon may be overlooked because of its preference for heavy forest or tangles, rarely appearing in the open. It has been reported that snakes up to three feet in length (1), lizards, and birds make up a substantial portion of its diet.

Adults appear in three color phases, dark brown to blackish above, but either white, buff or dull black below, the last perhaps the least common. All have long tails, half or more the bird's overall length, the feathers notably graduated to form a very circular tail-end when spread, with three narrow bands of white or buff color clearly displayed. The white or a buff collar across the nape is lacking in the blackish phase.

Immatures are dark brown above, the collar very obscure; the tail bands are duller; the underparts are boldly barred dark brown against white in one color phase, or buff in the other color phase (see *Accipiter b. bicolor* for similar phases); the upper breast becomes more uniformly rich tawny chestnut.

The call bears some resemblance to that of the Laughing Falcon (*Herpetotheres cachinnans*) but of slower tempo and shorter duration, a several-times-repeated long *ahr-ahr* falling off toward the end into a quavering, human-like moan (2); or a loud, half-human *ah-ow, ah-ow, ah-ow* (3).

I have found no information about its nest or eggs.

REFERENCES: Sutton 1951, p. 124, picture in black and white; and p. 180.

(1) Condor 55:1:fpc., picture in color.
(2) Slud 1964.
(3) Auk 59:1:10 (Sutton and Pettingill).

Micrastur ruficollis guerilla Cassin

Barred Forest-Falcon   Gavilancito de la Selva

Trop. Mid. Am. and S. Am.
Resident   14 in.   150 to 200 gr.   Plate 8

Somewhat more common than the much larger Collared Forest-Falcon (*M. semitorquatus*), the "barking" call of this small, very accipiter-like falcon may be heard more often than the bird is seen. It prefers the deeper forest and is seldom found away from forest shade, where it preys on birds, mice, lizards, and such.

The adult is dark brown to blackish gray above, and with distinct, evenly spaced, rather fine dark barring against a whitish ground color below. The tail, somewhat graduated, is long and well rounded, crossed by three very narrow whitish bands. The bill is black above, yellow below; cere and orbital areas orange-yellow; eyes light orange-brown; legs yellow. Immatures are brown above with an obscure, buff nuchal collar. Below they vary greatly, some having unbroken shades of buff or creamy white, others with the ground color ornamented by widely separated narrow bars of dark brown, others grading between these extremes. Tails are much like those of adults.

The notes of the characteristic, dog-like, barking call sound like the word *our,* when very quickly pronounced. The bird also utters other calls of a chicken-like cackling quality (1).

I have found no information regarding its nest or eggs.

REFERENCES: Blake 1953, p. 94, picture in black and white. (1) Slud 1964.

Falco deiroleucus Temminck

Orange-breasted Falcon   Halcón de Pecho Anaranjado

Local: Guatemala, Honduras, Nicaragua, Costa Rica, Panama, and S. Am.; Mexico (Veracruz, once)
Resident   ♂ 12 in.   ♀ 16 in.   ♀ 650 gr.   Plate 9

Not numerous but from 1958 through 1963 at least one pair (later probably others) resided at Tikal. Griscom (1932) spoke of them as nesting in church towers and belfries, "where it is impossible to collect without committing sacrilege." At Tikal we found them nesting in the roof-comb of Pyramid Temple II, in the Great Plaza, June 1963. We did not examine the nest. In previous years we suspected they nested in cavities in Temple I and in Temple III. Two nests in Trinidad had sets of three and two eggs each, whitish or yellowish, more or less obscured by brownish red blotches and smears. One was thirty feet up in a tree, one forty feet up in a palm (1).

Adults are blue-black above, the tail with several dull whitish bands; below largely bright rufous (conspicuously so on the breast), blending into a white throat, the belly and lower breast barred with black, the tail irregularly barred. Females are much larger than males, almost as large as small Peregrines (*F. peregrinus*), which they strongly suggest. The bill is dark gray, cere and bare area about the eyes greenish yellow, eyes brown, and legs yellow. Immatures are similar, with the black areas browner, the rufous areas paler, and barring present on the thighs.

The call is a penetrating, long-drawn-out whistle, recalling somewhat that of the Roadside Hawk, but of a clearer, smoother quality and falling in pitch toward the end. It is repeated a few times with short intervals.

REFERENCES:
(1) Oölogist's Record 26:3:42–46, eggs and nests (Coltart).

Falco rufigularis petoensis Chubb

Bat Falcon

Halcón Caza Murciélagos
Halcón Murcielaguero

E'pi'
Ah Chu'uy

Trop. Mid. Am. and S. Am.
Resident   ♂ 9 in. ♀ 11 in.   ♂ 130 gr. ♀ 200 gr.
Plate 9

Fairly common in forest edges, clearings, and open areas with scattered trees. It preys on bats and small birds, including hummingbirds.

They differ from the very similarly patterned Orange-breasted Falcon (*F. deiroleucus*) by their much smaller size (although a large female Bat Falcon closely approaches a small male Orange-breasted); and by their much more extensive and more narrowly barred black underparts, the black and white barring reaching all the way up to the whitish throat, with rufous only on the belly and under tail coverts. The throat is white, bordered with buff which extends around into the side of the neck. The tail is narrowly and obscurely barred above with dark gray, below with four or more whitish narrow bands. The bill is black and grayish, the cere, bare skin about the eyes and the legs are all lemon yellow, the eyes so dark a brown as to appear black.

Its call is a rapid series of *kik*'s, rather squeaky and nasal; also a short rippling *diditit* (1), and hear (2).

They nest in holes in trees. In Trinidad, two eggs are deposited, cream colored, marked with blotches and smears of brown (3).

REFERENCES: Sutton 1951, p. 160, picture in color. Condor 53:2:fpc., picture in color.

(1) Slud 1964.

(2) Mexican Bird Songs, recordings by L. Irby Davis.

(3) Herklots 1961.

Falco sparverius sparverius Linnaeus

American Sparrow Hawk   Clis-clis

American Kestrel

N. Am., West Indies, Mexico, Guatemala, Honduras, n. Nicaragua, also S. Am.; winters through Mid. Am. and S. Am.

Winter Resident   9 to 12 in.   100 gr.

Only two or three were seen at a time, but at least one appeared regularly in the months of February, March, April (to the ninth), and again in October (beginning the twenty-third) and November. Their *absence* was especially recorded during a visit from 22 April to 14 August. No doubt most are transients, merely passing through. They prefer open country and there is not enough of it at Tikal to expect them to reside here.

A bright rufous back and tail, with darker barring, a conspicuously harlequin face pattern in black and white, and a kingfisher-like habit of hovering on rapidly beating wings over possible prey are characteristics unique to this small falcon. A broad black band crosses the tail; underparts are buffy and whitish; wings of males are a rich blue-gray and black, of females rufous like their backs. The bill is dark gray, the cere, the bare skin about the eyes, and the legs are yellow. One beautiful male had distinctly orange legs.

The call is a high *klee-klee-klee-klee-klee-klee,* with a rising inflection (1), which gives it its name.

Nesting in the north is usually done in holes in trees, cliffs, or walls; very little if any material is added to the litter left there by the previous occupant; four or five eggs are laid, white or buff and spotted with brown (1), (2).

REFERENCES: Peterson 1960, p. 61, picture in color. Austin 1961, p. 85, picture in color. Murphy and Amadon 1953, plate 6, color photograph.

(1) Pough 1953.   (2) Herklots 1961.

CRACIDAE

Crax rubra rubra Linnaeus

Great Curassow   Paujil
                                                         Faisán Real

K'ambul
Bolonchan

Trop. Mid. Am. to Ecuador
Resident   36 in.   2700 to 3800 gr. (6 to 8½ lbs.)

A common bird at Tikal, almost as large as a turkey but more slender and lighter in bulk. They make flavorsome eating, and local hunting has severely reduced their numbers around Aguada Tikal, partly because they take to the lower branches of trees when alarmed, where they are readily shot. They are primarily ground feeders but also climb over the branches of trees for berries and fruit.

The male is mainly black, with a conspicuous crest of curling feathers, a bright yellow knob over the bill, and a white lower abdominal area. The female is mainly rusty brown, except for a black head and neck which are boldly barred and spotted with white. The broad brown tail is banded with buff. The bill lacks the yellow knob of the male.

They roost in trees at night. They also build their nests at moderate heights in trees, where they lay two or three very large, rough-shelled, dull white eggs. Nests are rather flimsy structures of twigs and leaves, set in an ample notch; one, unoccupied, was made entirely of green leaves (2).

The male calls at short intervals, usually from some large tree, with a low, throbbing, or grumbling *oomh,* difficult to locate. The female call is a faint whistling *quit-quit* (1), (2), (3).

REFERENCES:
(1) Sutton 1951, p. 240, picture in color.
(2) Auk 59:1:4, picture of nest; pp. 10, 11 descriptions (Sutton and Pettingill). Austin 1961, p. 86, pictures in color (of male and female).
(3) Mexican Bird Songs, recordings by L. Irby Davis.

Penelope purpurascens purpurascens Wagler

Crested Guan   Cojolita

Ah Cox

Trop. Mid. Am. and n. S. Am.
Resident   34 in.   1200 to 2400 gr. (4½ lbs.)

Somewhat less common than the curassows. A very edible bird, local hunting has reduced its numbers somewhat. It feeds in the trees as much as it does on the ground, and the forest is its essential habitat; clearings may therefore eliminate it even more effectively than hunting. It flies on noisy wings which sound *whuff, whuff, whuff* (1). Skutch (2) says that when alarmed "they perch conspicuously well above the ground and yelp absurdly in high-pitched voices . . . which in the presence of a gunner is suicidal." It has a distinctive single or double *honk* (3).

While nearly as large as the curassow, they weigh much less. Both male and female are alike, mainly dark or blackish brown in color, lighter on the underparts. Legs are red and a large patch of bright red-orange bare skin at the throat is conspicuous. Bare skin, dark blue in color, also surrounds the red-brown eyes.

They roost in trees at night. Nests are built some thirty feet up in trees. Eggs are white to creamy white (4). It seems strange not to find a report of clutch size of this fine game-bird.

REFERENCES: Aveledo 1958, p. 146, picture in color.
(1) Sutton 1953.
(2) Animal Kingdom 62:6:183 (Skutch).
(3) Slud 1964.
(4) Handbuch der Oölogie 4:202 (Schönwetter and Meise).

Ortalis vetula intermedia Peters

Plain Chachalaca   Chacha
                                                        Chachalaca

Bach
Ixbach

S.e. Texas, Mexico, Guatemala, Brit. Honduras, Honduras, El
   Salvador, Nicaragua
Resident   22 in.   450 gr. (1 lb.)

Common, numerous, and still to be seen right in the heart
of the village. They are not averse to cultivated land but
choose the clumps of thickets and the more heavily foliaged
trees, where they walk along the limbs and jump easily from
branch to branch. Early in the morning and again toward dusk
their loud, insistent, rhythmic chorus, *chachalac-chachalac,*
comes from coveys roosting in scattered flocks in the treetops of the surrounding forest; and hear (3).

They are good to eat, but their small size as compared with
other available game birds relieves them of hunting pressure.
They are much smaller than the cojolitas, but share with them
a slender build and long tail, brown eyes surrounded by bare,
dark blue skin, and a bare throat of red-orange. They are
mostly light brown-olive above, the rounded iridescent tail
tipped at the sides with white or tawny, the underparts much
paler and light gray. Legs are blue-gray.

Sturdy nests are built in dense underbrush, two to five feet
above ground (1) and to about twenty-five feet up in trees
(2). Nests are made of twigs and fibrous material woven into
a shallow saucer, lined with grasses and leaves. Eggs, two
or three in number, are white and glossy-shelled per Harry
Malleis (1); rough-shelled per Pough (2).

REFERENCES: Peterson 1960, p. 129, picture in color. Sutton
1951, p. 112, picture in color.
   (1) Van Tyne 1935.   (2) Pough 1953.
   (3) Mexican Bird Songs; recordings by L. Irby Davis.

PHASIANIDAE

*** *Colinus nigrogularis*

Black-throated Bobwhite   Codorniz

Ah Cul (in general)
Bech'

Mexico (Yucatán Pen.), Brit. Honduras, and Caribbean slope
of Guatemala, Honduras (Segovia River), and Nicaragua
Resident formerly?   8½ in.   140 gr.

Not found at Tikal, nor by Van Tyne (1935) at Uaxactún.
However, substantial quantities of their bones from Tikal have
been recently identified by Paynter (in litt.). Bones were
found not only in burials and caches where their presence
may be due to importation, but they were found in much
greater numbers in the debris of temples, roof-combs, and
other structures, where their occurrence would indicate that
they were once locally numerous. Since they prefer open,
even heavily cultivated country, and are not partial to forests,
it must be assumed that the habitat at Tikal was then very
different from that which we now see. One is tempted to place
them in time with the periods of Maya ascendancy, a thousand and more years ago.

They were reported by Taibel (1955) at Lake Petén-Itzá,
and also by Malleis (Van Tyne 1935), who found them to
be numerous in the savannah country south of that lake.

They are somewhat smaller than the northern Bobwhite
(*Colinus virginianus*) which they superficially resemble. The
male is distinguished by black superciliaries, chin and throat;
the female by brown in those same areas.

The call is the typical, whistled *bob-white* (Willis, in litt.).
A nest of grass and similar vegetation is made in a hollow
on the ground or among brush.

These four hawks are shown together because of obvious similarities: primarily their black color and number of tail bands, one band on the Common Black Hawk and the Kite, two bands on the Great Black Hawk and the Crane Hawk.

COMMON BLACK HAWK   *p. 35.*

ADULT: 21 inches; sooty black with brown tinge; small white window in spread wings; tail has one broad white band; facial area yellow; legs yellow, *smooth,* shorter than those of Great Black Hawk.

IMMATURE (tail only shown): dark brown above, paler and streaked below; tail has four to six narrow, tawny bands.

GREAT BLACK HAWK   *p. 36.*

ADULT: 24 inches; slaty black; tail has one wide, one narrow band; upper tail coverts (not rump) white; facial area slaty; legs orange-yellow, *coarse,* long.

IMMATURE (tail only shown): much like Common Black, but tail has many more bands (twelve or fourteen).

HOOK-BILLED KITE (Black Phase)   *p. 25.*

ADULT: 16 inches; leaden black; facial area green; tail has one broad white band; see Plate 3 for other phases (note scale is different).

CRANE HAWK   *p. 39.*

SUB-ADULT: 19 inches; illustrated instead of more uniformly slaty black adult in order to show grayish white on head and upper throat, and buffy barring on underparts; otherwise like adult, the tail notably long with two conspicuous white bands, a white bar on spread wings, lanky bright orange legs, orange-red eyes.

PLATE 4

GREAT BLACK HAWK

COMMON BLACK HAWK

Tail of
Immature

Tail of
Immature

CRANE HAWK

Sub-adult

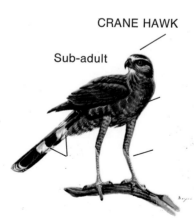

HOOK-BILLED
KITE
Black phase

inches	6
cms	15

ADULTS	**BROAD-WINGED HAWK** *p. 31*	**ROADSIDE HAWK** *p. 32*
size	15 to 17 inches; 400 to 500 gr.	14 to 16 inches; 275 to 320 gr.
head	*brown;* cere yellow	*gray;* cere yellow
upperparts	dark brown	gray brown
wings	below, dull white linings	above, show rufous in flight
underparts	throat *white; black whiskers*	throat gray, streaked white
	chest rufous	chest gray
	breast slightly barred, belly coarsely barred, thighs barred	breast brown barring, continuing down belly, thighs pale barring
tail	two white bands, the one near the end wider (a third partly hidden at base)	about four gray bands
eyes	pale red-brown	yellow

IMMATURES	**BROAD-WING**	**GRAY** *p. 33*	**ROADSIDE**
size	as above	15 to 18 inches; 400 to 600 gr.	as above
head	brown, white streaks	dark brown, russet streaks	brown, buff streaks, *pale line over eye*
upperparts	brown, mottled with white and buff	dark brown, blotched with much rufous	brown, the least mottling effect
underparts	throat creamy	throat has *dark side whiskers*	throat creamy
	body creamy, sparsely streaked with dark brown	body creamy, heavier streaking than on Broad-wing	body buff, coarsely streaked on breast, more spotted (wedges) below, with trend to barring
	thighs lightly streaked	thighs clearly barred	thighs lightly barred
tail	four narrow gray bands	much like the Broad-wing	wide gray bands (narrow dark in-between bands)
eyes	yellowish	*brown*	yellow

PLATE 5

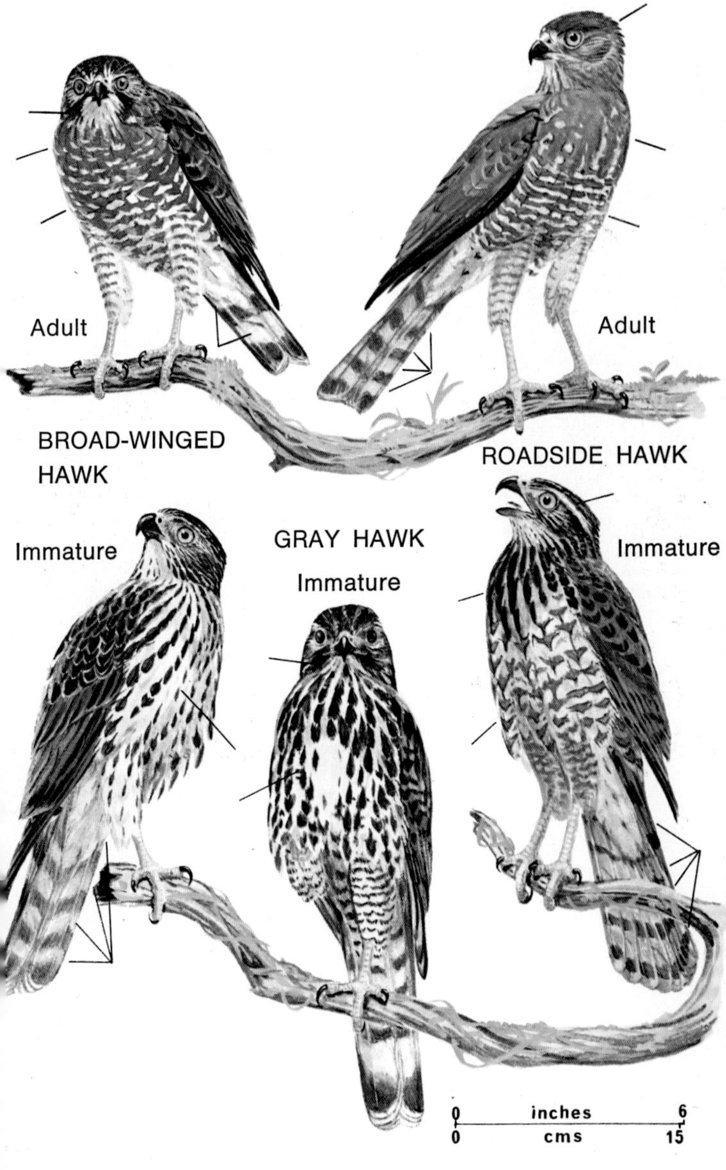

Adult

Adult

BROAD-WINGED
HAWK

ROADSIDE HAWK

Immature

GRAY HAWK

Immature

Immature

| 0 | inches | 6 |
| 0 | cms | 15 |

PLATE 6

Adult

Immature

BLACK HAWK-EAGLE

| 0 | inches | 6 |
| 0 | cms | 15 |

ADULT: 25 to 28 inches; short crest black; body black except for white and black barring on belly, thighs and feathered legs; three conspicuous pale gray bands on tail (a fourth partly concealed by coverts); wings barred below. Much white concealed under black of head.

Soars slowly about a great deal, calling noisily.

IMMATURES: head white; short crest tipped brown; back and wings brownish black; breast white, streaked lightly; rest of underparts barred white and black; tail with four conspicuous pale gray bands (a fifth partly concealed by coverts).

Odontophorus guttatus (Gould)

Spotted Wood-Quail   Codorniz
                                          Bolonchaco

Coban Chaco
Bulu'tok'

Trop. s. Mexico and chiefly highlands of Mid. Am. (except
El Salvador) to w. Panama
Resident   11 in.   300 gr.

Common and widespread. Found throughout the heavy forest with open understory, and in forest edges, either singly or
in small coveys of eight or ten birds.

These large quails display a conspicuous dark crest, partly
cinnamon in the males. The general effect is either olive-
brown or red-brown, mottled above with black and buff,
spotted below with white. The male has a black throat, the female a brown throat, both streaked with white.

Like all quails they nest on the ground.

The unmusical call is a repetitive *gahble-gahble*, or *ga-
gobble* (1).

REFERENCES: Blake 1953, p. 114, picture in black and white.
(1) Slud 1964.

Dactylortyx thoracicus sharpei Nelson

Singing Quail   Codorniz Gemidora
Long-toed Quail

Buluctok'
Chibilub

Highlands (chiefly) s. Mexico, Guatemala, El Salvador, and
Honduras
Resident   9½ in.   ♂ 200 gr. ♀ 180 gr.

Not uncommon. Found in flocks of four to eight birds.
Strictly terrestrial, they are usually shy and elusive, prefer-

ring areas with heavy underbrush where they scratch the ground debris in deliberate strokes with their long toes, in search of food. This activity may be heard in very dry weather.

They are slightly larger than Bobwhites (*Colinus virginianus*). Females are largely shades of brownish gray, darkest on the crown, the breast more uniform brown. Males display bright chestnut throats and superciliaries and darker mottling on the wings. Eyes are light brown, bill black, legs gray.

A rich, flute-like, two-part song begins with three or four penetrating whistles which rise in strength and pitch, followed by three to six rapid phrases, each phrase with notes of differing pitch. The song is best in April and May, but may be given as late as December (1). Sutton said (2) "the song began uncertainly, with an experimental whistle. After a pause the whistle was repeated. Gaining strength, it came more rapidly, three times, four times, five times—full-throated, sure of itself, even defiant—then broke into a rollicking

pitch wheeler! pitch wheeler! pitch wheeler!

and trailed off with a low twittering."

Nests seem not to have been described; eggs are white with a yellow cast; a set of five has been seen, but broods of only two to four.

REFERENCES:
(1) Wilson Bull. 69:2:fpc., pictures in color; pp. 123–148, life history (Warner and Harrell).
(2) Auk 59:1:12, description and picture of nestling (Sutton and Pettingill).

MELEAGRIDIDAE

Meleagris ocellata Cuvier
[*Agriocharis ocellata*]

Ocellated Turkey

Pavo del Petén
Pavo Ocelado

Kuts
Ucutz Ilchican

Mexico (Yucatán Pen., Chiapas), Brit. Honduras, and Guatemala (Petén)

Resident   36 in.   ♂ 5000 gr. (11 lbs.) ♀ 3000 gr. (7 lbs.)

Plate 15

These handsome and very flavorsome birds, widespread but not numerous, are about two-thirds as large as the more northern Common Turkey (*M. gallopavo*). Until local pot-hunting discouraged their presence, they were found in groups of three or more within a quarter mile of the Aguada Tikal, and nested within half a mile. The Government of Guatemala has wisely placed them on the fully protected list.

Their most distinguishing features are: the very bright blue naked head and neck, decorated with orange protuberances; the long gray tail decorated with blue and bronze eye-like spots; and an overall brilliant metallic bronze and greenish iridescence. (See Van Tyne 1935, p. 11, for a detailed color description.) Females are substantially smaller and less spectacularly marked than are the males.

Primarily a bird of the lowlands and with a very restricted range (see above), they prefer open forests where they feed mainly on the ground but roost in the trees.

The voice is a rather bell-like gobble, heard mostly in May and June. The nest is built on the ground where the litter and debris have been pushed about to form a depression, in which are laid eight or more large eggs, light brown in basic color, overlaid with speckles and small blotches of darker brown.

REFERENCES: Austin 1961, p. 99, picture in color. Gilliard 1958, p. 123, picture in black and white ("displaying" male). Russell 1964, picture in color.

ARAMIDAE

Aramus guarauna subsp.

Limpkin   Totolaca
                                               Correa

S. U. S., West Indies, Mid. Am., and S. Am.
Visitor   26 in.   1300 gr. (3 lbs.)

A single limpkin was seen at Aguada Tikal 29 April 1963 "which remained a few days, skirting the aguada edges" (Trik, in litt.). At nearby Uaxactún a male was collected by Van Tyne (1935), 28 March 1931. We may infer that the limpkin is an erratic visitor from some not-too-distant breeding ground. It is a long-legged brown bird, streaked with whitish down the head, neck, and breast, and ornamented across the back and wings with a distinctive effect of large whitish droplet-like spots.

It feeds mainly on snails and other shellfish, but will take insects, lizards, worms, and other such food. Its voice, a far-reaching, strident, wailing *kur-r-ee-ow, kree-ow,* repeated indefinitely, is heard mostly in the early evening and through the night.

The nest is a bulky structure of dead vines, reeds, and other vegetation, located over or close to water, rarely more than three feet up. Eggs (in Trinidad) are about three to six to the clutch, a pale buff or cream color with speckles and blotches of darker brown (1).

REFERENCES: Peterson 1960, p. 21, picture in color. Austin 1961, p. 109, picture in color; end papers, picture of egg in color.
(1) Herklots 1961.

RALLIDAE

Aramides cajanea albiventris Lawrence

Gray-necked Wood-Rail   Gallineta
                                             Chir-in-co-co

Ulumha (rails in general)

Trop. Mid. Am. and S. Am.
Resident   15 in.   500 gr.

Not uncommon but still not numerous, this large, long-legged, short-tailed rail frequented the Aguada Tikal steadily during the first two and a half years of camp activities, none of which caused it to leave. Although a rather shy bird, it was possible to observe it from within twenty feet, without the use of a blind. However, in late 1957 the aguada was cleared of its dense cover of vines, gourds, reeds, and shrubs, after which the bird departed and has not returned. It appears to prefer aguadas and swamps that have a very reedy cover.

The head (except for a small brown patch) and all the neck are gray (the throat whitish), contrasting with a darker olive-brown back and a rufous breast and sides, these in turn giving place to a black tail and abdomen. The bill is basally reddish shading rapidly through yellow to a rich green terminally. Eyes and legs are shades of red. All in all a very colorful bird.

The call, usually heard at dawn and dusk, begins with four quick cackles, followed by more slowly given, higher- but not high-pitched, emphatic notes, as kukukuku coh-coh-coh and other variations (1). From a distance, when the harsh, strained cackling is subdued, the voice is a clear, bell-like ringing; sometimes two birds respond in a sort of duet (2). A short *k-luk* may also reveal its presence (3).

The nest is a large compact mass of dead vegetation with

a shallow depression lined with twigs, located six to ten feet up (sometimes higher) in dense, vine-entangled thickets, usually near or even over water. Three nests had three large (two-inch-long) eggs each, dull white, spotted and blotched with pale lilac and bright brown (2).

REFERENCES: Blake 1953, p. 122, picture in black and white. Condor 31:1:fpc., picture in color.

(1) Mexican Bird Songs, recordings by L. Irby Davis.

(2) Audubon Magazine 61:1:20, 21 and 61:2:76, 77, partial history (Skutch).

(3) Slud 1964.

* *Porzana carolina* Linnaeus

Sora   Gallinetía

N. Am. to Mexico (Baja Calif.); recorded in winter from Mexico, Brit. Honduras, Guatemala, Honduras, Nicaragua, Costa Rica, Panama, and S. Am.

Winter Resident   8½ in.   85 gr. (75 to 125)

Uncommon. One (sometimes two) of these small rails was present at the Aguada Tikal almost daily from 28 March to 4 April 1956, 8 March to 23 March 1957, and 23 February to 12 March 1958. The clearing of the aguada late in 1957 (more completely in 1958) had the same effect on the Sora as it had on the Wood-Rail, and none was seen there for the next five or more years.

Adults are brown above and largely gray below, with a conspicuous black facial mask (indistinct in the female) and a short yellow bill. Immatures lack the black mask and the gray underparts, which are a buff color instead.

The voice was limited here to a dozen or so softly given throaty chuckles, as *kuk-kuk-kuk;* in the north a descending whinny and a plaintive whistled *ker-wee* (1).

REFERENCES:

(1) Peterson 1960, p. 29, pictures in color. Austin 1961, p. 110, picture in color.

Laterallus ruber (Sclater and Salvin)

Ruddy Crake   Gallineta Enana

Ulumha

Trop. Mexico, Brit. Honduras, Guatemala, El Salvador,
  Honduras, Nicaragua, and Costa Rica
Resident   6 in.   50 gr.

Not uncommon, but heard more readily than seen, this
small rail was resident in the Aguada Tikal until April 1958.
Like the Gray-necked Wood-Rail, the Sora, and other species,
it was no longer attracted to the aguada when it was cleared
of its maze of weeds, vines, and grasses. The bird was found
later (1962) in the weedy marshes to the east of the airstrip.

It is a very red-brown bird, darker above than below, the
head nearly black. Legs are greenish, eyes red-brown, the bill
black.

Its voice during the day is a clear, insect-like chatter, of
rapidly repeated notes on the same key; or a long, drawn-out,
descending whinny which is most frequently heard at dawn
and before sunset (1). The nest is built in dense grass, weeds,
or vine tangles, about one to three feet above ground or over
shallow water; the domed-over structure is made of coarse
grasses, with a lateral doorway (Skutch, in litt.); a mere mat,
damp and water-soaked (2).

Three or four eggs are deposited, white, thickly marked,
mainly at the large end, with large and small dots of cinnamon
brown and pale lilac (Skutch, in litt.).

REFERENCES: Blake 1953, p. 124, picture in black and white.
(1) Russell 1964.   (2) Griscom 1932, p. 122.

Porphyrula martinica (Linnaeus)

Purple Gallinule   Gallineta de Pecho Morada

S. U. S., West Indies, Mid. Am., and S. Am.
Visitor   13 in.   350 gr.

Uncommon. Only one has been sighted here, from 28
March through 4 April 1956, at which time, however, it

seemed very much at home. For breeding purposes it prefers larger bodies of fresh water with heavy aquatic vegetation, where nests are built above the water, anchored to clumps of reeds, high grasses, or other vegetation. A clutch may contain three or four (even five) buff eggs, spotted with darker brown and lilac (1), (2).

The adult is predominantly a brilliant blue-violet, some lustrous green on the back, white under the tail. The bill is red with a yellow tip, and a "shield" on the forehead is very pale blue. Eyes are red-brown, legs yellow.

Immatures lack the bright colors, being drab dark green above, pale buff below, and with a dark bill.

The voice includes a series of cackling, clucking, or guttural notes (1).

REFERENCES: Austin 1961, p. 108, picture in color. Gilliard 1958, plate 47, color photograph.

(1) Auk 46:4:431–446, pictures, nesting described (Gross and Van Tyne).

(2) Eisenmann 1952.

HELIORNITHIDAE

Heliornis fulica (Boddaert)

Sungrebe   Pájaro Cantil

Xpatux Já

Local: trop. Mid. Am. (except El Salvador), and S. Am.
Visitor   13 in.   130 gr.

Rare, although it seems reasonable to expect to find them along a stream like the Río de la Pasión, in southern Petén. "The bird collected from the Aguada Tikal on 27 July 1959 is the only record of the Sungrebe from the Petén" (Smithe and Paynter 1963).

The head is conspicuously patterned in black and white except for buff cheeks and a red eye-ring. Upperparts are mainly olive-brown, the darker brown tail tipped white. Underparts are mainly white becoming gray toward the rear, and with a collar below the throat of black, then buff, then gray. The bill is bright red above with a gray tip; below white with a central scarlet patch. Eyes are brown; legs yellow with a clear black stripe, the toes yellow with black bars.

The voice is said to resemble vaguely the bark of a dog, but more rolling and sonorous; in Panama it is a series of hollow whistles, as *whoh'k,* repeated two to ten times, about three per second (Willis, in litt.).

Nest and eggs appear to be unknown.

REFERENCES: Blake 1953, p. 126, picture in black and white.

JACANIDAE

* Jacana spinosa subsp.

Middle American Jaçana   Gallito de Pantano

Ulumha

Texas, Greater Antilles, Mid. Am., and S. Am.
Resident?   9 in.   80 gr.

Possibly a wanderer from lakes farther south in the Petén. We have recorded it at the Aguada Tikal, in March and April 1956, May to July 1960, August through October 1962, March 1963; it is also present at Uaxactún. However, it was absent during 1957 through 1961, and also in February and March 1964. No immatures have been found. Apparently the renovating of the aguada has not kept it away; one, sometimes two, have been seen feeding, not only about the edges of the aguada, but well up on the grassy slopes, close to the dormitories of the project's staff. Although wary, they were not excessively shy.

The adult plumage is very conspicuous; a rich red-brown body and blackish head and neck; wings which display a large yellow area when flying, and even more clearly when landing, at which time they are briefly held up vertically above the body; a yellow bill with a bright yellow shield above it; long greenish legs and extremely long toes and claws which enable it to walk over the top of floating vegetation.

The immature bird has the yellow wing-pattern of the adult, but otherwise it differs materially, the upperparts being gray-brown, with a wide white stripe above the eyes, the underparts mostly white with a tinge of buff across the breast.

The nest is a shallow structure among floating water plants. Eggs, about four in number, are brown, heavily scrawled with black (1).

Its voice is a sharp cackle, usually uttered during flight; also a plaintive whistle (1); or rasping single notes and a typewriter-like clacking (2).

REFERENCES: Peterson 1960, p. 88, pictures in black and white. Austin 1961, p. 116, picture in color; end papers, picture of egg in color.

(1) Bent, No. 146.   (2) Slud 1964.

CHARADRIIDAE

Charadrius vociferus vociferus Linnaeus

Killdeer   Collarejo

N. Am., Mexico, West Indies, Peru and n. Chile; winters
   through Mid. Am. and n.w. S. Am.
Winter Resident   10 in.   85 gr.

It seems strange that I have found no previous records of Killdeer in the Petén, whereas it is a common winter visitant here. It has been recorded from October through April. It has been noted as absent from 22 April to 14 August. As many as twenty-eight at a time have frequented the airstrip and the grassy meadows of the camp.

The upperparts are mainly brown, the rump a conspicuous bright rufous, the head with a broad white forehead and a white neckband. Underparts are mainly white, with two conspicuous black bands across the chest. The tail is blackish, edged with white.

The calls, a noisy repetition of *kill-deeah,* or a plaintive *dee-dee-dee* on a rising scale, are diagnostic (1).

REFERENCES:
(1) Peterson 1960, p. 96, picture in color. Austin 1961, p. 120, picture in color.

SCOLOPACIDAE

* *Capella gallinago* subsp.
[*Gallinago gallinago*]

Common Snipe
Wilson's Snipe

Holarctic regions to n. Mexico; the N. Am. form, *delicata,* winters through Mid. Am. to n. S. Am.

Transient   11 in.   115 gr. (105 to 135)

Two sight records are all that we know of this snipe at Tikal; one on 8 September 1960, at the edge of Aguada Tikal (Trik, in litt.), the other on 26 October 1962 in the low wet grounds between the airstrip and the camp cottages.

The upperparts are brown, strongly striped over the head and back with light buff; underparts are mainly white, the chest mottled with buff and brown, the flanks brown-barred. The very long straight bill (over 2½ inches) is greenish gray; eyes are brown; legs light gray.

When startled, it flushes with a rasping, nasal alarm note and flies off in a characteristic erratic, zigzag manner (1).

REFERENCES: Peterson 1960, p. 112, picture in color. Austin 1961, p. 122, picture in color.
(1) Bent, No. 142.

Actitis macularia (Linnaeus)

Spotted Sandpiper   Alzaculito

N. Am.; winters through Mid. Am. to S. Am.
Winter Resident   8 in.   40 gr.

One or two, rarely three, were noted year after year at Aguada Tikal, as late as 15 May and as early as 23 July. However, we have no records for the months of November through February. Perhaps we should consider the Spotted Sandpiper a transient in the Petén rather than a visitant.

A few characteristics readily separate it from other sandpipers, the most diagnostic being its wingbeat: short, stiff, shallow, quivering, always appearing to be below the body level. Although some other birds pump the head and tail up and down while feeding, this one tips up and down so constantly as to be called "Tip-up" and "Teeter-tail."

The breeding plumage is characterized by large, clear, blackish spots on the underparts. In the winter the spots are lacking and the bird is primarily white below; at this time a clear light mark just in front of the folded wing is helpful, as is a white border on the trailing edge of the wing when flying. The bill is dark brown above, yellowish below; legs are greenish yellow, eyes are brown.

The voice is a sharp, clearly whistled *peet-weet,* sometimes repeated in a long series (1).

REFERENCES: Peterson 1960, p. 113, pictures in color.
(1) Bent, No. 146.

Tringa solitaria solitaria Wilson

Solitary Sandpiper   Becacineta Solitaria

N. N. Am.; winters through Mid. Am. to S. Am.
Winter Resident   8 in.   50 gr.

One or two were present at Aguada Tikal as late as 17 May and as early as 14 August. A female on 25 September 1962 was extremely fat and weighed 79.2 grams. The Solitary and the Spotted seemed to get along very well together.

The white eye-ring and the dark wings are good field marks. In flight the wings and rump are solidly black and without stripes, but the tail displays white sides, barred with black. It nods its head, rather like a Yellowlegs, but does not teeter like the Spotted.

Upperparts are gray-brown; underparts white, except for grayish neck and chest; eyes brown; bill blackish or dark green; legs dark with a green tinge.

The voice is a sharp piping, usually of three-syllable *peep-weep-weep* notes, thinner and higher pitched than those of the Spotted (1).

REFERENCES: Peterson 1960, p. 112, picture in color; p. 92, picture in black and white, in flight.

(1) Bent, No. 146.

Calidris melanotos (Vieillot)
[*Erolia melanotos*—AOU 1957]

Pectoral Sandpiper   Becacineta
                                          Becacineta Pinta

Arctic N. Am.; winters in s. S. Am., migrates Mid. Am.
Transient   9 in.   55 gr.

Probably a regular migrant, having been noted in three different years, 28 February, 28 March, and 8 September. The September bird was quite fat, but not heavy. At Sayaxché, some sixty miles to the south, large flocks of forty or more were seen on 13 March (Hundley, in litt.).

The clearest field mark for this shore bird is its buff chest, which contrasts sharply with the white throat above and white breast below; additionally the back is streaked (snipe-like), wings lack all white stripes, and the tail lacks any white at sides. It flies with the head held high. Upperparts in general are streaky rusty brown; underparts white, with pectoral buff band; bill is dark brown above, shading below to light brown at base; eyes are brown; legs yellow-green.

Voice is somewhat snipe-like, a sharp, abrupt, reedy *crrrik* or *kerr* (1).

REFERENCES: Peterson 1960, p. 113, picture in color; p. 93, picture in black and white.

(1) Bent, No. 142.

Calidris fuscicollis (*Vieillot*)
[*Erolia fuscicollis*—AOU 1957]

White-rumped Sandpiper   Becacineta

Arctic N. Am.; migrates through Mid. Am. to s. S. Am.
Transient   7½ in.

This first record for all of Guatemala was taken 12 May 1963 at Aguada Tikal.

The white rump is a good field mark when the bird is flying, less so when at rest. Upperparts are brown or brownish gray, and streaked; white underparts have a chest streaking, but not nearly as prominent as the larger Pectoral. Eyes are coffee color, legs greenish.

The voice (Peterson 1960) is a thin mouselike *jee-jeet* (1); or a feeble, lisping *tsip* (2).

REFERENCES:
(1) Peterson 1960, p. 113, picture in color; p. 93, picture in black and white.
(2) Bent, No. 142.

RECURVIROSTRIDAE

Himantopus himantopus mexicanus (Müller)
[*Himantopus mexicanus*—AOU 1957]

Black-necked Stilt   Candelero
                                          Soldadito

U. S., West Indies, locally Mexico and S. Am.; ranges (perhaps breeds) through Mid. Am.
Visitor   14½ in.   115 gr. (to 200 in some areas)

A female weighing 115.8 grams, taken at Aguada Tikal 24 September 1962, is a first record for the Petén. Males are mainly glossy black above, females a somewhat duller brownish black. Both have white foreheads, white about the eyes, and pure white underparts. In flight the white rump and light gray tail become visible. Since it is a bird of marshes and shallow waters, its long black bill (over 2½ inches) and long stilt-like bright red legs (close to 10 inches) are well suited to its feeding habits. The eyes of our bird were of two colors, an inner ring of brown and an outer ring of bright red.

When alarmed it utters a series of sharp *kyip-kyip-kyip*-ings, in a rising pitch (1). Other notes are a nasal, squeaky *pr-ep* or *prowp,* and a sort of *chek* (2).

They usually gather in small, loose colonies to breed. Nests are mere hollows in the mudflats, or they may be built up into small mounds to keep the eggs above water. Eggs, three or four, are buff, spotted with brownish black (1), (3).

REFERENCES:
(1) Peterson 1960, p. 97, picture in color. Gilliard 1958, plate 63, color photograph (with nest). Allen 1961, plate 28, color photograph (with nest).
(2) Slud 1964.   (3) Herklots 1961.

COLUMBIDAE

Columba speciosa Gmelin

Scaled Pigeon   Paloma Pecho Brillante
                                     Espumuy
                                     Paloma Escamosa

Chukib

Trop. Mid. Am. (except El Salvador) and S. Am.
Resident   12 in.   270 gr.   Plate 10

Fairly common; but its habit of frequenting the heavy foliage in the crowns of tall trees makes it difficult to see. It is found within the forest at Tikal, not far in from wide roads and trails; also in forest edge and thinned woodland.

This is the largest and bulkiest pigeon at Tikal, almost as large as a domestic pigeon, and makes very choice eating. Its name derives from the diagnostic scaly effect of the black nape and back, speckled with light brown spots, and the black throat and chest coarsely speckled with white spots. The head is brownish; the back and wings ruddy chestnut, darkening to nearly black on the tail and to brown on the flight feathers; the chin, upper throat, and lower breast are iridescent vinaceous; the crissum white. The bill is very bright red, the eyes brown with a red eye-ring, and the legs shades of lavender. Females are much the same as males but in duller tones, the scaly effect smaller but sharper black and white.

Its voice is a slow, subdued but far-carrying *cooo-coo-coo-coooo,* sounding to me much like a Mourning Dove (*Zenaidura macroura*), but softer, mellower, and less mournful.

Its nest is frequently located from seven to fifteen feet up in dense tangles and thickets; less often some fifty or more feet up in tall trees which are so densely covered with vines that the nests are hardly visible (1). The latter was the situation at Tikal of the only nest I found, at least seventy feet up, just below the crown of a large tree. It was a very bulky platform blended into a heavy growth of vines and epiphytes, all so thick that although I could hear the birds I could see nothing of them. Only one white egg is deposited (1), (2); two eggs per set are reported from Trinidad (3).

REFERENCES: Blake 1953, p. 181, picture in black and white.
(1) Wilson Bull. 76:3:211–214, life history (Skutch).
(2) Russell 1964.   (3) Herklots 1961.

Columba nigrirostris Sclater

Short-billed Pigeon   Paloma de Pico Corto
                                           Paloma Piquicorta

Tzusuy (pigeons in general)

Trop. Mid. Am. (except El Salvador)
Resident   11½ in.   160 gr.   Plate 10

Common, more numerous than the larger Scaled Pigeon, and perhaps the most numerous pigeon at Tikal. It is found in virgin forest and the adjacent semi-open woodlands, where it forages mainly from moderate heights to high in large trees, and where it is more readily heard than seen. Occasionally flocks of twelve or more are found feeding on fruits at lower levels; during that activity they can be closely approached.

They are deep purple about the head and neck, blending into a brightly vinaceous body; the back, wings, and tail are dark brown with an iridescent greenish sheen. The bill is short and black, the eyes reddish with a red eye-ring, the legs red.

Its call is a very distinctive, four-syllable phrase, heard far and wide, which sounds to me like a mournful

to / wah \ shac / toon advertising the neighboring village of Uaxactún; if close by, a purr may be heard at the end (2).

Nests are much like those of the Scaled Pigeon, and composed of branchlets and twigs torn with much effort from the trees by the males. They are located from twenty-five feet up in dense tangles in the undergrowth, to a hundred feet up in the heavy foliage of tall trees (1).

I have found no information on eggs.

REFERENCES:
(1) Wilson Bull. 76:3:214–216, life history (Skutch).
(2) Mexican Bird Songs, recordings by L. Irby Davis.

Columbina talpacoti rufipennis (Bonaparte)
[*Columbigallina talpacoti*—AOU 1957]

Ruddy Ground-Dove   Tortolita Rojiza

Mukuy (ground-doves in general)

Trop. Mid. Am. and S. Am.
Resident   6½ in.   45 gr.   Plate 10

Common in the cleared areas. At the camp they breed in the orange trees and forage among the taller grasses in flocks of a dozen, in groups of only two or three where the grass is cut short.

They are about the size of a sparrow, but appear larger. The male has a grayish head, upperparts cinnamon brown, underparts russet vinaceous, the wings conspicuously spotted with black. Females are similarly colored, but paler and grayer above, paler vinaceous brown below. Both sexes flash rufous wings in flight. The bill is dusky, eyes reddish, legs pink.

The voice is a soft, three-syllable *kitty-woo,* repeated, but not monotonously long (1); also a low, purring *co-oo, co-oo.*

The nest is built in shrubs or trees, usually four to eight feet up, occasionally twenty or even higher. It is a thick-walled, but not tightly woven open cup, with a saucer about one inch deep, made of straws, twigs, and rootlets, and lined with dry grasses. Eggs, usually two, rarely one or three to a clutch, are pure white (1).

REFERENCES:
(1) Condor 58:3:188–205, life history (Skutch).

Claravis pretiosa (Ferrari-Pérez)

Blue Ground-Dove   Tortolita Celeste

Tuch Mukuy

Trop. Mid. Am. and S. Am.
Resident   7½ in.   70 gr.

Common from 1956 through early 1962, in the months of February through mid-July, but absent during August, September, and October 1962. Strangely they were conspicuously absent in March 1963 and in February and March 1964. They frequent clearings skirting brushy forest edges such as wide grassy trails, and the sides of the airstrip and Aguada Dimick, rather than the more open areas of the camp.

The male is bright blue-gray, paler on the forehead and throat, boldly spotted and barred with black on the wings. The female is buff-brown above, paler on the forehead and throat, spotted and barred with chestnut on the wings, and bright russet tail coverts and central tail feathers. Legs and toes are reddish, nails are black; bills are pale gray. A pair of these richly contrasting doves presents a lovely picture.

The eyes of both sexes are a bright red, but I recorded four live birds (two males and two females) with eyes that showed double and triple rings of color; the outer ring was most frequently red, the central ring brown (in one instance these colors were reversed), the innermost ring a yellowish white. All had been captured in mist nets and it may be that their efforts to get free caused this condition.

The call is a low, soft *coot,* not especially mournful, and other notes (1).

Nests, usually located about five to twelve feet up in shrubs and trees covered with tangles of vines, are made of twiglets, weed stems, and vine tendrils, forming a slight, frail, shallow, almost transparent structure. Two pure white eggs are the normal clutch (1).

REFERENCES:
(1) Condor 61:21:65–74, life history (Skutch); fpc., pictures in color of male and female.

Leptotila plumbeiceps plumbeiceps Sclater and Salvin

Gray-headed Dove   Paloma de Cabeza Gris

Tzutsuy

Trop. Mid. Am. (except El Salvador) to w. Panama and w. Colombia

Resident   10 in.   160 gr.   Plate 10

Fairly common, but being a comparatively quiet, not very vocal forest bird, it gives the impression that it is uncommon. Here it forages on the ground and up to moderate heights, in the more open-canopy parts of the forest where the understory is fairly heavy.

The blue-gray head, becoming nearly white on the forehead, chin, and throat, contrasts strongly with the olive-brown back; underparts are pinkish vinaceous (white below the tail); the dark, lateral tail feathers have white tips. The bill is black, legs red, eyes almost white with a yellowish tinge.

At Gallon Jug, British Honduras, the song is a short, hollow *cooooo,* given once every two or three seconds. Nests there were thin platforms made of twigs, located on top of stumps, large palm leaves, and on crossed branches in trees, ranging from three to thirty-five feet above ground. Two white eggs are deposited (Willis, in litt.).

REFERENCES: None.

NOTE: The White-tipped Dove (*Leptotila verreauxi*) should be looked for in the forest here; recorded from the lake country of the Petén to the south, at Yaxha, Flores, Pacomón.

Geotrygon montana montana (Linnaeus)

Ruddy Quail-Dove   Paloma de Montaña
                              Paloma Terrestre

K'ankab Tzutsuy

Trop. Mid. Am. (except El Salvador), S. Am., and West Indies

| Resident | 9 in. | 140 gr. | Plate 10 |

Not uncommon, but the least common of the pigeons at Tikal. I always saw it on the ground, in the dense cover bordering low moist areas, where it walked quickly into hiding.

It is short-tailed, stocky, and quail-like. The male has lustrous purplish chestnut upperparts, richest in color on the back, fading to light cinnamon rufous on the forehead; the throat is pinkish cinnamon shading to a buff breast and lighter belly. The female lacks the bright purplish chestnut back and is, instead, a flat olive-brown. The bill and legs are reddish, sometimes bright red, sometimes brown-red. Eyes range in color from yellow or orange to brown and red-brown, surrounded by a red eye-ring and purplish red bare skin area, paler on the female.

The voice is a deep, mournful *coo-oo-oo,* heard mostly from March to June (1); or a low humming *mmmm,* repeated with half-second intervals (2).

The nest is a broad, slightly concave, frail structure, built of coarse twigs, covered with leaves, and located in the undergrowth, from one to eight feet above ground. The eggs are not the usual white of most pigeons, but buff or cream color, two to a clutch (1).

REFERENCES:
(1) Condor 51:1:3–19, life history (Skutch).
(2) Eisenmann 1952.

PSITTACIDAE

Ara macao (Linnaeus)

Scarlet Macaw   Guacamaya Roja

Moo
Ix-Oop
Ah-K'ota

Trop. Mid. Am. (except Brit. Honduras) and S. Am.
Visitor (Resident formerly?)   36 in. (20 in. tail)   1150 gr.

Unknown in life at Tikal and Uaxactún except for a single sight report, when two were seen flying over the ruins in April 1962 (Trik, in litt.). However, a great quantity of bones have been found and identified by Paynter (in litt.). Bones from caches and burials may represent importations for ceremonial purposes, but by far the greater number were found in debris and under conditions that indicate they were the leavings of predators. Perhaps macaws were once as common here as they are today in the more open forests and borders of the lake and savannah country and the Río de la Pasión, only twenty-five to fifty miles to the south.

Although the largest of Petén parrots, the nearly two-foot-long, bright red tail accounts for almost two-thirds of its size. It is brilliantly colored in bright red, scarlet, vermilion, chrome yellow, and blues. The bare skin of the face and the upper bill are pinkish white, the lower bill black; legs dark gray; eyes pale yellow.

The screeching calls are harsh and strident. The egg is pure white. It nests in holes in trees.

REFERENCES: Austin 1961, p. 148, picture in color; end papers, picture of egg in color.

Aratinga astec astec (Souancé)

Olive-throated Parakeet
Lorito
Perico Grande

Xkili (parakeets in general)
Xk'ali'i

Gulf and Caribbean slope of trop. Mid. Am. to w. Panama
Resident   9½ in.   80 gr.   Plate 11

Uncommon, although flocks of four to twelve are occasionally seen and heard flying across the airstrip and well into the bordering forest. Their flight is rapid and direct, accompanied by noisy, shriek-like chatter.

This is the smallest of the Tikal parrots, although the long, pointed tail, which extends far back of the wings and accounts for half its total length, makes it measure more than the Brown-hooded Parrot (*Pionopsitta haematotis*) which is twice its bulk. Upperparts are bright green with blue in the wings; throat and breast are brownish, belly greenish yellow; the bill is ivory and gray; the cere yellow with a bright orange spot in the center; feet are dark brown. The eyes are yellow (sometimes with a narrow outer ring of red), surrounded by white bare skin area.

They nest in cavities in trees and possibly also in termitaries. Eggs are white.

REFERENCES: Bond 1961, plate 2, picture in color (of very similar *Aratinga nana*).

Pionopsitta haematotis haematotis (Sclater and Salvin)

Brown-hooded Parrot   Cotorra de Cabeza Parda

Xthuth (parrots in general)

Trop. Mid. Am. (except El Salvador), and n.w. S. Am.
Resident   8½ in.   160 gr.   Plate 11

Common. These short, stocky little parrots, with their wide-eyed, owlish expression, frequent the crowns of trees where they feed quietly and do not readily take alarm. Sometimes they chatter together, but not noisily. The general appearance is of a square-tailed bird with a brown head and neck, dark green upperparts, lighter, brighter green below. There is considerable blue in the wings, some red over the ear coverts and in the neck, but none of it conspicuous. In flight a large brilliant scarlet patch is displayed on the sides and below the wings which normally hide it.

The bare area about the dull yellow eyes is blue-white, the bill a dirty white, the legs dark gray.

They nest in holes in trees. The eggs are white.

They utter *p'leek-p'leek* notes alternating with rough *zapp-zapp* calls when in flight; also gurgling and squeaky notes (at Gallon Jug, British Honduras, Willis, in litt.); and listen to (1).

REFERENCES: Blake 1953, p. 197, picture in black and white.
(1) Mexican Bird Songs, recordings by L. Irby Davis.

Pionus senilis senilis (Spix)

White-crowned Parrot   Cotorra de Corona Blanca

Xt'ut'

Trop. Mid. Am. (except El Salvador) to w. Panama
Resident   9 in.   200 gr.   Plate 11

Common. This and the White-fronted Parrot (*Amazona albifrons*) were the only ones found here with white on the head. One other, the Yellow-lored (*A. xantholora*) occurs farther north, preferring deciduous forests, but should be watched for.

The White-crowned Parrot is common here year after year, but it was not reported by Van Tyne (1935) at Uaxactún.

It is the darkest and bluest of all our parrots, with a deep blue chest and breast; the head and neck are also deep blue, contrasting strongly with the white forehead, white crown, and white upper throat and chin; the wings are dark green with much dark blue in the flight feathers and bronzy brown coverts; the back is dark green. The only *bright* green is on the rump and upper tail coverts; the outer tail feathers are blue. Some red appears in the tail and the under tail coverts. The bill is yellowish green, the feet orange, the brown eyes surrounded by bright orange bare skin.

It is generally silent when climbing deliberately and carefully through trees, but screeches noisily when flying (1).

They nest in holes in trees and the eggs are white, three to a clutch in British Honduras (2).

REFERENCES: Blake 1953, p. 197, picture in black and white.
(1) Slud 1964.   (2) Russell 1964.

Amazona albifrons nana W. de W. Miller

White-fronted Parrot   Loro de Frente Blanca

Cop (a general term)

Chiefly arid trop. areas Mid. Am. to w. Costa Rica
Resident   10 in.   215 gr.   Plate 11

Uncommon, although found breeding at Uaxactún (Van Tyne 1935). It may be more common than we presently believe but has certainly been difficult to find; more to be expected in open country with scattered trees. With a white forehead extending back into the deep blue crown, with bright red lores and bright red wing patch (lacking in females), it should be conspicuous and not readily overlooked. The remainder of the bird, head and face and neck, upperparts and lowerparts, is bright green with a yellow tinge, and blue wing tips. The bill is yellow, the cere pale yellow, the eyes pale yellow, the bare skin gray, the legs greenish yellow.

It voices a raucous, squally *ca-ca-ca-ca,* or a barking *yack-yack-yack,* quite different from the screeches of many parrots (1); and hear (2).

They nest in holes in trees and the eggs are white.

REFERENCES: Condor 51:2:fpc., pictures in color (male and female).
(1) Slud 1964.
(2) Mexican Bird Songs, recordings by L. Irby Davis.

Amazona autumnalis autumnalis (Linnaeus)

Red-lored Parrot   Loro Cariamarillo
Yellow-cheeked Parrot

E'xikin

Trop. Mid. Am. (except El Salvador) and n.w. S. Am.
Resident   12 to 13 in.   300 to 450 gr.   Plate 12

Fairly common in the forest and in the treetops of forest edges. This large parrot varies greatly in weight, some birds exceeding even the 450 grams listed above.

The bright red loral area extends up and across the forehead (reduced in immatures). The cheeks are chrome yellow, a very conspicuous mark (except for immatures which have greenish cheeks). The crown is lavender. Upperparts are mainly clear parrot green, lowerparts yellowish green; the flight feathers have dark blue tips and a red patch on the secondaries. The bill is yellowish above, black below; the cere yellow; the eyes yellow-orange surrounded by yellowish white bare skin; the feet are grayish.

It is somewhat vocal when feeding, arguing, and growling. When flying it has many different calls, one a short-note *kyake-kyake-r-kyake,* etc.; another *yoik-yoik,* etc., all quickly enunciated (1).

It nests in holes in trees; a nest in British Honduras contained two eggs (2).

REFERENCES: Blake 1953, p. 200, picture in black and white.
(1) Slud 1964.   (2) Russell 1964.

Amazona farinosa guatemalae (Sclater)

Blue-crowned Parrot   Loro Cabeza Azul
Mealy Parrot

Trop. Mid. Am. (except El Salvador) and S. Am.
Resident   14½ in.   600 gr.   Plate 12

Common, second only to *Pionus senilis.* It is most numerous in moist, heavily forested regions, where it is found near the edge of clearings, roads, and trails; also wherever fruiting trees attract it to feed.

It is conspicuous because of its noisy calling from treetops, where it chatters a great deal, and also because of the very characteristic flight call, a three-syllable phrase which sounds to me as though Tikal is being hailed,

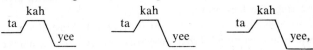

loud and clear; it also utters some typical parrot conversation followed by harsh *chock-chock-chock-chock*'s (1).

The plumage of this largest of Tikal parrots is mainly dull green, paler and richer on the cheeks and the underparts; the crown and nape are pale blue; the flight feathers have dark blue tips and a red patch on the secondaries. The bill is black and ivory above, gray below; the yellow cere is very small; feet are dirty yellow-green; the eyes are red-orange, surrounded by yellowish white bare skin.

REFERENCES:
(1) Mexican Bird Songs, recordings by L. Irby Davis.

CUCULIDAE

Piaya cayana thermophila Sclater

Squirrel Cuckoo   Piscoy

Kipcho

Trop. Mid. Am. and S. Am.
Resident   18 in. (10 in. tail)   100 gr.

Fairly common. It prefers forest edges, not in the dry high ridges, but in the moister areas, nearer marshy levels. It may be seen, usually solitary, running and hopping along branches at medium height in the trees about camp, silent and furtive, but smoothly agile, frequently displaying its extremely long, spectacularly marked tail. The tail feathers are graduated to an exceptional degree and from below they produce a decidedly checkerboard effect, each dark brown overlapping feather conspicuously tipped with white. Upperparts are bright rufous deepening in tone on the tail; underparts are pinkish buff about the throat, dark gray on the body. The bill is olive-yellow, the eyes bright red surrounded by a yellow-green eye-ring, the legs gray.

Its calls are too numerous to fully report. Most characteristic is an arresting, perhaps explosive *skwik-ahhhhh;* another is a short, sharply uttered, two or three times repeated *djit* (1); to Sutton an imperative *keep-rear* (2).

The nest is a shallow platform of many dead leaves (some placed while still green) on top of a foundation of coarse twigs, and sometimes located as low as three to eight feet up in a citrus tree, a bracken tangle, and such (Skutch, in litt.).

REFERENCES: Blake 1953, p. 204, picture in black and white. Condor 51:3:fpc., picture in color.
  (1) Slud 1964.
  (2) Auk 59:1:15 (Sutton and Pettingill).

Crotophaga sulcirostris sulcirostris Swainson

Groove-billed Ani   Pijuy

Chick-bul

Texas, Mid. Am., and n. S. Am.
Resident   12 in.   ♂ 85 gr. ♀ 75 gr.

Common locally. A small colony has been present year after year, first at the Aguada Tikal. When the aguada was cleared of its brushy cover they moved away to the thorny cover at the Aguada Dimick, located at the far end of the airstrip. There a group of six or eight has persisted, stragglers sometimes visiting the camp. I have not seen them elsewhere in Tikal, but Van Tyne (1935) reported a "flock of about eight anis lived in the Uaxactún clearing."

The ani is coal black, even the eyes appearing to be black. The tail is long and so loosely joined as to be floppy. The upper bill is high and very strongly arched; grooves parallel to the ridge account for its English name.

Its voice is a thrice-repeated two-syllabled *pee-huy, pee-huy, pee-huy,* not unpleasant, and which accounts for its Guatemalan name. It has a variety of other notes also, one a mournful wail, another a threatening, rasping *grrr* (1), (2); Eisenmann (3) said, a series of short, dry *hwilk*'s, sometimes accelerated so as to suggest the *wicka-wicka-wicka-wicka* of a flicker (*Colaptes*).

The nest is a bulky structure woven of coarse material such as dry twigs, lined with originally green leaves, and located in bushes and low trees. Dense, thorny vegetation is preferred. Eggs, three or four in number, are blue-green, covered with a chalky white deposit. Often communal nesting occurs, with three or four birds laying in the same nest (1).

REFERENCES: Blake 1953, p. 206, picture in black and white.
(1) Auk 76:3:281–317, life history (Skutch).
(2) Mexican Bird Songs, recordings by L. Irby Davis.
(3) Condor 59:4:253, in Panama (Eisenmann).

Dromococcyx phasianellus rufigularis (Lawrence)

Pheasant Cuckoo   Cuclillo
                                             Cuclillo Faisán

Baken-chulu

Trop. Mid. Am. (except Brit. Honduras) and S. Am.
Resident   14 in.   90 gr.

Uncommon but not rare. This terrestrial cuckoo is difficult to find, preferring the dense ground cover bordering the low moist areas rather than the high, dry, and more open ridges. It is mainly gray-brown above with numerous buffy white, smallish tips to the wing and tail coverts, and to the flight feathers and tail feathers. The tail coverts, seen close at hand, are very filmy. The crested head and neck are rusty brown; a white stripe extends back of the eye. Underparts are mainly white, with a light tinge of buff over the throat and chest, which are also streaked with brownish black. The eyes are yellowish (one bird had brown eyes), surrounded by a yellow-green eye-ring, the bare skin extending back over the ears where it shades into gray. The bill is long and slim, black above, gray below; the legs lead gray.

The voice (in Panama) is a three-noted whistle, *whoo-hee-wer'r'r'r'r'*, the second higher than the others, the third with a tinamou-like quaver (Willis, in litt.).

It is parasitic, using any available open nest.

REFERENCES: None.

TYTONIDAE

*** *Tyto alba* subsp.

Barn Owl   Lechuza Ratonera
                                                Lechuza Mono

Xooch

Practically cosmopolitan, N. Am., West Indies, Mid. Am. (not reported Brit. Honduras), S. Am.
Resident formerly?   17 in.

Not found at Tikal, nor by Van Tyne (1935) at Uaxactún, but he reported a "first" record for all Guatemala by Malleis, 22 June 1923, at Flores, Lake Petén-Itzá, a male *Tyto alba pratincola*. We list it here on the evidence of its bones, which were collected from the debris of temples and other structures in Tikal. None have been reported from burials or ceremonial caches. Perhaps the owls had been victims of other predators or possibly they died in their own dark retreats and so left this evidence of their former existence in Tikal.

It is a long-legged bird, with golden brown upperparts and pale buff or whitish underparts. The facial discs, nearly white, form a conspicuous heart shape. The flight is light and moth-like. Eyes are almost black. They live largely on small rodents.

Eggs, two to four in Trinidad (1), are white in color, and are laid in a litter of regurgitated fur pellets, located in any dark place such as old buildings, hollow trees, even burrows.

The voice is a rasping hiss; other shriller cries and a variety of sounds are also known.

REFERENCES: Peterson 1960, p. 128, picture in color. Blake 1953, p. 209, picture in black and white. Austin 1961, p. 156, picture in color.
(1) Herklots 1961.

STRIGIDAE

Otus guatemalae guatemalae (Sharpe)

Vermiculated Screech-Owl   Tecolotito de Guatemala
                                       Tecolotito Maullador

Kulte'

Trop. Mid. Am. and S. Am.
Resident   9 in.   100 gr.

Fairly common but not numerous. This small owl was frequently heard, at least from March through August, from low areas about Aguada Tikal to the high ridges of the Great Plaza. On the other hand, there were more frequent occasions when it was impossible to drum one up. The call (as well as the appearance) is very similar to that of the Common Screech-Owl (*Otus asio*), variously described as a soft but clear tremulous whinny, or a musical quavering trill. On one occasion a bird called steadily for twenty-five minutes, each trill lasting a full three seconds, with intervals of twenty-five to thirty seconds, about two calls a minute.

The Tikal birds were dark gray, generously vermiculated with black, the breast also streaked with very narrow black lines. No ruddy phases were seen. The bill is greenish above shading to brown at the base, and all gray below; feet are light brown; eyes yellow.

Nests are in holes in trees, both very high and low, and possibly in other cavities. Eggs, about three, are white.

NOTE: The screech-owl has been traditionally identified by archeologists with the *Moan-bird* of Maya glyphs (see illus-

COLLARED FOREST-FALCON

p. 41.

ADULT: 18 to 24 inches; occurs in three color-phases: (1) white underparts; (2) buff or tawny underparts; (3) dull black underparts (not illustrated); note thick-headed effect, pale collar (lacking in black phase), and dark, crescent-shaped extensions back of cheeks; tail is long (half of bird's length), strongly rounded, and has three clearly marked narrow pale bars. Eyes brown; facial area dull olive-green.

IMMATURE: occurs variably colored rather than in distinct phases; paler collar, sometimes obscure; underparts (whether white or tawny) boldly barred with dark brown.

NOTE: There are superficial resemblances between this falcon and the accipiter illustrated below it.

BICOLORED HAWK

p. 30.

ADULT: 14 to 18 inches; bright rufous thighs contrast sharply with gray underparts (but the gray varies widely from pale whitish to dark lead gray); wings from below are typical of accipiters in shape and pattern; long tail has two broad bars (a third partly visible), dusky from above, nearly white below. Eyes orange; facial area yellow.

IMMATURE: nuchal collar variable (buffy, or whitish, or obscure); thighs not always of contrasting color; underparts also are variable, from creamy white, through buff, to deep rufous; tail has three clear bars, narrower than on adults.

PLATE 7

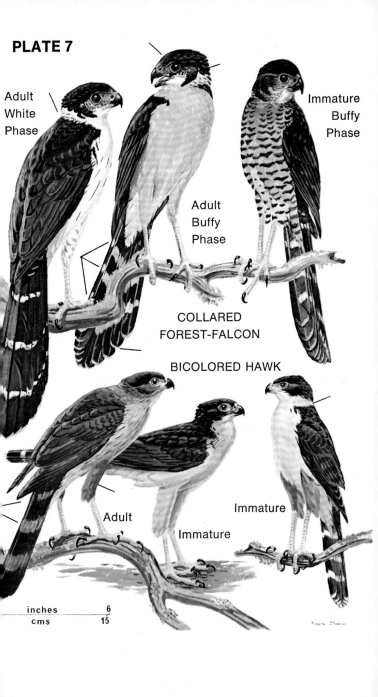

Adult
White
Phase

Adult
Buffy
Phase

Immature
Buffy
Phase

COLLARED
FOREST-FALCON

BICOLORED HAWK

Adult

Immature

Immature

inches 6
cms 15

Hawks on plates 7 and 8 have been grouped together because of their numerous similarities and their variable color patterns.

BARRED FOREST-FALCON p. 42

ADULT MALE: 14 inches; half the bulk of the Collared Forest-Falcon, but with a similar long, graduated, strongly rounded tail, crossed by three narrow whitish bars; above blackish gray; below whitish, distinctly marked with very fine black bars (almost vermiculated) on chest. Cere, facial skin, legs orange-yellow. Eyes pale brown.

ADULT FEMALE: black, strongly tinged with brown; distinctly barred below, but coarser than on male; cere, facial skin and eyes yellow; legs tinged with green.

IMMATURES: have buff collars, sometimes hidden; underparts extremely variable, from creamy white to deep buff; usually with widely spaced barring, but sometimes devoid of barring; otherwise much like adult female.

DOUBLE-TOOTHED KITE p. 27

ADULT FEMALE: 13 inches; blackish gray above; wings conspicuously barred with white below; white throat with diagnostic single black central stripe; tail has three narrow whitish bars; rest of underparts cream color, boldly barred with gray and rufous, blending to deep chestnut at sides of breast. Cere and facial skin greenish; eyes red-orange.

ADULT MALE (not illustrated): much like female except underparts grayer (less ruddy); the degree of rufous and barring variable; cere and facial skin yellower green; eyes orange (less red).

IMMATURE: upperparts dark brown streaked and mottled with white; below creamy white to buff, streaked with dark brown; the single diagnostic dark throat mark is present.

PLATE 8

Adult
♂

Adult
♀

BARRED
FOREST-FALCON

Immatures

DOUBLE-
TOOTHED
KITE

♀
Adult

Immature

0   Inches   6
0   cms   15

PLATE 9

♀
BAT
FALCON

ORANGE BREASTED
FALCON

♂

♀

BAT ♂
FALCON

0   inches   6
0   cms   15

The Orange-breasted Falcon is distinguished from the Bat Falcon by its wholly deep rufous chest and breast (black on the Bat Falcon), and by its much larger size; although a small male of the former may not be much larger than a large female of the latter.

The arrow above Temple II points to the cavity where a pair of Orange-breasted Falcons nested.

ORANGE-BREASTED FALCON   *p. 43.*

ADULT MALE: 11½ inches; above blue-black; throat white; chest, breast, under tail coverts and thighs all rich rufous; belly black with rufous barring (or rufous with black barring).

ADULT FEMALE: 16 inches; much the same as the male except for much *larger size.*

BAT FALCON   *p. 44.*

ADULT MALE: 9 inches; above blue-black; throat white, blending into narrow rufous band, then abruptly into black chest, breast, and upper belly (very narrowly barred with gray and rufous); under tail coverts and thighs rufous.

ADULT FEMALE: 11 inches; much the same as the male except for *larger size.*

tration on cover). Its bones might therefore be looked for in ceremonial burials and caches, but none have been found there. However, bones of the pygmy-owl (see *Glaucidium brasilianum*) *have* been found in such places, though lacking the "horns" usually shown on glyphs.

REFERENCES: Peterson 1960, p. 128, pictures in color (of Common Screech-Owl, gray and ruddy phases).

*** *Glaucidium brasilianum* subsp.

Ferruginous Pygmy-Owl   Tecolotito Listado

Toj-caj-xnuk

S.w. U. S., Mid. Am., and S. Am.
Resident formerly?   6 in.   ♂ 55 gr. ♀ 70 gr.

Not found at Tikal or in any other part of the Petén as far as I know, despite the fact that it hunts in daylight and has a distinctive, not easily overlooked call. It is noted here because the bones of at least six individuals have been found, all in burials and ceremonial caches in Tikal. None, however, was found in the debris among the ruins. This situation is directly opposite to that of the Barn Owl bones, all of which came from debris. Did pygmy-owls live here when the forests were thinned out for ancient milpas? Or were they imported by the ancient Maya, possibly for ceremonial purposes?

This very small owl is a ruddy or rusty brown, narrowly streaked with white over the head, broadly streaked with brown on the underparts. The hind neck has a black patch on each side, a good field mark. The tail is banded with alternately rufous and dark brown bars. Eyes are yellowish.

The voice is a series of fifteen to thirty slowly repeated characteristic whistles, continuing for about a minute and given at a rate of about two per second (Willis, in litt.); it is readily imitated and used to "call up" other birds for which it has a curious attraction; and hear (1).

Nests are in holes or cavities in trees. Eggs, about three per clutch, are white (2).

REFERENCES:
(1) Mexican Bird Songs, recordings by L. Irby Davis.
(2) Peterson 1960, p. 126, picture in black and white. Austin 1961, p. 157, picture in color.

Ciccaba virgata centralis Griscom

Mottled Wood-Owl   Lechuza Café

Icim (owls in general)

Trop. Mid. Am. and n. S. Am.
Resident   13 in.   ♂ 240 gr. ♀ 300 gr.

Common. They were frequently heard not only around the Aguada Tikal, but throughout the forest bordering thinned-out areas. The calls started with a low grunt, heard best when fairly close, followed by one to four (usually three) deliberate, loud hoots. The hooting overlapped the *hut-hut* of the Blue-crowned Motmots (*Momotus momota*) in the morning and again in the evening, both birds calling together for about half an hour. On one occasion I heard a call of the same tonal quality, but which began with six short, sharp hoots, followed by the three slow and deliberate ones typical of this species. Another call, which may have been this bird's also, began with two short, low hoots followed by three slow, two-tone $\dfrac{\text{hoo}}{\diagdown\text{oo}},$ $\dfrac{\text{hoo}}{\diagdown\text{oo}},$ $\dfrac{\text{hoo}}{\diagdown\text{oo's}}$ and closed with one short, sharp *hut*.

The soft, mottled plumage recalled that of goatsuckers more than did other owls, although the *Otus guatemalae* had a similar effect. The upperparts are dull dark brown mixed with buff mottling; underparts are lighter, tawny, the chest mottled dusky, the breast and belly broadly streaked with dark brown. The tail has a series of lighter bars. Toes are yellow-brown, the bill yellow-green, eyes brown.

They nest in cavities in trees. Two dull white eggs are deposited (1).

REFERENCES: Blake 1953, p. 219, picture in black and white.
(1) Herklots 1961.

Ciccaba nigrolineata Sclater

Black-and-White Owl   Lechuza Listada

Trop. Mid. Am. and n.w. S. Am.
Resident   15 in.   350 gr.

Rare. One individual is all I have seen at Tikal. It is mainly black above, sharply barred with white across the neck and shoulders, and with spots of white in a line above the eyes; underparts are white, heavily and sharply barred with black; the black tail has four or five narrow white bands. The bill is brownish yellow; the feet orange-yellow, the eyes (Blake 1953, p. 219) "brown, reddish or yellow."

About the same time I saw this bird, I heard "towards midnight a most penetrating scream, very human-like or at least mammal-like. It was repeated once." I did not connect this (and perhaps should not now) with the possible call of this owl until I read (Paynter 1955, p. 136) "the unusual mammal-like cry of this widely distributed but rare species, led to its collection." Russell (1964, p. 80) imitated its "loud, high-pitched *who-ah*" to the same end. The call is also described as *wooff-whooo*.

I have no definite data on nesting or eggs.

REFERENCES: Blake 1953, p. 220, picture in black and white.

NYCTIBIIDAE

Nyctibius griseus mexicanus Nelson

Common Potoo   Caballero

Hap-mu-hap

Greater Antilles, trop. Mid. Am., and S. Am.
Resident   15 in.   250 gr.

Rare. Except for a male in juvenal plumage, captured and photographed by Van Tyne (1) at Uaxactún on 5 May 1931, no potoo has been reported in the Petén. It is a nocturnal feeder; hunting more like a flycatcher than a nighthawk, it returns to a selected perch after each dash for its prey. During the daytime the quiet, characteristic bolt-upright posture, on a post or tree stub into which it seems to blend, makes detection almost impossible.

Upperparts are a mottled and vermiculated mixture of grays, browns, and black, producing an overall gray-brown effect; underparts are lighter gray, the chest darkened by black spots. There is also a reddish brown phase, less often seen. The eyes are golden yellow, which reflects bright ruby red in the beam of a flashlight.

The calls ascribed to different races are confusingly varied. They are heard evenings and early mornings, even all night through when the moonlight is bright. Because the potoo's presence is best revealed by its calls, they are noted here, roughly in their variety from north to south. The race *N.g. mexicanus* has a loud *baw-woo*, strong enough to be the yowl of a big cat (Austin 1961). The cry heard in Tamaulipas was a rough, throaty *baw* (Sutton 1951); and rough squawks, screams, and hoots (Sutton, Auk 59:1:16). In Costa Rica one call is an arresting, loud *wow, oo-wow, oo-wów;* another, a child-like *ugh, gwówer;* both have the quality of the cry of the guan or the Laughing Falcon (Slud 1964). In Panama it is a simple song, usually of six full notes slowly descending in scale, with a deliberate pause between each note, an interval apart; a melancholy series of loud, rich, long-drawn wailing notes; sometimes when more distant, only two or three notes are heard (Chapman 1929; Eisenmann 1952; Brewster and Chapman, Auk 12:3:208–211). Finally, a recording made by Paul Schwartz (2) beautifully reproduces the voice, probably of the Venezuelan race *N.g. griseus,* which comes closest to the words of Chapman. The Schwartz recording, when of a bird very near by, also confirms the northern versions, as the opening, highest-pitch note is then an explosive, piercing, nerve-tingling *baw-ooo!*

A single white egg, with faint brown and gray markings, is laid and incubated on top of a stub.

REFERENCES: Blake 1953, p. 225, picture in black and white. Auk 12:3:fpc., picture in color.

(1) Van Tyne 1935, fpc. and p. 20, pictures in black and white.

(2) Bird Songs, recordings by Paul Schwartz.

CAPRIMULGIDAE

* *Chordeiles minor* subsp.

Common Nighthawk   Tapacamino

Pujuy

N. Am., West Indies, Mexico (s. to Veracruz, Chiapas), probably Brit. Honduras, Honduras, Costa Rica, Panama; migrates through Mid. Am.; winters in S. Am.

Transient   9½ in.   70 gr.

They have been recorded here only from 18 September through 10 October 1962. They were then seen in late afternoons and until dark, flying at moderate heights mainly south across the airstrip, some returning in wide circles over the treetops for another sweep over the field. A peak of about twenty occurred on 23 September, although even then they did not fly together as a flock. After 10 October none were seen. Positive identification was not made, but it is unlikely that they were Lesser Nighthawks (*Chordeiles acutipennis*), a species which usually flies lower and hunts closer to the ground.

They are graceful, swallow-like fliers with long, pointed wings. The plumage is dark gray above, mottled with brown and black; underparts are barred black and white; chin and throat are white; the forked tail is crossed near the tip with a white band; white crosses the flight feathers fairly well up on the wing (the Lesser, a smaller, buffier bird, has this band nearer the wing tips). Females have the white replaced by buff.

The voice is described as a buzzy, nasal *bzheent* (1), or

pee-ee. (The Lesser calls *chuck-chuck-chuck* followed by a soft *pur-r-r-r-r-r-r.*)

Two creamy white eggs, heavily spotted with dark markings, are laid on the bare ground or ground litter, even on gravel roofs of buildings (2).

REFERENCES: Peterson 1960, p. 133, pictures in black and white. Austin 1961, p. 164, picture in color; end papers, picture of egg in color. Gilliard 1958, plate 100, color photograph (of Lesser, with two eggs).

(1) Novitates 1962, No. 2094, breeding in Central America (Eisenmann).

(2) Bent, No. 176.

Nyctidromus albicollis yucatanensis Nelson

Pauraque   Pucuyo

Pujuy

S.w. U. S., Mid. Am., and S. Am.
Resident   11½ in.   65 gr.

Common, wherever open areas are available, along with light cover. From time to time they disappear for days at a stretch, to return again, seemingly more active in semi-moonlight periods than in either full moon or complete darkness. When feeding at night they often sit on the ground, take short fluttering flights after their prey, and return to the ground or to a low shrub.

The general appearance is of a brown bird, though upperparts are brownish gray. The chin and face are brown, the throat crossed by a narrow white band. The forward part of the back and shoulders is richly mottled with bold black and dark brown triangles. Underparts are mainly barred black and buff; wings have a white bar rather like that of a nighthawk, but are short and rounded; the long tail is rounded and displays a wide streak of white at each side. Females replace the white marks with buff.

The large, staring, liquid-looking eyes are dark brown (red

when reflecting a flashlight). The very short legs are an oily gray.

The call is a characteristic, three-syllable, soft, mellow whistle, _whe_ /‾ ‾ \ _ew_ sometimes preceded by two more deliberate *whew*'s (3), (4).

Two eggs (sometimes only one), buff-colored, with brown blotches, are laid on the ground in fairly open areas or among scattered bushes (1), (2).

REFERENCES: Peterson 1960, p. 133, pictures in black and white. Austin 1961, end papers, picture of egg in color.
(1) Bent, No. 176.   (2) Russell 1964.
(3) Mexican Bird Songs, recordings by L. Irby Davis.
(4) Bird Songs, recordings by Paul Schwartz.

Otophanes yucatanicus (Hartert)

Yucatán Poorwill   Pucuyo

Chak Pujuy
Xt'unkiyaj

Mexico (Yucatán Pen.) and Guatemala (Petén)
Resident   7½ in.   ♂ 22 gr. ♀ 30 gr.

Fairly common and widespread but less common than the Pauraque. We found them feeding at night along with the Pauraques; in the daytime along edges of trails and clearings, not far from forest growth where they may roost. Paynter (1) said "it is arboreal, often occurring in high trees."

They vary in color, some rufous, some brown, others light gray to dark gray. All have the crown streaked with black, the shoulders mottled with black angular spots, a white band across the lower throat, and the lateral tail feathers with white only on the tips (a patch of white, not a long streak, as occurs on pauraques). Females substitute buff for the white of males.

The bill is dark brown to black, the wide chin area of the lower bill bare of feathers. Legs vary, flesh, brown or gray. Eyes are very dark brown, appearing black.

The call is a rapid ree′ ⌣ ree′ repeated several

times (1).

Two cream-colored, gray-spotted eggs are laid on the ground, within the forest but near clearings (2).

REFERENCES:
(1) Paynter 1955, p. 141.   (2) Van Tyne 1935, pp. 20, 21.

Caprimulgus carolinensis Gmelin

Chuck-will's-widow   Tapacamino

S.e. U. S.; winters to Greater Antilles, through Mid. Am.
(not reported Brit. Honduras), Colombia, and Venezuela
Transient   12 in.   80 gr.

Uncommon. About 7 A.M. on 11 October 1962 we found an adult female lying on the trunk of a tree which had recently fallen across a trail. She was in so torpid a condition that, when slowly approached and picked up by hand, the only protest was an opened, hissing mouth and a slight lift of the body; she seemed thin and weak, and perhaps blinded by daylight. I could not believe I held a live Chuck-will's-widow in my hands.

Larger than the local Pauraque, the plumage is a cryptic mixture of brown, gray, and black, with the ruddy browns predominating. Males have a thin white throat band and some white near the ends of the outer tail feathers; these are buff on females.

The four-syllable call, a low *chuck* followed by a loud, clearly whistled *will-wíd-ow,* is not heard here; neither are nests or eggs to be seen here.

REFERENCES: Peterson 1960, p. 133, picture in black and white. Austin 1961, end papers, picture of egg in color.

APODIDAE

Chaetura vauxi richmondi Ridgway

Vaux's Swift   Vencejillo Común
Dusky-backed Swift

K'usam
K'usamch'en

Trop. Mid. Am. (except Brit. Honduras) and n. S. Am.
Resident   4 in.   15 gr.

Common. Flocks of over fifty are frequently seen flying high in the air, often at the same time that swallows in still larger flocks are flying at lower elevations. Very rarely do they come down close over the aguadas, where the swallows often appear. In both appearance and style of flight they closely resemble the slightly larger Chimney Swift (*C. pelagica*) which is more or less aptly described as a "cigar with wings." The plumage is sooty black with a brown tinge, above and below, except for the throat and chest which are a pale, smoky gray. In the air the long, narrow wings are held stiffly bowed, and this, together with rapidly beating wings (sometimes slightly out of phase though not actually alternating), and short intervals of gliding, gives these swifts a characteristic flight.

They nest in hollow trees, where they build a bracket-like cup of small twigs, cemented together and to the wall of the hollow with glutinous secretions from the bird's mouth. Eggs, about four in number, are pure white (1).

The voice is a steady series of rapidly uttered twitterings. Slud describes it as measured *sit*'s, mixed with sibilant and buzzy sounds (2).

REFERENCES: Blake 1953, p. 235, picture in black and white. Austin 1961, p. 165, picture in color (of similar Chimney Swift).
(1) Bent, No. 176.   (2) Slud 1964.

SPECIAL NOTE

Apodidae (Swifts) are sometimes called Golondrina (Swallow) in Middle America, a name which should be used only for the superficially similar *Hirundinidae*. We have therefore chosen Vencejo and its derivatives for the Spanish names.

Panyptila cayennensis subsp.

Lesser Swallow-tailed Swift   Vencejillo Tijereta

Ah Cuzäm (a general term)

Mid. Am. from s. Mexico (Veracruz) to Panama (not recorded El Salvador), and S. Am.

Resident   5 in.   28 gr.

Uncommon. Since a nesting pair were first seen at Tikal on 9 April 1958 by Ernest P. Edwards, they have been seen from time to time, flying high. Edwards photographed the nest (1), which was attached to the side of a Ramón tree (*Brosimim alicastrum*) in the Great Plaza. Trik (in litt.) reported another nest which was fastened to a lintel inside one of the large pyramid temples near the Great Plaza. The nest had been abandoned. It was well protected from the elements and still in place in 1964.

The nest of the Swallow-tailed Swift is as interesting as is the bird. It is usually a vertical tube about four inches in diameter and from one to two feet long, composed of silky plant down taken from various possible sources, worked into a strong felt by the addition of the bird's glutinous secretions. The tube may be attached along its side or may hang loose from the top. Within the tube is a small shelf on which two white eggs are laid and where they are incubated and nestlings raised (2), (3).

The bird is velvety black above and below, except for some conspicuously contrasting white areas which occur in front of the very dark eyes, on the chin and throat, as a collar around the hind neck (where sometimes obscured with greenish brown), and as a patch at each side of the rump and flanks. The wings are long and curved. The tail is deeply forked but this is not always visible as it is spread only when a turn is being made in flight.

The voice is a high-pitched *dzip-dzip-dzip;* within the nest a soft *rrree-tee-tee* (2), (3).

REFERENCES:

(1) Auk 76:3:358, 359, picture and report (Edwards). Auk 15:1:7, picture in color.

(2) Auk 75:2:fpc., picture in black and white; pp. 121–130, life history (Haverschmidt).

(3) Auk 75:2:217–220, data on nests (Helmut Sick).

TROCHILIDAE

Phaethornis superciliosus longirostris (DeLattre)

Long-tailed Hermit   Chupaflor de Cola Larga
Tsunuum (hummingbirds in general)

Trop. Mid. Am. and S. Am.
Resident   6½ in.   5½ gr.   Plate 13

Common and conspicuous, especially where pools of water in depressions on roads and trails tempt it to bathe, along with other species. Prefers heavy forest growth, but feeds low, not in treetops. It is predominantly brown, appearing large for a hummingbird due to a long, strongly curved bill and a very long tail which has two mostly white central feathers extending far beyond the others; the bill and tail account for half the bird's length. Close at hand, the back is greenish bronze. The bill is black above, ochraceous below; legs are reddish brown. The name Hermit may derive from its brown, monkish attire.

The voice is a series of rapid twitters, not distinctive. When courting, groups of males gather together to perform aerial displays and to "sing"; this song is a single squeaky *sree* note, repeated incessantly, monotonously (1).

Nests of this bird and of most hermits are notably different from those of other hummingbirds. They build long inverted cones with the nest cup in the open top, much of the rest being a loose hanging tail. A favored location is the underside of a spiny-palm frond, near the tip of which the nest is constructed of fine rootlets, mosses, and fibrous material, bound together and to the frond by many cobweb filaments. The palm leaf becomes a roof over the nest and protects it from the rain (1). Two white eggs are deposited (2).

REFERENCES: Blake 1953, p. 246, picture in black and white.
(1) Auk 81:1:5–25, life history and sketch of nest (Skutch). Greenewalt 1960, plate 44, color photograph (*P. petreii* and nest).
(2) Eisenmann 1952.

SPECIAL NOTE
Hummingbirds are frequently named Gorrión (sparrow) in Guatemala, but other Latin American names are Colibrí,

Chupaflor, Picaflor, even Visitaflor; Ibarra reluctantly approved the use of Chupaflor (in litt.), which is also the choice of Miguel del Toro (1964).

Phaethornis longuemareus adolphi Gould

Little Hermit   Chupaflor Ocrillo

Trop. Mid. Am. (except El Salvador) and S. Am.
Resident   3¾ in.   2.5–3 gr.   Plate 13

Fairly common. About half the size of the Long-tailed Hermit (small enough to slip through a mist net like a butterfly), it is similarly marked, but lacks the extra long tail feathers, is a deeper, ruddier brown, and has an ear patch especially dark, almost black. The tail is decidedly graduated, the tips light buffy white. The bill is nearly one inch long, well curved, black above, some yellow and others reddish below; legs are pink or red-brown; eyes very dark brown.

The habits of the two Hermits are much alike, the little one perhaps preferring lighter forest, bathing in aguadas as well as puddles, building a smaller (but similar) nest and lining it with downy material (1).

It may utter a series of three or four squeaky notes during routine activities, but when singing with others in an "assembly" its song is more lively and varied; one form is a deliberate *chip-chip-chip-chip* followed by a rapid higher pitched *do-da-do-a-da,* of pleasant swing and cadence rather than musical.

REFERENCES:
(1) Auk 81:1:5–25, life history (Skutch). Ibis 93:2:180–195, life history (Skutch).

Phaeochroa cuvierii roberti (Salvin)

Scaly-breasted Hummingbird   Chupaflor

Guatemala, Brit. Honduras, Honduras, Nicaragua, Costa Rica, Panama, n. Colombia
Resident   5½ in.   8.5 gr.   Plate 13

Uncommon. A small, localized colony was found singing forty feet up in high trees, and flying back and forth over the wide, open road which begins just west of the archeologists' camp. They were seen nowhere else and even there it was difficult to detect them.

Upperparts are a flashy green, the tail with bluish tones; underparts look scaly only at close range, each green feather of the throat and chest being outlined with buff (gray on the females); the abdomen is buff (gray on females); the under tail coverts gray with a narrow white band across the belly. The outer tail feathers are broadly tipped with white, the others less so. The bill is strong, straight, and black; the legs black; the eyes very dark brown.

They utter very high pitched, but rather weak, squeaks as they chase about. Their assembly song includes a musical trill, and is described by Skutch as *chee-twe-twe-twe-twe*-trill-*chup chup* (1).

The breeding period ranges from May until the year's end. The nest is an open cup of soft materials covered on the outside with green mosses and lichens, an almost invisible excrescence on the chosen branch, six to thirty feet high (1).

REFERENCES: Condor 59:2:83, picture in black and white. (1) Condor 66:3:186–189, life history (Skutch).

Campylopterus curvipennis pampa (Lesson)

Wedge-tailed Sabrewing   Chupaflor Gritón

Trop. e. Mexico, Guatemala, and Honduras
Resident   5½ in.   ♂ 6½ gr. ♀ 5 gr.   Plate 13

Common and conspicuously numerous. This large hummingbird is bright green above, including the central tail feathers, which are tinged with iridescent blue; the head is crowned with flashing deep blue; there is a white spot close behind each eye; the outer tail feathers are blue-black tipped with white, the tail graduated, forming a wedge when partly spread. Underparts are mostly light gray with a light brown crissum. The bill is one inch long, strong and very slightly curved; legs are dark brown; eyes very dark brown, appearing black.

They frequent forest edges, using roads, trails, and clearings as flyways, feeding low and at moderate heights.

While in twisting, turning flight, with noisy wings whirring, they utter spirited, chippering squeals and squeaks (1).

Nests are normal camouflaged cups on branches, in which two white eggs are deposited.

REFERENCES:
(1) Sutton 1951.

Florisuga mellivora mellivora (Linnaeus)

White-necked Jacobin   Chupaflor de Cola Blanca

Trop. Mid. Am. (except El Salvador) and S. Am.
Resident   5 in.   6¾ gr.   Plate 14

Uncommon, perhaps rare. Two male specimens were taken at Tikal in June and July 1959. There is only one earlier record for the Petén, at Sabin (Paso Subín?) far to the south, by P. W. Schufeldt, 5 December 1917 (Van Tyne 1935).

Adult males are handsomely plumaged in rich blue, green, and white. The entire head and chest are blue-violet; the nape, back, and central tail feathers bright green, broken with a white crescent across the upper back; the tail (except for the central green) is white, with a very narrow terminal band of black; the green of the back carries down across the breast and sides; the remaining underparts are pure white. Wings extend beyond the tail.

Most females are bronzy green above, green and white below, and have a scaly-looking throat. However, they are sometimes dressed much like males, about one-fourth of them being dimorphic, with blue heads, white nape bands, white tails. Plate 14 shows a female in normal attire except for the male's type of white tail; separately shown is a dark, more normal female tail (1).

There appears to be nothing distinctive in its squeaky *tsitting* notes (2).

Three nests in Barro Colorado were cups of yellowish white down plastered on top of broad leaves, all less than five feet above ground, near small creeks deep within forest. Two nests contained two white eggs each. Young birds, clothed in yellowish down, make the nests look like mounds (Willis, in litt.).

REFERENCES: Blake 1953, p. 249, pictures in black and white. Austin 1961, p. 170, picture in color.
(1) Novitates 1950, No. 1450:9–11, plumages (Zimmer).
(2) Slud 1964.

* *Anthracothorax prevostii* subsp.

Green-breasted Mango   Chupaflor de Pecho Verde

Trop. Mid. Am. to n. Costa Rica, n.w. Venezuela, Old Providence and St. Andrew's in Caribbean
Resident   5 in.   6½ gr.   Plate 14

Uncommon. They are more to be expected in drier habitats and among deciduous trees, but a female was seen on her nest in trees near the hotel cottages, in March of both 1963 and 1964 (Margaret H. Hundley and C. Russell Mason, in litt.); populated areas attract them.

Both sexes are green above, the male more golden, but otherwise they differ materially. Males are very dark below, the green on the sides becoming velvety black on the chin and throat, the black shading down the body through rich dark blue to blue-green; the tail is iridescent reddish purple, edged with very dark brown. Females are white-bodied below, with green sides and under tail coverts, and an irregular conspicuous line of black all down the center.

The typical hummingbird nest is built on a bare branch, sometimes a hundred feet up, others low; rather in the open and unprotected. Two white eggs are deposited. Two young birds were found in a nest in Guatemala (Skutch, in litt.).

REFERENCES: Blake 1953, p. 250, picture in black and white. Allen 1961, plate 47, color photograph (with nest).

Chlorostilbon canivetii canivetii (Lesson)

Fork-tailed Emerald   Chupaflor Tijereta

Trop. Mid. Am. and Caribbean coast of S. Am.
Resident   3½ in.   2½ gr.   Plate 13

Uncommon, perhaps rare. They were found only at Aguada Dimick, where they may have been attracted by the new brushy growth of shrubs and small trees.

The forked tail separates them from other Tikal humming-birds. Both sexes are shining green above (males with more glitter), conspicuously red bills with black tips and small white tufts on the legs. Males are sparkling emerald green below, most brilliant on the throat and chest, and have blue-black tails. Females are gray below, the sides washed with green, the grayish tail ending with a black band and white tips. The bill is straight, needle-like; legs are dark brown; eyes dark brown.

It utters an endlessly repeated, characterless wiry *tseee-tseeree* (1).

A nest found in Oaxaca, Mexico, contained two white eggs. It was suspended, *vireo-like*, from plant stems, about two feet above ground. The exterior was formed of strips of inner bark which became progressively finer to end in a lining of downy plant material (2).

REFERENCES: Bond 1961, plate 3, picture in color (of similar but larger *C. recordii*).
(1) Slud 1964.   (2) Condor 66:1:51–55, nest (Wolf).

Amazilia candida candida (Bourcier and Mulsant)

White-bellied Emerald   Chupaflor Candido

Trop. Mid. Am. (except El Salvador) to Costa Rica
Resident   3¼ in.   4 gr.   Plate 13

Common. It is found feeding at low flowering bushes and
vines throughout the camp and also in the tops of the highest
flowering trees, almost always in competition with the larger,
noisy, Rufous-tailed Hummer (*A. tzacatl*). While busily feeding alone at low elevations, the whirring wings of a Rufous-tail
could be heard as it swooped in to chase the little fellow
completely away; but in the treetops they held their own better, perhaps because they flocked together there and were not
solitary victims.

It is the smallest of the Tikal hummingbirds, although
heavier than the brown Little Hermits. It is green above, the
green extending down over the sides of the neck where it
becomes the brightest emerald color; below it is white, purest
on the lower abdomen, the flanks washed somewhat with
green. The tail ends with grayish tips. The straight bill is black
above, pink or red below, with the tip black; legs are darkest
brown; eyes nearly black.

Small gatherings of males (leks) sing a series of two to five
lisping squeaks, as *tsk-seet-seet-seet-seet* (Willis, in litt.).

REFERENCES: Greenewalt 1960, plate 47, color photograph
(a similar bird).

Amazilia yucatanensis yucatanensis (Cabot)

Fawn-breasted Hummingbird   Chupaflor Vientre Castaño
Buff-bellied Hummingbird

S. Texas, Mexico, Guatemala, Brit. Honduras, and Honduras
Resident   4 in.   4 gr.   Plate 13

Rare. It is more likely to be found in a less humid climate;
the single one recorded was in the tintal, where trees are low
and scarce, the sun penetrates strongly, and the ground cover,

while hardly over twelve feet high for large areas, is very dense.

It closely resembles the Rufous-tailed Hummingbird (*A. tzacatl*), common and numerous here, from which it differs primarily by having a fawn-colored breast and belly, a slightly shorter bill which is colored scarlet above as well as below, middle tail feathers iridescent green, and perhaps more glitter in the green throat.

The voice can be noisy; a series of shrill, twittering squeaks (1).

The nest is a typical open cup, saddled on a branch or placed in a fork, in a bush or small tree, about three to ten feet above ground; two white eggs are deposited (1), (2).

REFERENCES: Peterson 1960, p. 144, picture in color.
(1) Pough 1953.
(2) Auk 59:1:16, 17, picture of bird on nest (Sutton and Pettingill).

Amazilia tzacatl tzacatl (de la Llave)

Rufous-tailed Hummingbird   Chupaflor de Cola Rufa

Trop. Mid. Am. (except El Salvador), Colombia, and Ecuador
Resident   4¼ in.   ♂ 5 gr. ♀ 4½ gr.   Plate 13

Common and the most numerous hummingbird here. Along with the smaller White-bellied Emerald (*A. candida*), this medium-sized hummer feeds both high and low, in the flowering crowns of tall trees and on bushes and shrubs in the clearings around the cottages. At lower levels it is readily seen as it swoops down at its little competitor with a noisy whirr of wings, to chase it completely away.

Upperparts are a shiny green, contrasting sharply with a dark rufous tail and tail coverts; underparts are a glittering green on the throat and chest, plain gray on the breast and belly, conspicuous chestnut on lower tail coverts and tail. The tail is obscurely edged with dark purple. The bill is rather long, black above, red below with a blackish tip; legs are dark brown; eyes very dark brown, appearing black.

Its "song" consists of two to four sibilant, piercing *tss*'s; also a not unmusical descending trill of rapidly given *stchup*'s (1); or a fast *tsip-tsip* repeated on and on at a rate of twelve per five seconds, sometimes accelerated into a trilling rattle (2).

The nest is a typical open cup located against a vertical or oblique anchoring twig and almost always close to a level perch, slender enough to be grasped by the bird's little feet during construction. Nests are placed from two to twenty feet up in a wide variety of trees, bushes, and vines. Two white eggs are deposited (3).

REFERENCES: Greenewalt 1960, plate 16, color photograph.
(1) Slud 1964.   (2) Condor 59:4:254 (Eisenmann).
(3) Auk 48:4:480–500, life history, nests pictured (Skutch).

Heliothryx barroti (Bourcier)

Purple-crowned Fairy   Chupaflor de Pecho Blanco

Mexico (Tabasco), Trop. Mid. Am. (except El Salvador) to Colombia and Ecuador

Resident   5 in.   5¼ gr.   Plate 14

Fairly common. This strikingly beautiful, large hummingbird is seen at its best when bathing, which occurs at most every aguada and roadside puddle. It is widespread, from camp, where a nesting bird was found, to the Great Plaza on top of the ridge.

Upperparts are mainly shining, bright green, underparts immaculate white. The crown of the male is flashing blue-violet; the face has a black patch ending near the neck in a small flashing spot like the crown; the four middle feathers of the tail are iridescent blue-green, the others pure white. The female is a somewhat larger bird, but is all green on the crown, lacking the blue-violet, and her facial patch is black with a dull brown tone.

The bill is short, straight, and very sharp, sharp enough to pierce the basal calyx of certain flowers in order to sip the nectar it cannot otherwise reach with its short bill.

About the only sound it makes is a weak *tsir* or *tsup* (1).

The nest is located from low to as much as thirty feet up, in a tree preferably near a clearing, where it is saddled well out on a slender branch; though made of the usual downy materials, it may lack the typical hummingbird's decorative lichens and mosses. Two pure white eggs are deposited (2).

REFERENCES: de Schauensee 1964, page 144, picture in color.
(1) Slud 1964.
(2) Audubon Magazine 63:1:8, 9, 13, life history (Skutch).

TROGONIDAE

Trogon massena massena Gould

Slaty-tailed Trogon   Aurora Grande

Trop. Mid. Am., Colombia, and Ecuador
Resident   12½ in.   150 gr. (141 to 171)   Plate 18
(Because weights of trogons vary greatly, extremes have been included in parentheses.)

Common. The largest of the four trogons at Tikal, it is as conspicuous as the much smaller Citreoline Trogon (*T. citreolus*), both frequenting the woodland around Aguada Tikal. It is, however, the more widespread of the two as it is also common on the high ridge occupied by the ruins which surround the Great Plaza.

It feeds on insects, which it chases in flycatcher fashion, returning to a perch after each essay (as do other trogons); feeds also on fruits. When perching it sits bolt upright (also typical of the other trogons), the tail hanging straight down. This is an aid to identification, as the tails have wide, square-tipped feathers which, when seen from below, disclose patterns which are distinctively marked on each species, and in most cases also differ for each sex.

The male is iridescent green above, becoming blue-green on the rump and on the middle tail feathers; the black wings have a large gray patch (a fine black and white vermiculation); the green of the upperparts continues below across the throat and breast, where it abruptly meets the bright carmine body; the tail below is black, obscurely shaded with gray tones. The bill is usually a rich salmon color; legs vary from yellow through orange and brown to gray; eyes are brownish yellow, with obscure orange-red eye-rings.

The female is dull slate gray instead of green, the abdomen a lighter scarlet red, the tail brownish, the upper bill sometimes black.

The general effect is that of a dark, chunky bird with a colorful bill, conspicuous red belly, and long blackish tail.

The voice is a subdued but far-carrying, clear *wuk-wuk-wuk-wuk-wuk* in rapid sequence and a slightly rising pitch, uttered up to ten times while the bird is perched motionless. At other times it sits in silence slowly raising and lowering its tail (1).

The nest is fully enclosed within one of the numerous dark brown termitaries or inside the soft wood of a decaying tree or stump. It is reached by a tube or tunnel which slants upward a foot or so and then arches over and downward to the unlined nest cup. This arduously carved-out structure may be anywhere from near ground level to thirty feet or more above. Three eggs of palest blue, nearly white, are usually deposited (1).

REFERENCES:
(1) Animal Kingdom 56:6:167–172, life history (Skutch).

Trogon citreolus melanocephala Gould
[*Trogon melanocephala*]

Citreoline Trogon   Aurora de Pecho Gris

Kux or Kuxtin

Trop. Mid. Am. to n. Costa Rica
Resident   11 in.   80 gr. (66 to 95)   Plate 18

Common, perhaps more common than *T. massena* in the vicinity of Aguada Tikal, where trees have been thinned out.

Sometimes called the Black-headed Citreoline, it is a race which enjoys humid climates more than do other races of *T. citreolus.*

On males the head, throat, chest, and wings are dull black; the back is iridescent golden green, becoming rich dark blue on the rump and dark green on the middle tail feathers; the outer tail feathers are black with large, overlapping patches of white on the ends; the body below is orange-yellow. The bill is greenish gray, legs dark gray, eyes brown and surrounded by conspicuous ruffles of very pale blue eye-rings.

The female is similar, the iridescent greens and blues replaced by dull black; but the large white tail patches are separated, that is, not overlapping as on males.

The general effect is that of a dark, medium-sized trogon, iridescent (or dull black) above, with pale blue eye-rings, an orange belly, and large white squares on the tail.

The voice is a low throaty, unmelodious, even harsh clucking, quickly accelerating into a falling chatter, as *chuck-chuck-chck-chkchkchkchk,* uttered along with a jerk of the tail with each note. At the nest they sometimes voice low, whining, not unpleasant notes (1), (2), (3).

It builds nests as described for *T. massena,* the nest tunnel smaller, only two inches in diameter. The two or three eggs are white (1).

REFERENCES:
(1) Condor 50:4:137–147, life history (Skutch).
(2) Slud.
(3) Mexican Bird Songs, recordings by L. Irby Davis.

Trogon collaris puella Gould

Bar-tailed Trogon   Aurora de Cola Rayada
Collared Trogon

Chiefly highlands trop. Mid. Am. and S. Am.
Resident   9½ in.   60 gr. (41 to 67)   Plate 18

Uncommon. Most reports of this medium-sized trogon come from substantially higher altitudes than the 600- to 800-foot level of Tikal, although it is also found at levels even below 300 feet in Quintana Roo (Paynter 1955). We found it in the cool forest shade, but not in dense ground cover. Its calls vary; one is a soft, very low but clear, two- or three-syllable *caow-caow* or *caow-caow-caow,* deliberately uttered; another, very different and used more as an alarm or warning call, is a low long-drawn-out *ch-u-r-r-r,* which is accompanied by a slow elevation of the tail. The comparatively quiet voice and other habits of this bird may make it seem rare rather than uncommon (1).

The sexes differ more than do any of the other three trogons at Tikal. Males are a golden green above, the wings with gray shoulders and white-streaked flight feathers; the face, chin, and throat are black; the chest, green like the back, is separated from the bright red body by a band of white; the tail, from below, is narrowly barred black and white throughout its length, some of which is visible also from above at each side of the green middle feathers. The bill is yellow, legs brownish, eyes dark brown with obscure brownish eye-rings.

Females replace all the golden green of the males, and also the gray wing coverts, with a soft sandy brown, darker on the crown; the bright red of the abdomen by pale rose, liberally tinged with white; the yellow bill with black above; the brownish eye-rings with a crescent of white behind the eyes. The tail from below is entirely individual (see plate 18); only one pair of black and white bars is present, at the feather tips; the rest of each of these three pairs of outer feathers is silvery gray, with some brownish tones.

Nests are in cavities, carved into soft wood, the incubating bird visible from the open front of the niche. Two white eggs are deposited (1).

REFERENCES: de Schauensee 1964, p. 162, picture in black and white. Austin 1961, p. 172, picture in color (of slightly different race).

(1) Auk 73:3:354–366, life history (Skutch).

Trogon violaceus braccatus (Cabanis and Heine)

Violaceous Trogon   Aurora de Pecho Violeta

Trop. Mid. Am. and S. Am.
Resident   9 in.   56 gr. (53¾ to 59)   Plate 18

Uncommon. They prefer clearings and cultivated land bordered by trees; they may increase along with the continued opening up of the woodland around Aguada Tikal. Some such increase may have occurred already, as they are reported more frequently than was the case in 1957.

The male is golden green on the back and on the middle, dark-tipped tail feathers; the head and throat are black, bordered by dark blue on the nape and across the chest; the breast and belly rich orange; the wings have gray shoulders and white-streaked flight feathers; the tail below is narrowly barred black and white, except for broad white ends to each of the outer tail feathers. The bill is pale blue-gray; eyes are dark brown, surrounded by very conspicuous yellow eye-rings.

Females replace the golden greens with slaty black, the orange body with yellow liberally tinged on the breast with whitish, and the barring of the tail with solid brownish black on the inner webs; the yellow eye-ring is replaced by a spot of white before and a white crescent behind the eye.

Nests are frequently carved (not tunneled) into the large, gray, paper-like nests of wasps, a complicated procedure, as the live wasps are present during the operation (1). They probably also tunnel into tree cavities and termitaries as described for *T. massena*. Two white eggs are the usual clutch (1).

The voice is an incessantly repeated *cow-cow-cow*-etc., soft, sweet-voiced, and pleasant (1); in Panama it is repeated ten or fifteen times, at a rate of about two per second (2).

REFERENCES: Condor 61:5:fpc., picture in color.
(1) Nature 52:9:464–468, life history (Skutch).
(2) Eisenmann 1952.

ALCEDINIDAE

Ceryle torquata torquata (Linnaeus)
[*Megaceryle torquata*—AOU 1957]

Ringed Kingfisher   Martín Pescador Grande

Mid. Am., Lesser Antilles, and S. Am.
Visitor, Resident?   16 in.   300 gr.   Plate 19

Uncommon. Solitary visitors have appeared from time to time throughout the year. On two occasions one was seen several hundred feet away from Aguada Tikal, rather than at its edge, clearly outlined against the sky as it perched on a bare branch high in a tall tree, a habit also noted by Slud (1).

It is much larger and has much greater brown chest-area than the Belted Kingfisher (*M. alcyon*). Males are heavily crested, grayish blue above, bright chestnut below, and with a white throat and collar. Females *add* a grayish blue band across the chest. The very large, heavy bill is black, shading to yellow at its base; legs are green; eyes are brown.

It voices a loud, scratchy, ten-syllable rattle (1); and hear (3).

Nests are in long burrows in some bank near water. Three white eggs are usual (2).

REFERENCES: Peterson 1960, p. 176, picture in color (of female).
(1) Slud 1964.
(2) Bond 1961, p. 49, picture in color (male of Lesser Antillean race).
(3) Mexican Bird Songs, recordings by L. Irby Davis.

Ceryle alcyon alcyon (Linnaeus)
[*Megaceryle alcyon*—AOU 1957]

Belted Kingfisher   Martín Pescador
                                                        Pescador Norteño

N. Am.; winters through Mid. Am. to n. S. Am.
Winter Resident?   13 in.   150 gr.   Plate 19

A not uncommon migrant, since fish were introduced at Aguada Tikal. At times several have been seen together; from 20 September through 18 October 1962, two were noted, though not present every day; solitary birds have been reported throughout the year.

Males have a raggedly bushy crest, are grayish blue above with a white collar, mainly white below with a grayish blue band across the chest. In addition, females have a bright chestnut band across the breast and chestnut on the flanks. The bill is black shading to blue at the base; legs are gray and brown; eyes dark brown.

The voice is a high-pitched, loud, harsh, rattle (1).

REFERENCES:
(1) Peterson 1960, p. 176, picture in color (of female). Allen 1961, plate 54, color photograph (of male). Pough 1953, pictures in color (both male and female).

Chloroceryle amazona mexicana Brodkorb

Amazon Kingfisher   Martín Pescador

Trop. Mid. Am. and S. Am.
Visitor   12 in.   125 gr.   Plate 19

Uncommon. It prefers open waterways with deep pools. While only one has been found here, other possibilities may have been overlooked.

Males have large, crested heads, are glossy dark green above with a white collar, mainly white below with a broad chestnut band across the chest and upper breast. Females are similar, but *lack* the chestnut-colored band; they have large green patches on the flanks which extend in a narrow band nearly to the center of the breast. The bill is black, legs are black, eyes very dark brown.

They voice a hard, loud, rattling *kreck-kreck-kreck,* froglike in tone. They are also reported to have a flute-like, tunefully repeated series of *cheet-cheet*'s (1).

The nest is at the end of a long burrow in a stream bank. Four white eggs are deposited (1).

REFERENCES: Austin 1961, p. 176, picture in color (of male). (1) Condor 59:4:217–225, life history (Skutch).

Chloroceryle americana isthmica (Goldman)

Green Kingfisher   Martín Pescador Chico

S.w. U. S., Mid. Am., and S. Am.
Visitor   7½ in.   38 gr.

Very uncommon. The only one recorded (20 February) had flown into a roadside mist net, not close to water. It ranges from coastal lagoons and quiet waters bordered by shrubs to moderately high altitudes and usually follows rapid, forested brooks.

It is very similar in attire to the Amazon Kingfisher (*C. amazona*), but much smaller, with more conspicuous white spots on wings and tail, and much less conspicuous crest. Females differ additionally by having two narrow greenish, white-spotted breast bands, instead of one.

The bill is blackish gray, legs yellowish brown, eyes dark brown.

It utters a low pebble-clicking note when perched; a sharp, insect-like, twittering rattle when alarmed or in flight (1), (2).

Nests are in burrows in sandy or earthen banks. A set of three white eggs and one of five eggs were found in Guatemala (Skutch, in litt.).

REFERENCES: Peterson 1960, p. 176, picture in color (of male). Sutton 1951, p. 32, picture in color (of male). Wilson Bull. 64:3:fpc., picture in color (of male).
(1) Slud 1964.
(2) Pough 1953, pictures in color (both male and female).

Chloroceryle aenea stictoptera (Ridgway)

Pygmy Kingfisher   Martincito Pescador

Trop. Mid. Am. and S. Am.
Resident   5½ in.   17.5 gr.

Fairly common, localized. This tiny kingfisher is almost always present at darkly shaded aguadas, when small fish are available (as at Naranjal); it will also readily eat insects, which it catches in flycatcher-like fashion (1).

It is glossy dark green above, mainly rufous orange below, brightest on the throat, and white on the belly. Females have additionally a greenish band across the breast. Bills and legs are black, eyes dark brown.

They utter a variety of sounds: a low pebble-clicking note, a scratchy *tsweek*, little *tsick*'s that sound like creaking bones, and a songbird-like chirpy *tsip* (2).

A nest found on Barro Colorado was an upward-slanting hole in an earthen bank around roots of a fallen tree, and located about three feet above a pool of water. Two young just out of the nest were near by (Willis, in litt.). The race in Trinidad may nest some distance from water; it lays four pure white, glossy eggs (3).

REFERENCES:
(1) Blake 1953, p. 276, pictures in black and white.
(2) Slud.   (3) Herklots 1961.

MOMOTIDAE

Hylomanes momotula momotula Lichtenstein

Tody Motmot   Tolobojo Enano

Trop. Mid. Am. and n.w. Colombia
Resident   7 in.   27½ gr.

Common. A small, stocky motmot, which perches so quietly at eye level in shadowy undergrowth as to be easily over-looked. The dark green back contrasts with a rusty brown nape and crown; the face is broadly striped, greenish blue above the eye, black behind the eye, whitish below it and again on the side of the neck, all against a brown ground color which shades to greenish brown on the breast. The dull greenish brown tail feathers are strongly graduated, rounded, and lack the extended racket-tipped tail of some other motmots. The bill is black above, variably yellowish brown or dull green below; legs are similarly varied from straw to brown to greenish; eyes are dark brown.

At Gallon Jug, British Honduras, it utters a rapid screech-owl-like quavering *cooooooo-o-o-o-oh;* also a low *hŏŏt-hŏŏt-hŏŏt*—which is continued indefinitely (Willis, in litt.).

REFERENCES: Blake 1953, p. 277, picture in black and white.

Electron carinatum subsp.

Keel-billed Motmot   Tolobojo Pico Ancho

Caribbean slope Mid. Am. from s. Mexico to n. Costa Rica
Visitor?   13–15 in.

There has been only one sight report of this Motmot, by Ernest P. Edwards (in litt.), 10 June 1958. Characteristics and voice were described in detail. It appeared to be calling and searching for a mate. It is distinguished from the resident Blue-crowned Motmot (*Momotus momota lessonii*) by its lack of a blue-bordered, black crown (having only a blue stripe over the eye, otherwise all green above); a much broader bill with a diagnostic keel-like, central ridge; a loud far-reaching *cut-cut-cadack* similar to the cackle of a hen, entirely different from the hollow, paired *hutt-hutt* of the other motmot (1). It should be noted, however, that the Blue-crowned may also occasionally voice a clucking call when excited.

REFERENCES:
(1) Slud 1964.

Momotus momota lessonii Lesson

Blue-crowned Motmot   Tolobojo

Toh
Jut-Jut
Bukpic

Trop. Mid. Am. and S. Am.
Resident   16 to 17 in. (9-in.-long tail)   120 gr.
                                                          Plate 17

Common. Frequently seen in the forest and back in the trees along roads and trails, perched quietly well above eye level but not high. Now and then they slowly swing the racket-tipped tail from side to side like a pendulum.

The general effect is of a long-tailed, heavy-billed motmot, green above, brownish below, with flashes of bright blue. The crown is black with a conspicuous border of blue and turquoise; the face has a large black patch, narrowly edged with turquoise; flight feathers and tail (above) are bluish or bluish green; the two middle tail feathers extend far beyond the others and are bare-shafted for a short space a little above the blue, black-tipped ends (racket-shaped). The brown chest has a showy triangular patch of black, bordered with turquoise. The heavy bill is black, the short legs dark gray, the eyes vivid red or brownish red.

The voice most often heard, uttered from early morning before the wood-owls stop their hooting until late evening when the owls are again calling, is a deep, resonant, far-reaching *hutt-hutt,* usually given in pairs, with a leisurely interval before the next pair (see Maya name above) (1), (2), (3).

Nests are in burrows, the entrance often invisible because it starts within the depths of some natural hole or cavity already available to the bird. Such burrows have been found in Temple I and other cave-like ruins. Three glossy pure white eggs are the usual clutch (1).

SCALED PIGEON p. 66.

12 inches, largest pigeon at Tikal; upper back, neck, throat, and chest coarsely scaled effect; belly whitish; bill and eye-ring red; legs lavender.

MALE: ruddier head and back than female, darkening to nearly black tail and dark brown wings; breast tinged vinaceous; scaly effect coarser than on female.

FEMALE: dull brown on head and back, buff instead of vinaceous on breast; scaly effect finer and more sharply black and white.

SHORT-BILLED PIGEON p. 67.

Slightly smaller than the Scaled Pigeon. Sexes alike; head and neck purplish, blending through dark vinaceous to iridescent greenish brown on lower back, wings, and tail, and to grayish on belly; bill black, eyes reddish, eye-ring and legs red.

GRAY-HEADED DOVE p. 70.

10 inches, smallest of the three pigeons at Tikal, with delicate appearance. Sexes alike; head blue-gray with white forehead; chin and throat white, cheeks buff; chest brightly vinaceous, blending down to white belly; dark outer tail feathers with white tips, conspicuous in flight; rest of tail, back and wings deep olive-brown; bill black, eyes yellowish white; small eye-ring and legs red.

RUDDY QUAIL-DOVE p. 71.

9 inches, terrestrial, short-tailed, stocky. Sexes distinct.

MALE: brown with purplish tones, deepest on head and neck, ruddier on back, cinnamon on tail; darkish line below the cheek; breast buff, belly paler; eyes vary from orange to red-brown; eye-ring purplish red; bill and legs red-brown.

FEMALE: much darker, lacking purplish shades, the back brown with greenish tones, more ruddy on forehead and face; breast dull brown, belly paler.

PLATE 10

SHORT-BILLED PIGEON

GRAY-
HEADED
DOVE

SCALED
PIGEON

♂
♀

RUDDY QUAIL-DOVE

♂
♀

♂

RUDDY
GROUND-
DOVE

♀

inches 6
cms 15

OLIVE-THROATED PARAKEET
p. 73

9½ inches, but half is tail, long and pointed. Bright emerald green upperparts and tail, with blue in the wings (some blue is present in all our parrots); throat and breast brownish, belly greenish yellow. Eyes yellow, legs dull orange.

WHITE-FRONTED PARROT
p. 75

10 inches, chunky. Mainly yellowish green, with white forehead (less extensive than on White-crowned), and bright red patch before the eyes; red patch on wing of male only; some females show less white on the forehead. Eyes and bill yellow, legs greenish yellow.

WHITE-CROWNED PARROT
p. 74

9 inches, chunky. The bluest of all Tikal parrots, giving a dark appearance, contrasting strongly with extensive white on the head and throat. Orange bare skin surrounds the brown eyes; red on under tail coverts; legs bright orange.

BROWN-HOODED PARROT
p. 73

8 inches. Dull olive-brown of head and neck give it its name, Brown-hooded; dark green upperparts, paler green below with tawny chest; wings in flight disclose scarlet patch on flanks. Blue-white area surrounding the dull yellow eyes give an owlish effect. Tail has some red at base, visible from below.

PLATE 11

OLIVE-THROATED PARAKEET

WHITE-FRONTED PARROT

WHITE-CROWNED PARROT

BROWN-HOODED PARROT

0   inches   3
0   cms   7

PLATE 12

RED-LORED or
YELLOW-CHEEKED PARROT

MEALY or BLUE-CROWNED PARROT

0 inches 3
0 cms 7

RUDDY GROUND-DOVE *p. 68.*

6½ inches, but looks larger; terrestrial. Sexes differ, but both show rufous on wings in flight, have gray heads, numerous spots on wings but none on underparts, dark-edged wings and tails; bills are dark brown, eyes reddish, legs pink.

MALE: brown above, vinaceous below.

FEMALE: paler and grayer above, paler vinaceous below.

MEALY or BLUE-CROWNED PARROT *p. 76.*

14½ inches; our largest and noisiest parrot. Plumage is mainly green, rather dull on upperparts, paler and richer on cheeks and underparts; crown and nape pale blue; wings with blue tips and red on secondaries. Pale yellow bare skin surrounds brown eyes.

RED-LORED or YELLOW-CHEEKED PARROT *p. 76.*

12 inches; next to largest parrot here. Plumaged in green, red, and blue much like Mealy Parrot, but green is brighter; chrome yellow cheek conspicuous (but lacking on immatures, which have green cheeks); bright red before the eyes often extends across forehead and into the yellow; crown lavender (not blue as on Mealy Parrot). Eyes are yellowish.

REFERENCES:

(1) Ibis 106:3:321–332, life history (Skutch). Allen 1961, **plate** 55, color photograph.

(2) Slud 1964.

(3) Mexican Bird Songs, recordings by L. Irby Davis.

GALBULIDAE

Galbula ruficauda melanogenia Sclater

Rufous-tailed Jacamar   Martín Gorrión
                                                    Pico Largo

Trop. Mid. Am. (except El Salvador) to w. Panama and S. Am.

Resident   11 in.   28.5 gr.

Common. Although primarily a forest bird, it is often seen among the trees beside roads and trails, quietly perched with uptilted bill on some bare twig, not high but well above eye level. It is exceptionally unwary of humans and may be closely approached.

Upperparts are glittering iridescent green, including the middle tail feathers. The glittering green extends below in a broad band across the chest where it separates the white throat (pale buff on females) from the bright chestnut breast, belly, and outer tail feathers. The bill, conspicuously long, slim, and sharp-pointed, is black; the short legs are yellowish straw, shading to blackish near the toes; eyes are dark brown. A black face patch is obscured by the dark green around it.

It utters a great variety of rather high-pitched songs (2). One is a series of gentle squeals, not unmusical, which start with slow deliberation, then accelerate and rise in pitch to an excited climax; another is a high-pitched, rapid trill (1); or a nasal *peet-peet-peet-peet-peet* (3).

Nests are in burrows with exposed entrance holes, located in any available bank, even those only a foot or so in height; sometimes the root-bound earth of a fallen tree will serve. Two to four white eggs are deposited (1).

REFERENCES: Blake 1953, p. 281, picture in black and white.
(1) Ibis 105:3:354–368, life history (Skutch). Allen 1961, plate
57, color photograph.
(2) Slud 1964.
(3) Condor 57:2:73 (Amadon and Eckelberry).

BUCCONIDAE

Notharcus macrorhynchos hyperrhynchus (Sclater)

White-necked Puffbird   Páparo Collarejo

Trop. Mid. Am. and S. Am.
Resident   10 in.   90 gr.

Very uncommon. It prefers the bare branches of high trees
for its perch. The only one found was in such a location.
Though relying largely on insects for food, this one had eaten
a large lizard which weighed nearly nine grams.

It is mainly glossy black above, with a large white forehead
and a narrow, obscure white collar; the face and underparts
are mostly white, with a strongly contrasting black band across
the lower breast, and gray barring on the flanks. The black
bill is broad, thick, and strongly hooked at the tip; legs are
black; eyes reddish brown.

The voice is nearly nonexistent; sometimes a weak, whispered, falling note in a minor key; sometimes a nasal sound
uttered through its closed beak (1).

Nests are sometimes dug into termitaries located thirty or
forty feet above ground (1). For *N. pectoralis* the tunnel is
horizontal, not slanted upward as for trogons. Three white
eggs are deposited (2).

REFERENCES: Blake 1953, p. 282, picture in black and white.
Austin 1961, p. 188, picture in color.
(1) Slud 1964.
(2) Wilson Bull. 60:2:82–85, life history of *N. pectoralis*
(Skutch).

Malacoptila panamensis inornata (DuBus)

White-whiskered Puffbird   Páparo Barbón

Trop. Mid. Am. (except El Salvador) and S. Am.
Resident   8 in.   36 gr.

Not uncommon, but they are easily overlooked, preferring
the shadowy forest, thickets, and tangles. However, they often
perch in semi-open cover on a more or less exposed branch,
some fifteen feet above ground. There they sit motionless and
voiceless for the most part, on the alert for their prey, which
ranges from moths to lizards. They are not shy, in fact seem
hardly aware of human beings; once located they can be
closely approached.

Upperparts are reddish brown, darker on the rump, generously spotted with light buff; the face is diagnostic, the shaggy
cheeks with soft yellow-brown feathers, and whiskers of lighter
buffy white; underparts are light red-brown, streaked with
dark brown, and shading to whitish below the tail. Females
are duller, grayer browns both above and below. Bills are
black above, greenish yellow below; legs pale gray; eyes
reddish.

The voice is seldom heard, and then is usually a high-
pitched, thin *peep,* or a long-drawn-out, weak, plaintive
tzeeee (1).

Nests are in burrows, the entrance well concealed, the
tunnel inclined downward, the cup lined with dead leaves.
Two white eggs, rarely three, are deposited (1).

REFERENCES: Blake 1953, p. 283, picture in black and white.
(1) Ibis 100:2:209–231, life history (Skutch).

RAMPHASTIDAE

Aulacorhynchus prasinus virescens Ridgway

Emerald Toucanet
Pico de Nabaja
Tucancillo Verde

Ah Pichic

Chiefly highlands s. Mexico, Guatemala, Brit. Honduras,
Honduras, El Salvador, and Nicaragua
Resident   14 in.   150 gr.

Not uncommon. This small green toucan is more numerous
in higher altitudes but is not rare here at 600 to 800 feet
above sea level. It usually feeds in the crowns of tall trees
where fruits are available, but will forage less frequently close
to the ground. Along with other species of toucans, it has the
regrettable habit of robbing other birds' nests of their young.

Upperparts are bright green, slightly tinged with brown on
the head and toward the tail; underparts are brilliant green
with a yellowish tone, the throat dingy white, the under tail
coverts a rich dark brown, the tail tipped red-brown. The
large but well-shaped bill is mainly yellow above, in various
shades, blending to amber and brown on the ridge and sharply
contrasting with a broad crescent of black, just above the
serrated cutting edge; below it is black except for a narrow
yellow border at the base. Legs are blue-green, eyes very dark
brown.

The voice is extremely variable, sometimes mimicking
neighboring birds, usually loud and penetrating barks and
croaks (2).

It nests in cavities in trees or high stumps, the holes perhaps
previously carved out by large woodpeckers. The entrance,
well concealed by a tangle of vegetation, is a foot or so above
the bare nest cup, where two white eggs are deposited (1).

REFERENCES: Austin 1961, p. 189, picture in color. Sutton 1951, p. 256, picture in color.
(1) Wilson Bull. 56:2:65–76, life history (Wagner).
(2) Slud 1964.

Pteroglossus torquatus erythrozonus Ridgway

Collared Araçari   Cucharón
                                        Tucancillo Collarejo

Panch'el

Trop. Mid. Am., Colombia, and Venezuela
Resident   15 in.   170 gr. (147 to 182)

Common and numerous. They range widely through the forest, high and low, straggling along one after the other rather than in compact flocks. They are often found feeding with the larger Keel-billed Toucans (*Ramphastos sulfuratus*). The race is smaller-bodied than some others; even within the area the weight varies materially and so do the details of coloring, both feathers and bill.

The general effect is of a large-billed bird, dark above and on the throat, yellow below, with a bright red rump and a red belly-band.

The head and throat are black, the back and mantle dark green, wings and tail dark greenish gray; an obscure brown collar crosses the neck and the rump area is conspicuously red. Below the black neck the yellow breast is strongly washed with red and has a black central patch; a band of bright red (at sides) and black (in center) separates the breast from a clear yellow belly which becomes tinged with red near the tail. The upper bill has coarse, tooth-like notches along its biting edges. It is largely ivory yellow, blending with shades of gray and brown, the ridge and tip black. The lower bill is all black, the whole with a narrow but conspicuous border at the base of light yellow. Legs are dark green, the thighs feathered dark brown. The eyes are light yellow, surrounded by bare skin, usually black before and red behind the eye.

Calls include a high-pitched, squeaky series, as *pe-tit, pe-tit, pe-tit,* repeated many times at a steady, moderately fast rate (1), (2), (3); another is a thin high-pitched, two-syllable hiccup which sounds like *fe-líz* (the name for the bird in Costa Rica) (2).

Nests are in cavities, with narrow entrances and deep pockets, located high in trees. Three white eggs are deposited in the unlined cup (1).

REFERENCES: Blake 1953, fpc., picture in color.
(1) Condor 60:4:201–219, life history (Skutch).
(2) Slud 1964.
(3) Mexican Bird Songs, recordings by L. Irby Davis.

Ramphastos sulfuratus sulfuratus Lesson

Keel-billed Toucan   Pito Real
                                                                 Tucán Grande

Ah Pam

Trop. Mid. Am. (except El Salvador) and n. S. Am.
Resident   19 in.   400 gr. (360 to 450)

Common, the most conspicuous of the toucans. Small flocks, sometimes accompanied by the smaller araçaris, feed throughout the forest wherever fruit occurs; a heavy rustle of wings and the dropping of debris then reveal their presence. The voice is an infallible clue, it is so characteristic and still so unlike a birdcall; a longish series of loud, croaking *crrek-crrek-crrek-crrek*'s, given with a deliberate rhythm, frog-like to some listeners (1), and hear (3).

When in flight, the conspicuously lemon yellow chest and face blend into the equally conspicuous large, yellow-green bill, and make the bill appear much longer than it really is. The body and tail are black, with a white patch above and a crimson patch below, located at the base of the tail. The upper bill is largely yellow-green, broadly tipped with dark red, and with a large wedge of orange just above the sharp, serrated cutting edges. The lower bill, also yellow-green and red-tipped, has a middle area of light blue. A narrow black border separates the bill from the face of the bird. Eyes are dark greenish yellow, surrounded by an area of bare skin delicately colored in light green, yellow, and blue. Legs are rich glossy blue. In death the colors of both bill and bare skin areas fade rapidly and much is lost within a single day.

Nests are in natural cavities in trees, both high and low, where one to four dull white eggs are laid. The eggs are sculptured with irregular pitted grooves extending lengthwise. The nest cup may be located anywhere from a few inches to as much as six feet below the entrance hole (2).

REFERENCES: Austin 1961, p. 189, picture in color. Gilliard 1958, plate 110, color photograph.
(1) Slud 1964.
(2) Misc. Pub. No. 19, U.M.M.Z., life history (Van Tyne 1929).
(3) Mexican Bird Songs, recordings by L. Irby Davis.

PICIDAE

Piculus rubiginosus yucatanensis (Cabot)

Golden-olive Woodpecker   Carpintero Verde

Chahum (woodpeckers in general)

Trop. Mid. Am. (the species, in much of its range chiefly in the highlands; the race, a lowland bird), and S. Am.
Resident   8½ in.   75 gr.   Plate 20

Uncommon. It frequents the heavy forest and is seldom seen.

It is the greenest woodpecker at Tikal, largely olive-green with a golden cast above, more yellowish below. The gray crown is surrounded by crimson, broadly so toward the nape; the cheek is grayish with a wide crimson stripe below it (lacking on females who wear it in dark gray). Underparts are sharply barred dark olive-green against pale yellow. The bill is black, legs gray, eyes very dark brown.

Its flicker-like call is diagnostic (1) (but see *Dryocopus lineatus*); in Costa Rica the male voices a powerful, high-pitched clear note, very rapidly repeated to form a long-continued roll or trill; both sexes utter a high, loud, sharp *beee* and also a dry *churr* (2).

Nests are in cavities in decaying trees and stumps, both high and low, the cup lined with wood chips. Eggs are four in number, pure white (2).

REFERENCES:
(1) Blake 1953, p. 291, picture in black and white.
(2) Wilson Bull. 68:2:118–126, life history (Skutch).

Celeus castaneus (Wagler)

Chestnut-colored Woodpecker   Carpintero Atabacado
                                              Carpintero Rubio

Uchichil Chemach

Trop. s.e. Mexico and Caribbean slope of Mid. Am. to n.w. Panama

Resident   9½ in.   90 gr.   Plate 20

Fairly common. It is seen quite often in the heavy forest, somewhat back from the roads and trails.

The head with its longish, conspicuous crest extending over the nape, the nape itself, and the throat are all tawny or light brown; the male has a large patch of dull red below and before the eyes; otherwise it is mainly chestnut above and below, spotted with numerous blackish v-shaped marks, which make a barred effect on back and belly, a scaly effect on the breast; the rump is yellowish, the tail tipped black. The bill is pale yellow-green, legs are green, eyes are red-brown, surrounded by a smallish area of black bare skin.

The voice is not helpful to recognition, occurring in too great a variety of squeaks, a nasal *skahr* followed by a lower level, weaker *heh-heh-heh,* and other calls (1).

Three nests in British Honduras were from three to over forty feet up in dead trees. One contained four eggs (2), (and Willis, in litt.).

REFERENCES: Blake 1953, p. 292, picture in black and white.
(1) Slud 1964.   (2) Russell 1964.

Dryocopus lineatus similis (Lesson)

Lineated Woodpecker   Carpintero Grande

Colonté

Trop. Mid. Am. and S. Am.
Resident   12 in.   155 gr.   Plate 21

Not uncommon, but still not numerous. Though mostly found in the forest, it shows some preference for partially cleared areas with scattered trees, as in Group E at Tikal.

It is a large woodpecker, although much smaller than the northern Pileated (*D. pileatus*) which it otherwise closely resembles, and only slightly smaller than the Pale-billed (*Phloeoceastes guatemalensis*) which it also superficially resembles, and which is more common. The bright red crest is long and pointed, with a flowing quality; a blackish area around the eye and over the ear is outlined below by a narrow white line from the bill to the nape; below the white line is a wide stripe of red; the chin is white, streaked with black. Females retain only part of the red crest (black on the forehead and forecrown) and none of the wide red stripe—which becomes black. The body (both sexes) is mainly black above, with a white stripe from the nape to the sides, below the wing, and with white shoulders on the wing. The breast is black, the belly pale buff barred with black. In flight the under wing flashes white. The bill is ivory, legs dark gray, eyes white (sometimes tinged pale yellow).

It is not especially vocal. Its drumming on trees is of a rolling nature, not like the imperative two raps or hammer blows of the Pale-billed. One call is a loud flicker-like *wícka, wícka, wícka* (1), (2); another, perhaps more common, is *oook-churrrrr* (2); and hear (3).

Nests are in cavities in trees, both high and moderately low. A set of three and one of four white eggs were found in Guatemala (Skutch, in litt.).

REFERENCES: Blake 1953, p. 293, pictures in black and white. Sutton 1951, p. 144, picture in color.
(1) Eisenmann 1952.   (2) Slud 1964.
(3) Mexican Bird Songs, recordings by L. Irby Davis.

Centurus aurifrons dubius (Cabot)

Golden-fronted Woodpecker   Cheje Común

Ch'ujut

Texas and Mid. Am. to Costa Rica
Resident   10 in.   83 gr. (71 to 95)   Plate 20

Uncommon. It was reported as common in the clearings of Uaxactún (Van Tyne 1935) and may increase at Tikal as more open areas develop. Although it is not averse to habitations, I found it a rather wary bird when met along forest edges; usually high in tall trees, but not in dense foliage.

The *races* of the Golden-fronted vary in a number of details. In general the race here has clearly but rather finely barred wings and back (zebra-backed), a black tail with white rump, and light buff-gray underparts. The head has a small orange-red forehead patch just above the bill, and a large wholly red patch running *continuously* from the crown down the nape, the two separated by a narrow grayish area. On females the large red patch is greatly reduced, leaving only a red nape. Buff-gray underparts are palest about the face and throat, deepening to yellow-gray down the breast; the belly is washed strongly with red. The bill is black, legs greenish, eyes reddish.

A comparatively noisy woodpecker, it utters a rolling *churr-churr*, rapidly repeated, and confusingly similar to other woodpeckers.

Nests are in holes in trees, both high and low. Four white eggs were found in a nest in British Honduras (1).

REFERENCES: Peterson 1960, p. 145, picture in color (of northern race, which lacks continuous red crown and nape, otherwise very similar).
(1) Russell 1964.

Centurus pucherani perileucus (Todd)

Black-cheeked Woodpecker   Carpintero Selvático

Trop. Mid. Am. (except El Salvador) and n.w. S. Am.
Resident   7½ in.   50 gr.   Plate 20

Not uncommon but not widespread. It shows a preference for more open areas and is found along forest edges beside roads which are open to the sky. It is a very active little bird and quite unmindful of humans.

Its color pattern bears some resemblance to the Golden-fronted (*C. aurifrons*), prime distinctions residing in its smaller size and the conspicuous black facial mask across the eye and down to the side of the neck (with a slight interruption of white above the eye). Wings and back are coarsely barred black and white; the tail is black, the middle feathers barred, the rump white; the head has a small yellow patch just above the bill, the crown and nape a bright red (on females this red occurs only on the nape). Underparts are buff-gray, barred on the sides, and with a red patch on the belly. The bill is black, legs greenish, eyes dark brown.

The voice is a smooth *churr*-ing rattle (1); in British Honduras a rapid *chi-chi-chi* (Willis, in litt.).

Nests are in holes in dead palms and trees, from twelve to over fifty feet up (2). Three eggs are usually laid. An interesting nest was found (July 1959) about twenty-five feet up in a dead palm tree, and hardly more than three feet below another nest which was occupied at the same time by a pair of Pale-billed Woodpeckers (*Phloeoceastes guatemalensis*). Both pairs appeared quite tolerant of each other.

REFERENCES: Blake 1953, p. 298, picture in black and white. de Schauensee 1964, p. 160, picture in color.
(1) Slud 1964.   (2) Russell 1964.

Sphyrapicus varius subsp.

Yellow-bellied Sapsucker　　　　　Carpintero Pecho Tinto
　　　　　　　　　　　　　　　　　　Carpintero Bebedor

N. Am.; winters through Mid. Am. to Panama
Transient　　　　　8 in.　　　　　50 gr.

Rare. This migrant is noted because of a verbal report to me of a specimen taken at Tikal by James Greenway sometime in the first half of 1962 and left with Jorge A. Ibarra at the Museum of Natural History in Guatemala. It has not been identified to subspecies.

Whether at rest or in flight, a conspicuous, longitudinal patch of white on each wing, present in all plumages, will separate it from most other woodpeckers. Males have a patch of red not only on the forehead but also on the throat. Females replace the red throat with white. The upper breast is black; the face has a striking pattern of broad black and white stripes; the back and wing tips are black, coarsely barred with white; tails are mainly black with a white rump. Underparts are light colored with an obscure tinge of yellow. Different races vary from this description, and juveniles and birds in winter plumage make for confusion, but the long white wing patch is still a good clue.

Its distinctive drumming, several rapid thumps followed by several slow rhythmic ones, is confined to its nesting grounds. It may utter a squealing, whining, nasal note, or a downwardly slurred *keeyew* (2).

REFERENCES:
(1) Peterson 1960, p. 145, pictures in color. Austin 1961, p. 192, picture in color.
(2) Pough 1953.

Veniliornis fumigatus sanguinolentus (Sclater)

Smoky-brown Woodpecker   Carpintero Atabacado

Trop. Mid. Am. and S. Am.
Resident   6½ in.   33 gr.   Plate 21

Common. This smallest of Tikal woodpeckers is usually found within fifteen feet of the ground, in open-canopy forest areas which permit the growth of a fairly heavy understory. It is a drab and quiet little bird, a dull brown color above and below, paler about the face, the male only having a dark red crown and nape with a checkerboard effect of small black spots. Occasional birds, not all, have a shiny suffusion of orange across the back and shoulders. The tail is blackish brown; the bill black or dark brown, legs dark green-gray. Eyes are brown, surrounded by a smallish area of black bare skin.

The voice is "a queer little wooden rattle" (1); or a harsh rasping series of rapidly given *zur-zur-zur-zur* notes, and other shorter calls (2).

Nests are in holes in trees, in British Honduras located from three to five feet up (3).

REFERENCES:
(1) Wilson Bull. 68:2:119 (Skutch).
(2) Slud 1964.   (3) Russell 1964.

Phloeoceastes guatemalensis guatemalensis (Hartlaub)

Pale-billed Woodpecker   Cheje Grande
                                              Carpintero Real

Colonté

Trop. Mid. Am. to w. Panama
Resident   13½ in.   220 gr. (200 to 240)   Plate 21

Fairly common. Because it is the largest and most spectacular of Tikal woodpeckers, it may seem more numerous than is actually the case. It shows a decided preference for large, heavy-bodied trees and mature forest, but is also found in semi-open areas, where it meets the superficially similar Lineated Woodpecker (*Dryocopus lineatus*). I found a pair apparently nesting about twenty-five feet up in a comparatively slim, dead palm tree, located at the edge of a wide open road. Less than four feet below the nest hole was another smaller one, being used by a pair of Black-cheeked Woodpeckers (*Centurus pucherani*).

Although the Pale-billed is similar in appearance to the Lineated, the male is easily recognized, with its all-red head, crest, nape, neck, and throat, lacking black in any of those parts. The female is more of a problem, having black on the forehead and over the top of the crest, black on the hind neck, ear patch, and throat; but she still has more red across the face than either the male or female of the smaller bird. On both male and female the large crest appears firm and stiff rather than flowing, the whole head presenting a large, solid, even wooden effect.

Upperparts are mainly black, with white stripes starting high on each side of the neck and joining at the middle of the back. Underparts are black on the chest, coarsely barred on the breast and belly with black and white. In flight the underwing flashes yellowish white. The bill is ivory color, legs greenish gray, eyes yellow.

It drums a diagnostic loud, resonant, imperative double-rap, distinctly different from other Tikal woodpeckers. On occasion it utters a series of reedy rattles (1).

Nests are in holes in trees. A set of two glossy, pure white eggs was seen in Costa Rica (Skutch, in litt.).

REFERENCES: Sutton 1951, p. 96, picture in color. Blake 1953, p. 303, picture in black and white. Condor 52:1:fpc., pictures in color.

(1) Slud 1964.

LONG-TAILED HERMIT

p. 94.

6½ inches, more than half the long tail and bill. This and Little Hermit the only predominantly buff-colored hummers here; back bronze green in some lights. Bill ochre-colored below.

LITTLE HERMIT

p. 95.

4 inches, a butterfly-like hummingbird. Plumage like that of larger Long-tailed Hermit, but tail lacks the *extended* white central feathers, and bill is yellower below.

SCALY-BREASTED HUMMINGBIRD

p. 95.

5½ inches, same size as rather similar Wedge-tailed Sabrewing, shown just below. Upperparts flashing green, continuing down neck and throat where mixed with gray; narrow white band across belly; outer tail feathers conspicuously white-tipped. Males buff below, females gray. Scaly effect visible only nearby.

WEDGE-TAILED SABREWING

p. 96.

5½ inches. Upperparts flashing green, with flashes of blue on crown (much duller on females), and white spot behind the eye; throat and underparts gray, some buff below tail; tail pointed, outer tail feathers white-tipped (grayish on females).

WHITE-BELLIED EMERALD

p. 100.

3¼ inches. Upperparts bright green; underparts white; tail tipped gray. Short bill shows red below.

RUFOUS-TAILED HUMMINGBIRD

p. 101.

4¼ inches. Above bright green; below flashing green on throat and chest (females duller), breast and belly gray. Bill flesh color, below. All brown tail also shown, from above, with green rump, but lacking green central feathers of Fawn-breasted.

PLATE 13

SCALY-BREASTED
HUMMINGBIRD

LONG-TAILED
HERMIT

LITTLE HERMIT

WHITE-BELLIED
EMERALD

WEDGE-TAILED
SABREWING

RUFOUS-TAILED HUMMINGBIRD

FORK-TAILED
EMERALD

FAWN-BREASTED HUMMINGBIRD

0	inches	3
0	cms	7

WHITE-NECKED JACOBIN p. 96

5 inches. Sexes differ.

The male has dark blue head, throat, and chest; a conspicuous white collar across the back; much white in the tail.

The female usually is bronzy green above, green and white below with practically no white in the tail; but a large percentage of females have varying degrees of male plumage, a dimorphic condition which should be given further study.

GREEN-BREASTED MANGO p. 98

5 inches. Sexes differ greatly.

The male is green above and below, becoming almost black on chin, throat, and breast. The tail is purple (middle feathers green), edged with dark brown.

The female is green above, but mainly white below, with a conspicuous irregular black line down the middle. The tail is darker and tipped with white.

PURPLE-CROWNED FAIRY p. 102

5 inches. Sexes differ, but only slightly. Both have bright green upperparts and immaculate white underparts, with long blue and white tails.

The male has flashing blue-violet in the crown and just back of the black eye patch.

The female lacks the blue-violet entirely, and has a brownish black eye patch. She also seems to be larger than the male.

PLATE 14

WHITE-NECKED JACOBIN

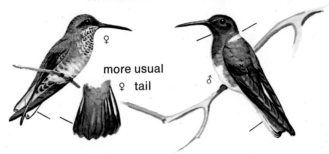

more usual ♀ tail

♀

♂

GREEN-BREASTED MANGO

♂

♀

PURPLE-CROWNED FAIRY

♀

♂

0   inches   3
0   cms   7

PLATE 15

OCELLATED TURKEY

♂

0 — inches — 6
0 — cms — 15

FAWN-BREASTED HUMMINGBIRD

p. 100.

4 inches. Above bright green; below glittering green on chest (more brilliant than Rufous-tailed), buff on belly. Bill bright red above as well as below. Brown tail also shown, from above, with green central feathers (lacking on Rufous-tailed).

FORK-TAILED EMERALD

p. 99.

3½ inches. Sexes differ, but both have decidedly forked tails, conspicuously red bills with black tips, bronze green upperparts (bronzier on females). MALE: glittering emerald throat and chest, continuing green on body; tail dark blue and brownish black. FEMALE: gray underparts, washed with green at sides; tail gray, terminating in blue-black band and white tips.

OCELLATED TURKEY

p. 54.

Male only illustrated: about 36 inches, or two-thirds as large as the wild Common Turkey. A knob on the crown and a wattle which usually hangs over to left side of the bill (illustrated in deflated condition) become greatly enlarged when "displaying" before females.

The head and neck are forget-me-not blue, the tail gray with eye-spots of blue and bronze, the wing with a white patch. The spurs are conspicuously long.

Female is substantially smaller, lacks the knob and wattle, and has a border of white at the base of the bare neck.

DENDROCOLAPTIDAE

Dendrocincla anabatina anabatina Sclater

Tawny-winged Woodcreeper   Trepador Cola Lisa

Trop. Mid. Am. (except El Salvador) to w. Panama
Resident   7½ in.   ♂ 40 gr., ♀ 31 gr.

Common. Woodcreepers in general are abundant through-out the forest and this one is among the more numerous. It feeds primarily on insects, for which it probes into cracks and crevices in trees with its sturdy bill, climbing up to a moderate height and then flying down to the base of another tree; small lizards are also eaten; army ants are followed for the insects which they stir into activity.

Upperparts are olive-brown, the tail a rustier brown, the wings with a patch of tawny or yellow-brown which is more conspicuous in flight, or when the bird flicks its wings open and shut. Underparts are largely gray-brown, the throat buff, palest on the chin. The bill is dark brown above, gray below; legs are gray; eyes light brown. An immature bird has white eyes.

It voices a reedy, sometimes quavering *squirp;* also a long-drawn-out rattle (1).

Nests are made in old woodpecker holes, to which strips of bark and leaves are added. This vegetable matter is sometimes used to cover the two white eggs when they are left alone (1).

REFERENCES: Blake 1953, p. 306, picture in black and white.
(1) Animal Kingdom 65:15:151–155, life history, partial (Skutch).
(2) Slud 1964.

Dendrocincla homochroa homochroa (Sclater)

Ruddy Woodcreeper   Trepador Rojizo

Trop. Mid. Am. (except El Salvador) and Venezuela
Resident   7½ in.   37 gr.

Common. About as numerous as *D. anabatina,* it is also
similar in habits, size, and build, but of a richer, ruddier color;
the two species are often seen together, especially when foraging over swarms of army ants. It is mainly red-brown, a
deeper brown on the crown and tail, pale on the throat. The
sturdy bill is dark brown, sometimes becoming gray on the
lower bill; legs are gray, sometimes with a ruddy tinge; eyes
are light brown.

It utters reedy or squeaky notes, a chattering rattle, and
other calls (1).

Nests are in holes or cavities in trees, the entrances preferably small and concealed. One of two nests found in British
Honduras was located about two feet up in a decayed stump
and held two white eggs; the other was about five feet up in
a palm and held three eggs (2).

REFERENCES:
(1) Slud 1964.   (2) Russell 1964.

Sittasomus griseicapillus gracileus Bangs and Peters

Olivaceous Woodcreeper   Trepadorcito Aceitunado

Takaj-ché

Trop. Mid. Am. and S. Am.
Resident   6 in.   11 gr.

Common. This, second only to the Ivory-billed (*Xiphorhynchus flavigaster*), is the most numerous of all the wood-
creepers at Tikal. It is also the smallest and one of the most
active, feeding along branches as well as on tree trunks, from
ground level to moderate heights.

Underparts are grayish olive, deepening slightly above on
head, shoulders, and upper back to olive-brown, all contrast-

ing with the brighter rufous of the wings, rump, and tail. The wings have a small darker rusty patch and dark tips. The bill is black above, grayish below; legs are shades of gray; eyes are very dark brown, almost black.

It voices a woodpecker-like rattling trill (1).

An individual was seen carrying small dead leaves into a tall hollow palm trunk (Skutch, in litt.).

REFERENCES: Blake 1953, p. 307, picture in black and white. Austin 1961, p. 179, picture in color. de Schauensee 1964, p. 208, picture in color (of similar race *S. g. levis*).

(1) Slud 1964.

Xiphocolaptes promeropirhynchus emigrans Sclater and Salvin

Strong-billed Woodcreeper Trepador Gigante

Chiefly highlands trop. Mid. Am. to w. Panama, also S. Am.
Visitor 12½ in. 135 gr.

Rare. It prefers pine forests and higher altitudes, and is unexpected here; however, it has been recorded in March 1957, August 1959, and March 1964. On the first occasion two were seen, in the company of a large mixed group of birds, all busily feeding above a stream of army ants. The August bird may have been breeding.

Upperparts are shades of brown, dark sepia, and rufous, narrowly streaked with buff about the head and back. The underparts are paler shades of duller brown, also narrowly streaked with paler buff about the face, neck, breast, and sides. The bill is gray, legs green-gray, eyes red-brown.

Its large size (one measured thirteen inches), its long, heavy bill, and its numerous streaks, distinguish it from all others, with the possible exception of the Ivory-billed (*Xiphorhynchus flavigaster*). The latter is substantially smaller (about nine inches), has broad stripes rather than narrow streaks, forming a characteristic string of "beads," and a bill with a downward droop.

In British Honduras it sings at dawn, occasionally later, a loud rough *schifferty-schifferty-schifferty-schiff;* also call notes, as *yip-yip-yip* and *pee-yub* (Willis, in litt.).

REFERENCES: de Schauensee 1964, p. 208, picture in color (of similar race *X. p. rostratus*).

Dendrocolaptes certhia sancti-thomae (Lafresnaye)

Barred Woodcreeper   Trepador Rayado
                                          Trepador Barrado

Trop. Mid. Am. and S. Am.
Resident   10 in.   61 gr.

Uncommon? A fair-sized forest bird, a typical climber of tree trunks and limbs. It may cling immobile while an observer passes by and hence is seldom seen; however, it was frequently caught in mist nets. It tends to forage over swarming army ants which are traveling in vertical columns on the trees, rather than over ants which are traveling on the ground (1).

It is distinctly barred, more narrowly about the head and neck, more coarsely below, and obscurely on the back, with black and brown of about equal width, except on the wings and tail, which are a smooth rufous brown. It is the only *barred* woodcreeper present. The bill is long and heavy, usually black, occasionally brown or gray below; legs are gray; eyes are dull brown (one was red-brown).

It voices a distinctive, slow *oi–ink,* repeated two or three times (2); also a loud *téw-wee, téw-wee, téw-wee* (3).

REFERENCES: Blake 1953, p. 309, picture in black and white. de Schauensee 1964, p. 208, picture in color (of similar race *D. c. colombianus*).
   (1) Auk 77:2:159 (Willis).   (2) Slud 1964.
   (3) Condor 59:2:87 (Howell).

SPECIAL NOTE
   On April 3, 1962, a single specimen was taken by Ibarra and Greenway which was referred to *D. c. legtersi* Paynter (verbal comm.); other examples of this woodcreeper at Tikal are somewhat intermediate between *D. c. sancti-thomae* and the paler, perhaps smaller race, *legtersi,* from Yucatán.

Xiphorhynchus flavigaster eburneirostris (Des Murs)

Ivory-billed Woodcreeper   Trepador Goteado

Takaj-ché

Trop. Mid. Am. to n.w. Costa Rica
Resident   9 in.   ♂ 48 gr.   ♀ 40 gr.

Common. It is probably the most numerous of the wood-creepers at Tikal, ranging widely throughout the forest, frequently seen on tree trunks and limbs along the wider roads and more open sunny trails. It is conspicuously deliberate as it climbs from about eye level upward, probing for insects, and continuing higher than other species before it comes whistling down to begin another climb.

The crown and nape are blackish brown (but appearing lighter due to buff streaking), the back brown, the breast and sides brown-olive, all conspicuously brightened by broad buff stripes made up of droplet-shaped spots, looking somewhat like loose strings of beads. The chin and throat are creamy buff; wings and tail are uniformly rich red-brown. The bill, long and sturdy, has a slight downward droop; it is light-colored but not true ivory, being rather a pale grayish ivory, often with additions of brownish tones. Legs are greenish or greenish gray. Eyes are brown.

It voices a distinctive, melodious, "laughing" whistle, that begins on an even pitch and rapidly slides trippingly down the scale, sometimes ending with two clear *weet-weet* whistles (1), (2). Sutton (1951) considers it strikingly like the song of the Canyon Wren (*Catherpes mexicanus*). Less frequently used are woodpecker-like rattles and other calls (1).

Nests are in holes or cavities in trees.

REFERENCES: Blake 1953, p. 309, picture in black and white. Condor 53:3:fpc., pictures in color.
   (1) Slud 1964.
   (2) Mexican Bird Songs, recordings by L. Irby Davis.

Lepidocolaptes souleyetii insignis (Nelson)

Streak-headed Woodcreeper   Trepador Punteado

Trop. Mid. Am. and S. Am.
Resident?   7½ in.   30 gr.

Rare. None have been found at Tikal, but a male was found at Uaxactún, 28 March 1931 (Van Tyne 1935). Unlike other woodcreepers, it is partial to man-made environment, clearings with scattered trees, light woodlands; Tikal may yet attract it.

Its blackish crown and nape, its brown upper back and shoulders, are brightened with buff streaks; upperparts are otherwise mainly chestnut. The face and throat are light buff, becoming marked with dark scallops on the throat and chest; the rest of the underparts are gray-brown, boldly streaked with buff on the breast and sides. The bill is pale, long and slender, somewhat down-curved.

It voices a beautiful, long-drawn, clear trill, sometimes full-voiced, sometimes weakened (1), (2).

Nests, usually high in trees, are preferably made in natural cavities with small cranny-like, well-concealed entrances. The nest floor contains a loose accumulation of bits of wood, on which two white eggs are laid (1), (3).

REFERENCES:
(1) Animal Kingdom 65:5:151–155, life history (Skutch).
(2) Slud 1964.   (3) Russell 1964.

FURNARIIDAE

Automolus ochrolaemus cervinigularis (Sclater)

Buff-throated Foliage-gleaner   Hojarasquero Pardo

Trop. Mid. Am. (except El Salvador) and S. Am.
Resident   7½ in.   ♂ 48 gr. ♀ 40 gr.   Plate 22

Uncommon, perhaps rare. This brown ovenbird is found in heavy ground cover, tangles, and in vine-covered trees in such cover. It may easily be overlooked despite its restless feeding habits.

Upperparts are dark brown, somewhat rust-colored on the wings, very red-brown on the tail, and with a light buff line over the eye. Underparts are buff, darkest on the belly, very pale on the throat, somewhat ochraceous on the lower face. There is a rather scaly effect to the feathers of the lower throat. The bill is dark brown above, yellowish below; legs are greenish; eyes dark brown.

Its voice is a harsh, slow, long-continued croak or rattle, incessantly repeated mornings and evenings, when its song most readily reveals its presence; seldom heard during the day. It also utters low throaty notes (1).

Nests are in burrows in the ground, with a bulky cup at the end composed of leaf stems and having a shallow depression in which two or three white eggs are deposited (1), (2).

REFERENCES:
(1) Condor 54:2:93–100, life history (Skutch); 59:2:89, picture in black and white.
(2) Auk 43:4:546, nest (Van Tyne).

Xenops minutus mexicanus Sclater

Plain Xenops   Pájaro Pico Chato

Jana'-sinik

Trop. Mid. Am. (except El Salvador) and S. Am.
Resident   4¾ in.   11 gr. (10 to 12.5)

Common. It is a restless acrobatic little forager in semi-open forest, where it explores branches, twigs, and leaves from all angles. Not shy, it is readily seen, usually above eye level to moderate heights, although it may also feed from ground level to high in trees.

Its small size and active habits, its conspicuously upturned lower bill, and a conspicuous clear white, short stripe, from well below the eye to the ear, combine to make it comparatively easy to identify. Upperparts are olive-brown, the dusky wings have a wide streak of brown, the tail is bright rufous (with some black showing when spread). The throat is dull white, becoming streaked with brown on the breast and all brown on the belly. The bill is black above, light brown below; legs are gray; eyes dark brown.

The voice is a persistent chipping, sometimes quickened into a somewhat musical trill. It also utters a high thin *tsiss* and other hiss-like notes (1).

The nest is a hole in a tree, woodpecker-fashion, the cup lined with fine strips of plant fibers. Two young birds were being fed in such a nest (2).

REFERENCES: Austin 1961, p. 198, picture in color. Condor 59:2:91, picture in black and white.
(1) Slud 1964.   (2) Van Tyne 1935.

Sclerurus guatemalensis guatemalensis (Hartlaub)

Scaly-throated Leafscraper   Escarbador

Trop. Mid. Am. (except El Salvador), Colombia, and Ecuador
Resident   7½ in.   34 gr.   Plate 22

Uncommon but not rare. Primarily a ground-feeder, scratching in the ground litter, tossing leaves about, it prefers the fairly open understory of the forest, even damp and muddy ground which it can probe with its notably slender bill. Its jerky movements help to disclose its presence.

It is a rich, dark brown above and below, only the throat showing white with a scaly or scalloped effect. The tail is largely black. The bill is black above, light brown below; legs are dark brown; eyes very dark brown.

It utters an unusually sharp squeak, sometimes a series of *squick*'s. It also has a song, described as a rising and falling, an accelerating and slowing, *pwik-wik-wik-wik-wik-wik-wik* (1).

The nest is in a burrow 21 to 33 inches long in a bank; one was in a mass of clay adhering to roots of a fallen tree. At the inner end is a loose shallow structure of leaf-stems, where two pure white eggs are deposited (Skutch, in litt.).

REFERENCES: Blake 1953, p. 316, picture in black and white.
(1) Slud 1964.

FORMICARIIDAE

Thamnophilus doliatus yucatanensis Ridgway

Barred Antshrike   Pájaro Hormiguero Rayado
                                        Gritón

Balan-ch'ich'

Trop. Mid. Am. and S. Am.
Resident   6½ in.   25 gr.   Plate 22

Not uncommon, but localized in sunny, dense low growth, such as occurs along the north edge of the airstrip. It keeps within ten feet or so of the ground.

The male is very conspicuously barred black and white. The female is a much smoother-looking bird, rich red-brown above, with an obscure paler brown collar; underparts are buff, palest on the throat; the face and sides of the neck are finely streaked with black. The bill is black above, blue-gray below, the cutting edges yellowish on females; legs are blue-gray; eyes are pale yellowish white.

The voice is a not unmusical series of rapidly repeated chuckles, first on a level pitch, then accelerating and falling, to close with a single, short, upward, nasal hiccup (1), (3), (4). Other calls are heard (1).

The nest is a simple cup of loosely woven, fine vegetable fibers, fully suspended at the rim from the forked twigs of a bush or small tree located from three to thirty feet up. Two or three pale buff, lightly spotted eggs are deposited (2).

REFERENCES: Blake 1953, p. 318, picture in black and white.
(1) Slud 1964.
(2) Austin 1961, p. 200, picture in color (of male); p. 202, nesting described. Allen 1961, plate 63, color photograph (with nest). Gilliard 1958, plate 119, color photograph (of female).
(3) Mexican Bird Songs, recordings by L. Irby Davis.
(4) Bird Songs, recordings by Paul Schwartz.

Thamnistes anabatinus anabatinus Sclater and Salvin

Russet Antshrike   Pájaro Hormiguero
                                        Larvero

Trop. Mid. Am. (except El Salvador), and w. S. Am.
Resident   6 in.   19 gr.   Plate 22

Rare. It is found in heavy forest, high in trees more often
than low, rarely on the ground. It may be inconspicuous
rather than rare.

Upperparts are mainly yellow-brown, contrasting with dark
red-brown rump and tail; underparts are paler yellow-brown,
becoming yellow-gray on the sides and belly. Males have a
partly concealed, inconspicuous area of brighter orange-brown
on the back. The bill is black above, gray below, the lower
bill being noticeably bulbous; legs are blue-gray; eyes red-
brown.

Among a variety of calls, one is a *switsit,* another a piercing *weesawisst;* a song is a measured series of *tswit*'s, first
intensifying, then falling (1).

REFERENCES:
(1) Slud 1964.

Dysithamnus mentalis septentrionalis Ridgway

Plain Antvireo   Pájaro Hormiguero
                                       Matagusano

S. Mexico (Campeche), Guatemala, Honduras, Costa Rica,
    Panama, and S. Am.
Resident   4½ in.   12½ gr. (11 to 13½)   Plate 25

Common and numerous. It frequents the lower branches
of trees, the understory in general, and the low growth bordering roads and trails.

The illustrations of the male and female of this small antbird are on the same plate with entirely unrelated birds, because of superficial resemblances throughout the group shown.

The male is gray above, darkest on the head; underparts
are paler gray, lightest on the belly, which is tinged with yel-

low. Some white shows in two obscure wing bars, at the bend of the wing, and at the very tips of the stubby tail feathers. The female is dull grayish olive on the back and rump; red-brown on the crown, nape, wings, and tail, brightest on the forehead and crown; the throat is dull white, the breast and sides brownish gray, the belly and crissum pale yellow. Some buff shows in two very obscure wing bars and at the tail tips. The bill (both sexes), conspicuously heavy for so small a bird, is black above, dark gray below; legs are gray; eyes very dark brown.

It utters a large variety of sounds. One is a soft *woo-tóo*, a two-syllable whistle with the second note higher in pitch; this may be repeated a few times to become a gentle song. Another is a descending rolling cackle, soft and weak, gradually fading out (1).

The nest is a frail, openly woven cup, suspended vireo-like at the rim from a small forked branch and made of dark filamentous material, the outside with more or less green moss. Two whitish eggs are deposited, variably flecked and blotched with purplish brown (Skutch, in litt.).

REFERENCES:
(1) Slud 1964.

Microrhopias quixensis boucardi (Sclater)

Dot-winged Antwren
Pájaro Hormiguero
Motorralero

Trop. Mid. Am. (except El Salvador) and S. Am.
Resident   4¼ in.   8.5 gr. (7 to 10)   Plate 22

Fairly common. It is found from eye level to the tops of tall thickets and in denser understory where the open canopy lets much light through.

The male is glossy black above and below, with smallish white spots on the wings and large white tips on the strongly graduated tail feathers. A large patch of white is concealed under the black back except when the male is excited. The female is a flat dark gray above, rich red-brown below, shows white on the wings and tail, and has the concealed white patch on the back as does the male. The bill is black, legs are gray, eyes very dark brown.

In addition to sweetly whistled peeps and cheeps, it voices a musical high-pitched descending roll or trill, light and sweet (1).

A nest at Gallon Jug, British Honduras, was located about twenty feet up in a tree, a deep cup or pouch of palm strips (others of leaves, dark fibers, and cobweb) suspended vireo-like by its rim from a forked twig; a very different one, on Barro Colorado, was a bulky leaf-and-grass cup located about ten feet up in a clump of leaves in a bamboo (Willis, in litt.). Other nests range from about three to twenty-five feet above ground and contain two white eggs each, spotted and blotched with brown (Skutch, in litt.).

REFERENCES:
(1) Slud 1964.

Cercomacra tyrannina crepera Bangs

Dusky Antbird
Pájaro Hormiguero
Marañero

Trop. Mid. Am. (except El Salvador) and S. Am.
Resident   5½ in.   16 gr.   Plate 22

Not uncommon, but less common than *Microrhopias quixensis*. Both occur in similar habitat: tall thickets and heavy, sunny understory, seldom high above ground.

The male is dark gray, almost black on the crown and wings, the latter with two very minute white wing bars. The female is dull grayish olive above, becoming rufescent on the wings; underparts are tawny orange color which continues up into the face, shading to grayish olive on the flanks. Both sexes have a concealed white patch on the back. The bill is black on the male, the female dark brown above and light gray below; legs are dark gray; eyes are light brown.

It sings a "cosy little trill" (1) of one to three slow notes followed by a dozen or so faster ones, rising in pitch, as *byou-byou-byou*-etc., then *beepeepeepeebe bebe* (2); and a call *teé-oo, teé-oo* (3).

The nest, some two to nine feet up, often near an opening in the woods, is a deep, open cup or pouch, slung vireo-like from the fork of a slender drooping vine or branch; composed of leaves and fibers. The open top slopes strongly down from the fork. The bird usually sits facing out, the head just visible over the low rim, the tail held upright against the much higher rear wall. Two dull white eggs are deposited, spotted all over with red-brown, heaviest at the large end (Skutch, in litt.).

REFERENCES:
(1) Chapman 1929.   (2) Slud 1964.
(3) Eisenmann 1952.

Formicarius analis intermedius Ridgway

Black-faced Antthrush   Pájaro Hormiguero Cantor

Xbech'lu'um

Trop. Mid. Am. (except El Salvador) and S. Am.
Resident   7½ in.   63 gr. (55 to 71)

Fairly common. It is one of the few antbirds which is essentially terrestrial, preferring well-shaded but fairly open understory rather than dense brush. There it may be found stepping slowly and deliberately along over the ground litter, sometimes flicking leaves about, feeding on snails, beetles, lizards, even small snakes, as it goes. During the dry season its foraging activities may reveal its presence.

This chunky, thrush-like bird is a rich dark brown above, darkest on the crown and on the short, almost stubby tail; below, it is dusky gray on the breast, shading to a whitish belly and red-brown under tail coverts. The face and throat are conspicuously black, bordered below by a bright rufous band which continues up across the ears and neck to form a narrow collar on the nape. The bill is black; legs are varied shades of flesh, brown, and gray; the eyes are dark brown with a reddish tone, and are surrounded by light blue-gray bare skin.

It has a distinctive, readily imitated song; a full, mellow, three-syllable whistle, *kyéw-kyew-kyew,* the first note higher and longer than the others, the phrase repeated at about fifteen-second intervals; sometimes the shorter notes are repeated many times, going down-scale, with a very different effect (1), (2), (3),* (4). Its alarm call is a sharp *tleet-tleet,* also quite characteristic (1).

The nest, like the bird's habits, differs materially from that of most other antbirds; one was located in the cavity of a tree or hollow stump, the entrance about six feet above ground, the cup some two feet below the hole and lined with leaves, flower stalks, and flowers. Two eggs, white, faintly stippled with brown, are deposited (1).

REFERENCES: Blake 1953, p. 321, picture in black and white.
(1) Wilson Bull. 57:2:122–128, life history (Skutch).
(2) Slud 1964.   (3) Condor 59:4:254 (Eisenmann).
(4) Mexican Bird Songs, recordings by L. Irby Davis.

COTINGIDAE

Attila spadiceus flammulatus Lafresnaye

Bright-rumped Attila   Bigotón

Trop. Mid. Am. and S. Am.
Resident   8 in.   43 gr. (35 to 48)

Fairly common. Found in almost every part of the forest, but especially where there is strong but not dense understory, where it forages both high and low.

It is mainly brown above, shading to very dark brown on the head and somewhat redder brown on the tail; the rump is conspicuously orange-yellow (sometimes with a brownish tinge); underparts are pale gray, sometimes heavily washed with yellow on the breast and belly; the throat is lightly streaked, the chest more heavily streaked. The bill is dark brown above, usually gray below, and has heavy bristles at its base; legs are blue-gray; eyes are usually reddish brown, sometimes yellowish.

Its song is flycatcher-like. One form is of paired whistles in two keys, as *weét-it, weét-it, weét-it, weét-it, weeeee* (1), (2), (3); another, quite different, is a short run of trills followed by two deliberate notes; also a series of about ten pairs of short, high whistles (3). The singer is difficult to trace, as it perches near the tree trunk, well concealed by foliage (5).

The race in Trinidad builds a nest of weed stems and small twigs in a hole in a tree, where two smooth, creamy white eggs are deposited, thickly covered with purplish brown marks and blotches (4).

REFERENCES: Blake 1953, p. 323, picture in black and white. Condor 56:3:fpc., pictures in color.

(1) Slud 1964.   (2) Chapman 1929 (Panama race).
(3) Mexican Bird Songs, recordings by L. Irby Davis.
(4) Herklots 1961.
(5) Condor 59:4:254 (Eisenmann).

SPECIAL NOTE

The following three cotingas are very similar in color and pattern: Rufous Mourner (*Rhytipterna holerythra*), Rufous Piha (*Lipaugus unirufus*), and Cinnamon Becard (*Pachyramphus cinnamomeus*). Only the last is illustrated (see plate 23); it is rustier above and much paler below than are the other two; it is also decidedly the smallest (5½ inches); the others are conspicuously larger, the Rufous Mourner eight inches, the Piha ten inches. A good ear and knowledge of their calls is also helpful, as each has a distinctive voice.

Rhytipterna holerythra holerythra (Sclater and Salvin)

Rufous Mourner   Bobo Alazán

Trop. Mid. Am. (except Brit. Honduras and El Salvador) and n.w. S. Am.
Resident   8 in.   35 gr.

Fairly common. It is reputed to prefer open woodland and well-shaded clearings; here it is found well distributed throughout the semi-open forest, most often at moderate heights, sometimes high in trees.

PLATE 16

PLATE 17

BLUE-CROWNED MOTMOT

inches | 0 — 6
cms | 0 — 15

17 inches, about half of which is in the long tail with its racket-shaped tips. The race at Tikal is browner below than more northern races.

The bill is heavy, the black crown bordered by blue and turquoise above a large black facial patch and red eyes; a triangular patch of black and turquoise on center of chest; flight feathers and tail (from above) blue-green.

The tail is often slowly swung, pendulum-like, from side to side.

This rather smooth-looking bird is uniform, somewhat red-brown above (hazel-colored) and a paler tawny color below. The bill is very dark brown, nearly black; legs are dark gray; eyes, a dull brown.

Its call is diagnostic, a two-syllable "wolf-whistle," given in a melancholy, minor key (1).

REFERENCES:
(1) Slud 1964.

Lipaugus unirufus unirufus Sclater

Rufous Piha   Guardabosque

Trop. Mid. Am. (except El Salvador) and n.w. S. Am.
Resident   10 in.   84 gr.

Uncommon but not rare. It frequents semi-open forest ranging from the top of the understory up to medium heights in trees.

About the size of an American Robin (*Turdus migratorius*), this largest of the cotingas is a smooth-appearing bright cinnamon brown above, and a pale tawny color below, very pale on the throat. The bill is dark brown to black above, lighter brown below; legs are gray with a greenish cast; eyes are dull brown with a grayish cast and surrounded by a small area of grayish white bare skin.

It is usually quiet, but when alarmed utters one of the clearest, loudest, most emphatic musical whistles heard in the forest, a sudden, arresting, *wee-weéoo-weeooweét* (1); also described as a long but explosive, silvery, whistled *see-you, I-see-you* (2).

A nest in British Honduras, located about ten feet up in the crotch of a large tree, was a shallow depression at one side of a sizable bromeliad; it contained two pale brown eggs (3).

REFERENCES:
(1) Slud 1964.   (2) Eisenmann 1952.
(3) Russell 1964.

Pachyramphus cinnamomeus fulvidior Griscom

Cinnamon Becard   Mosquero Atabacado

Trop. Mid. Am. (except El Salvador) and n. S. Am.
Resident   5½ in.   20 gr.   Plate 23

Common. It is found in cleared land with shade trees, and throughout the very open parts of the forest and forest edges, where it forages from eye level to medium heights in trees.

It is a small, very ruddy, large-headed becard, with a conspicuously wide bill. Upperparts are a bright cinnamon rufous, dark and rich on the crown, light tawny on the cheeks, with an orange-colored line before the eyes; wing tips are blackish brown; underparts are shades of ochre buff, paler on the belly, very pale on the chin and throat. The bill is black above, light-colored below, shading from an ivory tip, through gray, to a flesh-colored base; legs are grayish black; eyes very dark brown, appearing black. Sexes are alike.

Its more usual song is a slow-paced, thinly musical *wee-tee-tee-tee-tee-too,* and variants such as a descending series of *pee*'s in minor key. At times it utters a succession of thin squeaks for lengthy periods (1).

Four conspicuous nests have been found at Tikal. The nest is wider than high (about twelve inches across), a bulky globular mass woven of twigs and leaves, the entrance hole very low, almost at the bottom. One was built on (not hung from) the extreme end of a branch which was bent down by its weight to within five feet of the surface of Aguada Tikal. Another, similarly located at the end of a limb, overhung a wide forest road, and was some thirty or more feet above ground.

REFERENCES:
(1) Slud 1964.

Pachyramphus major australis Miller and Griscom

Gray-collared Becard   Huilo de Corona Gris

Trop. Mid. Am. from Mexico to e. Nicaragua
Resident   6 in.   22½ gr.   Plate 23

Uncommon. It is reputed to prefer a dry habitat, or forests of oaks or of pines, or second growth in more humid forests, none of which preferences is fully satisfied at Tikal, though the climate is dry half the time, and a small amount of second growth is developing. Nevertheless, it has been found here year after year since the first record was made in 1957.

The male is distinctly individual, mainly blue-black above, the crown glossy, the lower back and rump blue-gray; there are conspicuous white bars and white streaks on the wings, and white tips on the tail feathers; underparts are gray with a slightly bluish tinge, which continues up into the cheeks and neck, to form a gray collar across the upper back.

The female is largely cinnamon rufous or tan above, with a paler, tawny collar; yellowish below, liberally washed with shades of tawny. While similar to *P. cinnamomeus* and also similar to the female and immature of *P. aglaiae,* its crown is brown on the forehead only, mixed with black and becoming solid black on the nape; this separates it from *P. cinnamomeus,* which has no black in the head at all, and from *P. aglaiae* females and immatures, which have an all-black (or dark brownish black) crown and nape. The female, otherwise, replaces the male's white markings with bright tawny, and retains some black in the webs of the tail feathers.

The bill is blue-gray, legs dark gray, eyes dark brown.

Both sexes utter simple, low-volume, but sweetly musical notes, two syllables repeated five or six times (Skutch, in litt.), and hear (1).

REFERENCES:
(1) Mexican Bird Songs, recordings by L. Irby Davis.

Pachyramphus aglaiae hypophaeus (Ridgway)
[*Platypsaris aglaiae*—AOU 1957]

Rose-throated Becard   Huilo de Pecho Rosado

S.w. U. S. and Mid. Am. to n. Costa Rica
Resident   6½ in.   30½ gr.   Plate 23

Not uncommon. Like *P. major,* it is reputed to prefer open second growth and clearings with shade trees, but finds enough suitable habitat at Tikal to be present regularly from 1956 on, seen too frequently to be called uncommon. It is found in open understory at moderate heights (not low), and in fairly high trees along wide roads. It nests high in trees.

A bird of many "races," this is the darkest one of all. The male is almost black above, slightly tinged with brown, rarely disclosing a pure white patch which is concealed under the black back; the rose color on the throat, for which the species is named, is essentially lacking, being extremely faint even on the rare occasions when present at all; underparts are dark gray, paler on the chin and throat. Females are shades of red-brown above, brightest on the tail, but black (with a faintly brownish cast) on the crown and nape; the cheeks are light brown; underparts are ochre brown, palest on the chin, smudged with dull brown on the breast and belly. Immature males (see plate 23) are similar to the female, but the browns are much darker, the cheeks dark gray. The bill is noticeably heavy, black above, gray below; legs are gray, eyes very dark brown.

A nest was found at Tikal some thirty feet up in a palm tree, suspended pendant-like from a vine-like tendril, practically pensile rather than a globular mass clustered about the end of a branch as described for *P. cinnamomeus.* This arrangement produces an oval effect, about twelve inches high and nine inches through. The entrance hole was somewhat below the center of the mass. Four black nestlings were in the nest. Eggs vary from white to buff shades, often blotched with darker colors (1).

Its song opens with a low rapid chatter, followed by a soft

but high-pitched thin whistle, which then drops down the
scale and trails off to nothing, as

chee-o
chatter-chatter   ⎯ o
                     o
                      o
                       o
                        o
                         o (1)

or a conversational *chi-zoo, wheez-oo, chi-zoo, kee-zoo,* repeated over and over, with short pauses between each group
of four syllables (2).

REFERENCES:
(1) Bent, No. 179, pp. 3–9, partial history (from Skutch Ms.);
p. 538, plate 1, photograph of nest. Peterson 1960, p. 161, pictures
in color (N. Am. race). Condor 52:6:fpc., pictures in color
(northern race).

(2) Auk 59:1:20, voice; p. 28, picture of nest (Sutton and
Pettingill).

Tityra semifasciata personata Jardine and Selby

Masked Tityra   Torrejo

Ppilankeuel (4)

Trop. Mid. Am. and S. Am.
Resident   8 in.   87 gr.

Fairly common. It is strictly arboreal, almost always in the
crowns of tall trees, often in those which are bare of leaves.
It shows some preference for open areas and clearings adjoining the forest, provided tall trees are present.

It is a decidedly chunky bird with a sturdy bill.

The male is light gray above including most of the crown,
very pale gray below, almost white on the throat; the tail has
a broad black band tipped with white; flight feathers are
black. The eye is surrounded by a conspicuous red area of
bare skin which extends forward to the bill; the forehead
and forecrown are black and the black encircles the red
bare skin area to meet the black chin. The female is brownish

gray above including the crown, and has a smaller and paler red bare skin area, giving her a duller appearance. The bill of both sexes is basally red, shading through gray to a black tip; legs are gray; eyes vary, light brown, brown, or reddish.

The voice is diagnostic, once it is learned: a queer, low grunt, some say pig-like, others insect-like, no one bird-like (1); Eisenmann calls it a dry *quert-quert* (2).

Nests are in cavities, either natural or stolen from woodpeckers, located from forty to a hundred feet up; the cup is lined with dead leaves, twiglets, bark, and other vegetation removed from the treetops. Two eggs are deposited, café-au-lait color, marbled with darker brown, and with small black spots (1). Five nests in British Honduras contained three eggs in each (3).

REFERENCES: Blake 1953, p. 327, pictures in black and white. Austin 1961, p. 204, picture in color. Auk 59:1:fpc., picture in color.
(1) Auk 63:3:326–362, life history (Skutch).
(2) Eisenmann 1952. (3) Russell 1964.
(4) Cruz 1939, p. 101.

Tityra inquisitor fraserii (Kaup)

Black-crowned Tityra   Torrejo
                                                           Rechinador

Trop. Mid. Am. (except El Salvador) and S. Am.
Resident   7¼ in.   48 gr.

Not uncommon. It frequents habitat similar to that used by *T. semifasciata,* tending to forage a bit lower in the trees. It may have increased in recent years, since the forest was thinned out.

It is superficially similar to *T. semifasciata,* but smaller and slimmer (hardly more than half as heavy), lacks all red about the eye and on the bill, has an all-black crown and forehead, a pale gray face, and, when in flight, the underside of the wings flash a white "window." Otherwise, the male is light gray above, pale gray below, mainly black on the flight feathers and tail, the latter white-tipped. The female is brownish gray above, bright reddish brown on the side of the face; the crown, flight feathers, and tail are mainly black; the pale gray underparts are slightly washed with brown. The bill is black, legs are black, eyes dark brown.

It utters a drier, less grunty call than that of the Masked Tityra (3), with a sawing or "squicking" note, given in sets of two or three, as well as frog-like and other sounds (1).

Nests are in cavities, often high in trees, sometimes in the same tree used by *T. semifasciata*. Two in British Honduras were only three to twelve feet above ground and contained two eggs in each; another was forty feet up in a palm (1), (2).

REFERENCES:
(1) Slud 1964.　　(2) Russell 1964.
(3) Eisenmann 1952.

PIPRIDAE

Pipra mentalis mentalis Sclater

Red-capped Manakin　　　　　　　　　　Sargento

Trop. Mid. Am. (except El Salvador) and S. Am.
Resident　　4¼ in.　　15½ gr. (12½ to 18½)　　Plate 27

Common. This very small, stub-tailed, restless bird frequents the high forest, but is confined mostly to the understory, both fairly heavy and semi-open.

Males are conspicuously red on the head, nape, and upper back, the chin yellow, elsewhere mainly black; the thighs are lemon yellow, as are the undersides of the wings. The eyes are white, sometimes with a yellow tone; the bill brown above, yellowish below; legs are shades of brown. Females and immatures of both sexes lack the male plumage and closely resemble each other; they are olive-green above, darker on the head, brighter on the back; below more grayish green, the belly often washed with yellow. Eyes of females are brown (though I recorded one with white eyes); eyes of immature males are white (though I recorded two out of a total of nine with brown eyes). Bills and legs are much like adult males.

While most immature males lack the slightest red on the head they occasionally show a red feather or two. They sometimes retain the green plumage well into their first breeding period. One all-green bird, with brown eyes, and larger than average, was recorded with very enlarged gonads.

Some three or more males assemble in a small group day after day in the same chosen location, where they perform complicated courtship displays, often called dances. Displays are accompanied by high-pitched, buzzy *psit* notes; by longer songs, as *psit-psit-psit-ptseeee—psip;* and by loud wing-snapping which sounds like the breaking of a dry stick. The performances are most active from March through May, but are known to continue on a reduced scale through November (1), (2).

The nest is a frail, shallow, hammock-like cup, slung in the fork of a thin, horizontal branch, usually about ten feet above ground, occasionally only five, or up as high as thirty feet. It is made of grasses and fine vegetable fibers, usually brown in color. Two eggs are deposited, dark gray-buff, heavily mottled with brown (1).

REFERENCES: Blake 1953, p. 329, pictures in black and white. Austin 1961, p. 206, picture in color.

(1) Auk 66:1:1–24, life history (Skutch); fpc., pictures in black and white (with nest).

(2) Mexican Bird Songs, recordings by L. Irby Davis.

Manacus candei (Parzudaki)

White-collared Manakin   Señorita

Trop. Mid. Am. (chiefly Caribbean slope) to n.e. Costa Rica
Resident   4¾ in.   20 gr.   Plate 27

Not uncommon. This small, stubby-tailed, restless bird is found in the tangles and heavy undergrowth along sunny roadsides and sunny forest edges, usually within fifteen feet of the ground.

The male has conspicuous plumage: upperparts are black

on the crown, wings, and tail; green on the back and rump; pure white across the upper back and nape which continues below on the neck, throat, and breast, becoming bright yellow on the abdomen. The female is mainly green above (brownish on the flight feathers), green below on the throat, neck, and breast, becoming rich yellow-green on the abdomen. The rich yellow is the clearest mark to distinguish her from the female *Pipra mentalis*. Bills are black above, grayish below; legs are bright orange, sometimes with a ruddy tone; eyes are dark brown.

It utters a two-syllable *pee-wee,* a hard wren-like ripple, and other notes (2). The male snaps its wings loudly and performs a courtship dance which, while distinctly its own in details, is still much like the group assembly dances of other manakins (1), (2).

A nest in British Honduras was a tiny, shallow cup suspended in a fork of a shrub, vireo-like but much shallower and thinner. It held two speckled eggs (Willis, in litt.).

REFERENCES: Blake 1953, p. 331, pictures in black and white.
(1) Van Tyne 1935, p. 33, dancing described.
(2) Slud 1964.

Schiffornis turdinus veraepacis (Sclater and Salvin)

Thrush-like Manakin   Tordo Aceitunado

Trop. Mid. Am. (except El Salvador) and S. Am.
Resident   6½ in.   31 gr.   Plate 27

Fairly common. This long-tailed manakin, which looks more like a thrush and sings more like a cotinga, frequents moderately heavy undergrowth, in well-shaded forest, seldom more than twenty feet above ground.

It is sometimes called Brown Manakin, but the Tikal bird is too green to be so named; it is, however, obscurely colored and rather undistinguished. Above it is olive-green with a brownish tone, clearer brown on the edges of the flight feathers and on the tail; below a paler shade of green. The bill is black above, dark brown below; legs are dark gray to black; eyes usually very dark brown.

It voices a characteristic three-syllable call which opens with a prolonged whistle followed by a strongly accented one, ending on a short note. Other calls are also uttered (1).

A nest at Tikal was located in the hollowed top of a palm stump, only six feet above ground. It contained two whitish eggs. A nest in British Honduras was located within two feet of the ground, in the open-topped cavity of a palm stump, and made of skeletonized dead leaves with a thin lining of fine rootlets. It contained two grayish white eggs, with a ring at the larger end of large dots (Willis, in litt.).

REFERENCES:
(1) Slud 1964.

TYRANNIDAE

Muscivora forficata (Gmelin)

Scissor-tailed Flycatcher   Mosquero de Tijereta

W. U. S.; winters through Mid. Am.
Transient   14 in. (9 in. tail)

Uncommon. It was first recorded 2 December 1962 and since then has been reported 8 April and 10 August 1964, only one individual each time. It is found in the vicinity of the airstrip, wherever scattered shrubs or small trees occur. It may be a winter resident.

It is pearl gray above and below (*no* black on the head), with salmon pink sides, belly, and wing lining, the deepest color near the bend of the wing. The very long black and white, flimsy, forked tail is usually held closed and straight down when not in flight. The wings are brownish black; the lower back may be lightly washed with red. The bill is brown, legs are black, eyes dark brown.

The voice heard during migration may be muted to a nasal *chip* (1).

REFERENCES: Peterson 1960, p. 161, picture in color. Austin 1961, p. 208, picture in color.
(1) Slud 1964.

Tyrannus tyrannus (Linnaeus)

Eastern Kingbird   Chatilla Norteña

E. N. Am.; migrates through Mid. Am.; winters from Honduras to S. Am.

Transient   8½ in.   40 gr.

Common migrant. For a bird never before reported for the
Petén, their presence makes an interesting story. One was
first noted on 23 April 1959, one 28 April, three 8 May 1959.
In the fall of 1962 they arrived in a huge wave that started
slowly, reached a maximum which ran into hundreds, and
then fell off as most of the birds moved on. The following
records were made: a single bird was seen early in the morning of 13 September, on the 17th two were seen, on the 21st
twelve, on the 22d and 25th "many," on the 27th over two
hundred (perhaps hundreds more), on the 30th over twenty-
four, on 8 and 15 October "a few," on the 22d still "perhaps
twelve." The peak flocks were spread out in low trees, bushes,
and weeds and on the ground, from Aguada Tikal to Aguada
Dimick (about a mile apart), and were also scattered through
the forest all the way to the Great Plaza on the high ridge,
half a mile away (see Map B). Many were removed from
mist nets, as only two specimens were kept. Toward evening
they were very languid, as though tired out or affected by the
berries and fruits which they had eaten; so dull were they
that they could be approached to within fifteen or twenty
feet, and then they flew off only a short way. At night many
roosted in the weeds on the airstrip, perhaps even on the
ground.

This kingbird is dark gray above, almost black on the
head and tail, the latter with a conspicuous white band across
the tip; underparts are white, slightly washed with gray on
the breast; the red crown patch is concealed, on some birds
lacking. The plumage of these migrants did not have the sharp
contrast of black and white of breeding birds. The bill is black
with a brown basal area below; legs are black; eyes dark
brown.

The only voice heard was a squeaky twitter.

REFERENCES: Peterson 1960, p. 160, picture in color. Austin 1961, p. 208, picture in color. Murphy and Amadon 1953, plate 67, color photograph.

Tyrannus melancholicus chloronotus Perlepsch

Tropical Kingbird Chatilla Tropical

Xtakay (a general term for flycatchers with yellow bellies)

S.w. U. S., Mid. Am., and S. Am.
Resident 8½ in. 43 gr.

Common. It is found in open areas with scattered trees and shrubs, often close to forest edges. The sunny aguadas, one at each end of the airstrip, proved attractive to it, but none was ever seen at any of the forest-shaded pools.

It is a decidedly gray-headed kingbird, with a dark mask through the eye; the back is gray-green, the wings and tail a dingy brown; the tail is forked and has pale (but not whitish) edges to the sides of the outer feathers; the chin is white, the throat grayish white, the breast yellow becoming brilliant yellow on the belly. The bill, fairly large and with a broad base, is black; legs are black; eyes dark brown. The crown has a concealed orange patch.

With wings quivering nervously, it utters a rapid, high-pitched, bickering twitter, as *píriríri*, and also typical fly-catcher *beep*'s (2), (3). It has a song, voiced only at dawn from about February to June, which begins with a couple of short, clear *pit*'s, followed by two or three thin trills given in ascending steps, as *phwee, phwee, whe-whee, wheea-whéeoo*, the entire phrase repeated over and over for many minutes (1), (4).

Nests are untidy-looking, bulky bowls made of a variety of dried vegetation, the cup lined with finer materials. Usually located, unconcealed, within fifteen feet of the ground (sometimes forty feet up) in a shrub or tree. At Aguada Dimick nests were placed on each of three poles which had been driven into the central area of the pond, the tops only three feet above the water. Two or three eggs are usual, of a pale buff color, blotched with brownish marks (1).

REFERENCES: Blake 1953, p. 342, picture in black and white.
Peterson 1960, p. 160, picture in color.
(1) P.C.A. 34:349–352, life history (Skutch).
(2) Slud 1964.   (3) Eisenmann 1952.
(4) Mexican Bird Songs, recordings by L. Irby Davis.

SPECIAL NOTE

There are three *streaked* flycatchers, one rare, the others fairly common at Tikal:

Piratic—*Legatus leucophaius*—6 in., 30 gr.
Sulphur-bellied—*Myiodynastes luteiventris*—8 in., 47 gr.
Streaked—*Myiodynastes maculatus*—8 in., 47 gr.

The latter two are confusingly similar.

Legatus leucophaius variegatus (Sclater)

Piratic Flycatcher   Mosquero Ruidoso

Trop. Mid. Am. (not reported El Salvador) and S. Am.
Summer Resident   6 in.   30 gr.

Uncommon. It is a summer resident in Central America and parts of southern Mexico, uncommon north of Costa Rica, where it is present roughly from early February to late September, when it returns to South America (just where is not known). The only known evidence of its presence in the Petén is the record made at Tikal, 7 April 1957, and a report of an active nest in June 1962. It prefers cultivated areas with scattered tall trees, even though close to houses, and avoids regions of heavy forest.

It is the smallest by far of the three streaked flycatchers at Tikal, other distinguishing characteristics being a very stubby, broad bill; lack of streaks on the upperparts; clear white chin and throat; a diagnostic voice. Otherwise the plumage includes blackish brown on the crown and tail and brownish olive back; a broad dull whitish line over the eye which continues narrowly across the forehead and narrowly across the nape; a blackish brown mask through the eyes and a broad dull white stripe below it; inconspicuous bars and edges on the brown wing feathers; sulfur yellow and still paler yellow on the underparts from chest to tail; conspicuous streaks of dusky olive on the chest, breast, and sides. The crown has a hidden yellow patch. The bill is black, legs very dark gray, eyes dark brown.

Its voice is a not unmusical, high-pitched, long-drawn-out whistle, *pee-e-e-e* (1), *tiddle-dee-dee* (2), or a softer, partly trilled, complaining *weé-yee,* followed by *píririree;* often *weé-yee* alone (3). The song is given from a perch in the tiptop of a tree, where, though it has an open view, it is hard to see from the ground, and from which it calls and calls and calls; it is therefore heard much more often than it is seen (4).

It does not build its own nest, but steals that of some other bird, provided only that it is of an enclosed or covered-over type. At Tikal the domed nests of the Vermilion-crowned Flycatcher (*Myiozetetes similis*), the pensile, retort-shaped nests of the Eye-ringed Flatbill (*Rhynchocyclus brevirostris*), the globular nests of the Cinnamon Becard (*Pachyramphus cinnamomeus*), the swinging pouches of the Montezuma Oropendala (*Gymnostinops montezuma*), and even those made by the Violaceous Trogon (*Trogon violaceus*) when inside of wasp nests, should attract it.

Two eggs, sometimes three, are deposited. They are dark-colored, café-au-lait (and other shades of brown), with even darker brown blotches and scrawls (1).

REFERENCES:
(1) P.C.A. 34:451–464, life history (Skutch); p. 452, picture in black and white.
(2) Chapman 1929.   (3) Eisenmann 1952.
(4) Condor 59:4:254, voice and nests (Eisenmann).

Eight pairs of trogons are illustrated; the sexes differ materially.

SLATY-TAILED TROGON   *p. 103.*

MALE: 12½ inches, the largest of our trogons; head, chest, and back iridescent green, bluish on rump, blue-green on middle tail feathers; lower breast and belly carmine; black wings have large gray patch; eye-ring dull red; bill salmon color.

FEMALE: lacks green and blue plumage which is replaced mainly by dull gray, the tail with brownish black (but similarly patterned); upper bill may be black instead of salmon.

CITREOLINE TROGON   *p. 104.*

MALE: 11 inches; head and chest black, back iridescent green, rump deep blue; lower breast and belly orange-yellow; tail is dark green above on middle feathers, but outer feathers are black with large *overlapping*-white ends (see different tail pattern of female). Eye-ring is conspicuously pale blue.

FEMALE: green and blue of male replaced by dull black; outer tail feathers with smaller white ends forming three *separated white areas* surrounded by black (as when perching).

BAR-TAILED TROGON   *p. 105.*

Sexes differ more than those of the other trogons.

MALE: 9½ inches; head, chest, and upperparts mainly golden green with a black face and throat; wings black with gray shoulders; lower breast and belly bright red with narrow band of white across chest; outer tail feathers narrowly barred black and white throughout their length (entirely different from female's); eye-ring is obscure brown; bill yellowish.

FEMALE: lacks green plumage and gray shoulders, which are replaced by rich sandy brown; red underparts paler (pinkish), washed with white; bill black and gray; white crescent back of the eye; tail distinctive, silvery gray with brownish tones, the outer feathers narrowly black and white at the tips.

VIOLACEOUS TROGON   *p. 107.*

MALE: 9 inches; head and chest black with blue border, back golden green; lower breast and belly orange; eye-ring yellow; outer tail feathers narrowly barred black and white, as in Bar-tailed Trogon, but with more white at tips.

FEMALE: lacks green and blue plumage which is replaced by dull black; orange-yellow of lower breast and belly washed with whitish; yellow eye-ring replaced by small spot of white before the eye and a white crescent back of the eye; the outer tail feathers similar to the male's, but have much brownish black, especially on inner webs.

PLATE 18

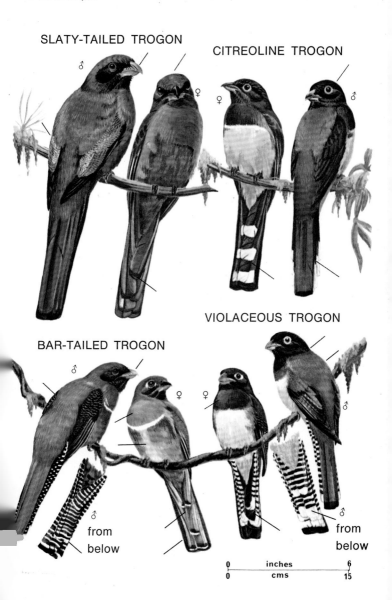

SLATY-TAILED TROGON

CITREOLINE TROGON

♂   ♀   ♀   ♂

VIOLACEOUS TROGON

BAR-TAILED TROGON

♂   ♀   ♀   ♂

♂
from
below

from
below

0   inches   6
0   cms   15

RINGED KINGFISHER p. 108

MALE: 16 inches, a very large, heavy-billed bird; upperparts blue-gray with white collar; underparts extensively chestnut, much more so than the female northern Belted Kingfisher; lacks that bird's gray chest band (but see female).

FEMALE: similar to male with underparts also extensively chestnut, but with addition of gray and white chest bands which might cause confusion with female Belted Kingfisher; its completely chestnut breast and belly thus identifies it (female Belted has white belly below rusty breast band).

BELTED KINGFISHER p. 109

MALE: 13 inches; upperparts blue-gray with white collar; gray band across chest and gray down the sides; all white breast and belly, lacking chestnut plumage (but see female).

FEMALE: similar to male, but with addition of chestnut band on breast and chestnut down the sides; belly white, lacking extensive chestnut plumage of Ringed Kingfisher.

AMAZON KINGFISHER p. 109

MALE: 12 inches, heavy billed; upperparts dark green (with few white spots) and white collar; underparts are chestnut on chest and breast, white on belly, scattered green at sides.

FEMALE: similar to male but *lacks all chestnut* plumage; underparts mainly white with green at sides which continues narrowly as partial band to center of breast.

NOTE: The much smaller Green Kingfisher (only 7½ inches) is not illustrated; it is very similar to the Amazon in pattern and color, but more conspicuously spotted with white on wings and tail, and female has two green bands across the breast instead of one partial band.

PLATE 19

RINGED KINGFISHER

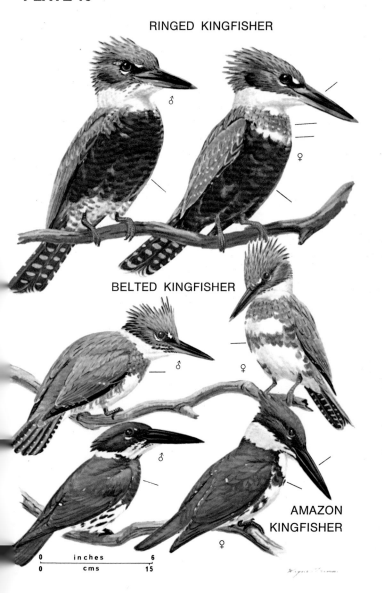

BELTED KINGFISHER

AMAZON KINGFISHER

0   inches   6
0   cms   15

PLATE 20

WOODPECKERS

CHESTNUT-COLORED ♂ ♀

GOLDEN-OLIVE ♀ ♂

BLACK-CHEEKED ♀ ♂

GOLDEN-FRONTED ♂ ♀

0   inches   3
0   c m s   7

CHESTNUT-COLORED WOODPECKER p. 123.

MALE: 9½ inches, conspicuously tawny crested; mainly pale chestnut above and below, with numerous dark v-shaped bars; facial patch red (lacking on female); tail and wing tips black. Bill pale greenish yellow.

FEMALE: same as male except for lack of red facial patch.

GOLDEN-OLIVE WOODPECKER p. 122.

MALE: 8½ inches, the greenest woodpecker at Tikal; upperparts olive-green with golden tinge; underparts yellow darkly barred with olive-green; crown is gray bordered by red, widest red on nape; mustache red.

FEMALE: same as male except for lack of red border of crown (red on nape only), and lack of red mustache.

BLACK-CHEEKED WOODPECKER p. 126.

MALE: 7½ inches; upperparts black, barred with white; head with large black facial patch, yellow forehead, bright red crown and nape; underparts buff-gray, barred with black at sides and red on belly. Tail black with some white bars and white rump.

FEMALE: very similar to male except red restricted to the nape.

GOLDEN-FRONTED WOODPECKER p. 125.

MALE: 10 inches; upperparts black, barred with white; head gray with small golden red forehead and bright red crown and nape, colors of forehead and crown interrupted by narrow gray band (there are many racial variations, a northern type having a second gray band between the red crown and an orange-red nape); underparts are buff-gray, with some red on belly. Tail is black, the rump white.

FEMALE: very similar to male except for lack of red on crown (retains red on nape and golden red forehead).

Myiodynastes luteiventris luteiventris Sclater

Sulphur-bellied Flycatcher   Mosquero Rayado
                                         Mosquero Cejiblanco

S.w. U. S., Mid. Am. to Costa Rica; winters s. to Panama
   and n.w. S. Am.
Summer Resident   8 in.   47 gr.

Fairly common. It prefers clearings with scattered tall trees,
open woodland, and forest edges, avoids the heavy forest, and
is usually found throughout the camp and the borders of
wide roads, from moderate heights to the tops of the trees;
should be watched for from early March to September.

It is similar in many ways to the Streaked Flycatcher (*M.
maculatus*), both generously streaked above as well as below,
and both fairly common here. It differs mainly by having a
crown of paler brown with fine black streaks (*maculatus* has
a dark brown crown with coarse streaks); prominent white
facial stripes, one above and one below the dusky mask
which extends from the bill to behind the eye (on *maculatus*
the upper one is decidedly yellowish, the lower one less
prominent); a conspicuous, almost black stripe on the side
of the throat which continues narrowly across the chin (on
maculatus greatly reduced, leaving the chin white); a pale or
sulfur yellow breast and belly (on *maculatus* mainly dull
white, both species streaked, however); an all-black bill (on
maculatus the basal half of the lower bill is quite pale);
finally, a call note which is much sharper and more insistent
than the soft, nasal call of *maculatus*.

Otherwise the wing feathers are dark brown edged with
very light buff; the back is a light buffy olive and heavily
streaked, becoming a reddish brown on the rump and tail;
each tail feather has a dark stripe down the center, widest on
the two middle feathers; the throat is white shading through
grayish white to the yellow underparts, which are heavily
streaked on the chest, lightly streaked on the sides. There is
a hidden yellow patch in the crown. The bill is black, legs
very dark gray, eyes dark brown.

It utters loud, quarrelsome, insistent cries, and harsh

screaming calls (1); a sharp *whee-zeé-ah;* a softer *chu-er* (2). However, it also has a musical song given only at dawn, and perhaps only in April and May, from a prominent perch in the top of a tree: a soft, liquid *tre-le-re-ree,* repeated over and over for ten or fifteen minutes (1).

A nest is made in a decaying tree, using an old woodpecker hole or some natural cavity, filling it up with a mass of sticks until the final cup permits the sitting bird to see out through the opening. They are located high and low. Three eggs are deposited, glossy white or creamy in color, heavily mottled with cherry red and pale lilac (1).

REFERENCES: Blake 1953, p. 344, picture in black and white. Peterson 1960, p. 160, picture in color.
(1) P.C.A. 34:385–391, life history (Skutch); p. 386, picture in black and white.
(2) Auk 59:1:21, voice described (Sutton and Pettingill).

Myiodynastes maculatus insolens Ridgway

Streaked Flycatcher   Mosquero Rayado
                                       Mosquero Cejiamarillo

Trop. Mid. Am. (not recorded El Salvador and Nicaragua) and S. Am.
Summer Resident   8 in.   47 gr.

Fairly common. It occurs in the scattered trees about camp and along the wider roads, from early March to the end of July (probably even through August). Its winter home—presumed to be in South America—is not known.

It is quieter vocally and less active than the similar Sulphur-bellied Flycatcher (*M. luteiventris*), and forages at lower levels, seldom over thirty feet up. The distinguishing characteristics of the two have been described under that bird, but the yellow eyebrows and whitish underparts of *maculatus* should be remembered. In other respects, its wings are edged pale buff; the back is grayish brown and heavily streaked, becoming reddish brown on the rump and tail; each tail feather has a dark stripe down the center, widest on the two middle feathers; both the chin and throat are white, becoming dull grayish white on the underparts, which are heavily streaked. There is a hidden yellow patch in the crown. Legs are dark gray, eyes very dark brown. The lower bill is pale basally.

It utters a variety of calls, all distinctly different from those of *M. luteiventris;* one, an agreeable nasal *tsuka-tsuka,* given singly or in series, sometimes followed by twitters (1); another a sharp woodpecker-like *skwit-askwít-askwít-askwíta* (2); and a four- or five-syllable song, given at both dawn and dusk during the months of April, May, and June, when it is repeated over and over for as long as half an hour at a stretch. The latter is clear but soft, and has been variously symbolized as *ka-wé-teedly-wink,* "right here to me" (1), and "work ought to be" (2).

Eisenmann describes the notes as a loud heavy *chup* or *check;* also *eéchup;* also *chupeé* or *chupeét;* also a song given by the male as *chup, weéarooweép,* the phrase portion following a slight pause after *chup,* and of such different, rather musical though squeaky quality that it seems as if given by another bird (3).

Nests are made in abandoned woodpecker holes, or are open saucers of twigs and grass placed in niches and crannies formed by bromeliads, old palm fronds, and such, or located under protecting eaves of roofs; usually from fifteen to thirty feet above ground but sometimes much higher in trees. When made in old woodpecker holes, the cavities are filled up close to the entrance, making the sitting bird visible to an observer. Three whitish eggs are deposited, heavily marked with cherry red and pale lilac (1).

REFERENCES:
(1) P.C.A. 34:374–384, life history (Skutch); p. 375, picture in black and white.
(2) Slud 1964.   (3) Eisenmann 1952.

SPECIAL NOTE

There are three confusingly similar flycatchers here, with conspicuous black and white, mask-like head markings; they differ strikingly in call notes and in shape of bill:

Boat-billed—*Megarhynchus pitangua*—10 in., 65 gr.
Social—*Myiozetetes similis*—7 in., 33 gr.
Great Kiskadee—*Pitangus sulphuratus*—9½ in., 65 gr.

Megarhynchus pitangua mexicanus (Lafresnaye)

Boat-billed Flycatcher Mosquero Picudo

Trop. Mid. Am. and S. Am.
Resident 10 in. 65 gr.

Uncommon. It sometimes forages over the heavy forest canopy, where it is difficult to find, but is usually seen in semi-open woodland, forest edges, and clearings with trees not too widely scattered. There it forages mostly at medium heights, although one was caught in a mist net at ground level.

Only two have been identified with certainty but others, seen high in trees, were probably this species. It is readily confused with the very similar Great Kiskadee (*Pitangus sulphuratus*), which usually occurs at lower levels. It may be distinguished from the Kiskadee by its much heavier, broader bill, more bullheaded appearance, and the lack of the Kiskadee's conspicuously bright red-brown in wings and tail.

It has a boldly patterned head, the black (brown-tinged) crown bordered from the bill to the nape with a broad white stripe, below which a black mask extends across the eyes, cheek, and hind neck; the throat is white, abruptly meeting the lemon yellow underparts; the back is gray-olive, the wings and tail brown with buff margins on the feathers (not reddish). The crown has a concealed patch of orange-yellow (more visible on Kiskadees). The bill is black, conspicuously heavy and broad at the base; legs blackish; eyes brown.

The usual call is a loud, rapidly repeated monosyllable, raucous when near by, but in the distance a pleasant *choip-choip-choip-choip;* a disagreeable, long-drawn, whining *churr* (1); a long single note, *dddditditerr,* amounting to a sustained harsh twitter, rising in pitch at the end (3); or a harsh, rattling, several-times-repeated *keerrrrrik-keé* (4); hear (5).

Skutch describes a song, given early in the morning, from early March through June: a loud, clear-ringing *cheer,* repeated over and over for more than twenty minutes at a stretch (1).

The nest differs entirely from that of the Kiskadee. It is located from twenty to a hundred feet up on a branch (Kiskadees usually use a tree crotch), sometimes in an exposed position. It is a broad, rather frail, shallow, open bowl (the Kiskadee's nest is domed over, oven-like) with a loosely woven base of coarse materials gathered from trees, the lining composed of rootlets, tendrils, and similar softer vegetation. Two or three eggs are laid, whitish in color, speckled and blotched with brown and pale lilac (1), (2).

REFERENCES: Auk 68:1:30–49, life history (Skutch).

(1) P.C.A. 34:353–355, life history (Skutch); p. 354, a picture in black and white. De Schauensee 1964, p. 304, picture in color (of race, *M. p. pitangua*).

(2) Auk 59:1:20–22, nests and songs (Boat-billed and Kiskadee together).

(3) Slud 1964.   (4) Eisenmann 1952.

(5) Mexican Bird Songs, recordings by L. Irby Davis.

Myiozetetes similis texensis (Girard)

Social Flycatcher   Mosquero de Corona Anaranjada
Vermilion-crowned Flycatcher

Trop. Mid. Am. and S. Am.
Resident   7 in.   33 gr.

Common, but localized about the camp and the aguadas at each end of the airfield, consistent with its preference for unforested terrain, open areas with scattered trees, and fresh water near at hand. It forages from the ground up to medium heights in shrubs and trees.

It has a bold color pattern which is similar to that of the Boat-billed and the Kiskadee, but it is not likely to be mistaken for them as it is hardly more than half their size, has a very small black bill, short and narrow, and is a grayer tone above (brownish but lacking all rusty shades).

The crown and the facial mask are dark gray or a dusky brown with a broad white (or slightly yellowish) stripe between them that stops short of the nape; the throat is white and abruptly meets the bright yellow underparts; upperparts are grayish brown or olive-brown, the wing and tail feathers with pale margins (but not rusty). The crown has a concealed patch of vermilion. Legs are black, eyes very dark brown.

Its voice is comparatively soft, with high-pitched but plaintive tones. A readily recognized call is an arresting, excited-sounding *cheé-cheecheé-cheecheé-cheecheé* (1). A complicated dawn song is heard before sunrise from about early April to early June (2).

The nest is a somewhat untidy, domed or roofed-over type, with the entrance hole to one side. The bulky mass is composed of straws, weed stems, dry vines, and the like; the interior cup is lined with finer vegetation. It is located from six to fifty feet up, preferably in a thorny tree or bush, almost always near the nest of some other bird, a practice which accounts for the name, "social" flycatcher (2). At Tikal, when trees still hung out over the aguada, nests were placed there, along with those of becards, only a few feet above the water.

Sets of three or four eggs are deposited, creamy white in color, spotted and blotched with brown and pale lilac (2).

REFERENCES: Blake 1953, p. 346, picture in black and white. Sutton 1951, p. 147, picture in black and white.

(1) Slud 1964.

(2) P.C.A. 34:427–446, life history (Skutch); p. 428, picture in black and white.

Pitangus sulphuratus guatimalensis (Lafresnaye)

Great Kiskadee   Kiscadi
                                       Mosquero Grande

Xtakay

S. Texas, Mid. Am. to n.w. Panama (Bocas del Toro), also
    S. Am.
Resident   9½ in.   65 gr.

Uncommon, but conspicuous. It normally avoids extensive heavy forest and has a strong preference for open country, even areas with few trees. It also enjoys the proximity
of water, both pools and streams, where it dives for small
fish (but not as deep as do kingfishers). It has been present
since early 1956 at least, but restricted to the immediate vicinity of Aguada Tikal.

It is strikingly similar to the Boat-billed Flycatcher (*Megarhynchus pitangua*), from which it may be distinguished by
its distinctive voice, by a bill which, though still black and
large, is long, more slender, and lacks the other's broad flat
base, and by wings and tail with conspicuous reddish brown
margins. It seldom forages as high in the trees, ranging from
very moderate heights down to the tops of shrubs.

The strikingly patterned head has a black crown, bordered
across the forehead, above the eyes, and across the nape with
a broad white stripe. A black mask extends across the eyes,
cheeks, and hind neck; the throat is white, abruptly meeting
the bright yellow underparts; the back is brown-olive (the
least green of the three birds), the wings and tail brown with
the feathers conspicuously edged with rich cinnamon rufous.
The black crown only partly conceals an inner patch of
chrome yellow. The legs are black, eyes a dull dark brown.

The voice is usually described as a noisy, peremptory,
three-syllable *kis-ka-dee,* which sometimes (as when two or
more birds get singing together) speeds up to a most excited,
confused chatter. Another version is a single *geep* or *wheep,*
loud and shrill, sometimes followed by a clear *career,* to
become *geep-geep-career* (1); and hear (3).

It builds a bulky nest of the domed or roofed-over type. One such was located in the crotch of a small tree close by the Aguada Tikal, a very untidy, droopy affair made of long grasses, weeds, and roots; the entrance hole in the side of the upper half is shrouded by the loose strands of material hanging down over it.

A set of three eggs and four sets of four eggs were found in Guatemala (Skutch, in litt.). They are white or cream-colored, sparingly spotted with brown (2).

REFERENCES: Blake 1953, p. 346, picture in black and white. Peterson 1960, p. 160, picture in color. Austin 1961, p. 207, picture in color. Gilliard 1958, plate 127, color photograph.

(1) Auk 59:1:20–22, picture in black and white (Sutton and Pettingill).

(2) Bent, No. 179.

(3) Bird Songs, recordings by Paul Schwartz.

SPECIAL NOTE

There are four confusingly similar flycatchers of the *Myiarchus* group in the Petén. All four have been found at Tikal. Three are residents, one is transient. They are illustrated in plate 24, shown one below the other in the order of their size (the largest at the top), with their bills vertically aligned to emphasize the size relationship. Reading from top to bottom, they are:

Brown-crested (resident)	(*Myiarchus tyrannulus cooperi*)	9	in. long, 40 gr.
Great-crested (transient)	(*Myiarchus crinitus boreas*)	8½	in. long, 33 gr.
Yucatán (resident)	(*Myiarchus yucatanensis*)	7	in. long, 22 gr.
Dusky-capped (resident)	(*Myiarchus tuberculifer platyrhynchus*)	6½	in. long, 22 gr.

The same sequence is followed in the description of each species.

Next to each illustration is a picture of a tail feather typical of the species, which shows the olive-brown outer web, and the combination of olive-brown and brighter cinnamon orange on the inner web. A "fifth" feather has been chosen in each case, avoiding the outer and the middle feathers, which do not give as distinctive a pattern for each species. The bright colors are mostly concealed unless the tail is spread; when spread varying degrees of ruddy effects occur.

A knowledge of the songs and calls of each species is the most positive aid to identification, but the birds are not accommodatingly vocal except during parts of their breeding periods.

Interesting discussions (W. E. Lanyon) of the tail-feather patterns and the vocalizations of flycatchers within the *Myiarchus* group are available in Condor 62:5:341–350 and 63:6:421–449, which also include many pertinent citations from other literature.

Myiarchus tyrannulus cooperi Baird

Brown-crested Flycatcher   Mosquero Copetón
                                                Copetón Costeño

S.w. U. S., Mid. Am. to n.w. Costa Rica, also n. and e. S. Am.,
    and Lesser Antilles
Resident   9 in. (8 to 9½)   40 gr.   Plate 24

Fairly common. It is usually found in open country, but also inhabits semi-open woodland and forest edges. To many it is known as Wied's Crested Flycatcher (A.O.U. 1957). At Tikal it forages from moderate heights to high in trees, wherever the forest has been substantially thinned, ranging from Aguada Tikal to the Great Plaza and even beyond. It becomes scarce or absent after July.

Comparing it with the very similar Great-crested Flycatcher (*M. crinitus*), it is somewhat longer and bulkier, its back less greenish, its head a lighter brown, its underparts paler gray on the throat and chest, paler yellow on the lower breast and belly; the tail feathers have less cinnamon on the inner webs (see illustration), but the ruddy effect is still conspicuous when the tail is spread; the bill is long and slender, dark below as well as above; legs are very dark gray, eyes dark brown. The mouth lining is pale ochre buff.

It has a short, noisy, harsh whistled *weerp,* given with great intensity, and not rising in pitch as does that of *M. crinitus;* it may be shown graphically as ⬛ (1), (2).

It nests in holes in trees. Two or three eggs are deposited, creamy buff, slightly marked with brownish scrawls (3), (4).

REFERENCES: Blake 1953, p. 349, picture in black and white. Peterson 1960, p. 160, picture in color. Murphy and Amadon 1953, plate 75, color photograph (with nesting hole).

(1) Condor 62:5:341–350, voice and feather data (Lanyon).
(2) Slud 1964.   (3) Bent, No. 179.
(4) Herklots 1961.

Myiarchus crinitus boreus Bangs

Great-crested Flycatcher   Mosquero Copetón
                                                                     Mosquero Viajero

E. N. Am.; winters through Mid. Am. to Colombia
Transient   8½ in. (7½ to 9)   33 gr.   Plate 24

Uncommon spring, common fall migrant. None were recorded in the Petén until a wave of this species began to arrive at Tikal, 21 September 1962, along with a very much larger influx of Eastern Kingbirds (*Tyrannus tyrannus*). They were widely scattered through the forest, from the Aguada Tikal to beyond the Great Plaza. They continued to be present in fair numbers through 27 October, when I left the area. At first I thought they were resident Brown-crested Flycatchers, but investigation showed that not a single Brown-crested was seen in Tikal from at least 17 August through 27 October 1962, while a few resident Yucatán Flycatchers (*M. yucatanensis*) and Dusky-capped Flycatchers (*M. tuberculifer*) *were* present during that period.

It is found in semi-open woodland, in forest edges and second growth, and in cleared land with scattered trees, where it forages both high and low. Its back is olive-green, the head darker and browner; the wings are olive-brown with cinnamon rufous margins, the tail similar, but with most all of each inner feather-web cinnamon orange, showing a ruddy flash when spread; the throat and breast are gray, shading to brilliant yellow on the lower breast and belly. The bill is black above; below it is brown, pale brown on the basal half; legs are black; eyes brown. The mouth lining is orange.

The fall migrants were not vocal. The voice is a distinctive loudly whistled *wheep* or *whirp,* with a sharply rising inflection, and repeated several times at two-second intervals; it may be shown graphically as (1), (2).

REFERENCES: Peterson 1960, p. 160, picture in color. Austin 1961, p. 208, picture in color; end papers, picture of egg in color.
  (1) Condor 62:5:341–350, voice (Lanyon).
  (2) Slud 1964.

Myiarchus yucatanensis Lawrence

Yucatán Flycatcher   Mosquero Copetón

Mexico (n. Yucatán Pen. and Cozumel I.), Guatemala (Petén), and Brit. Honduras

Resident   7 in.   22 gr.   Plate 24

Uncommon and very local. It is usually found in thin woodland, light second growth, and clearings. Here it has been found only in the forest edge and scrubby growth around Aguada Dimick, an artificial reservoir which catches the drainage at the east end of the airstrip. It is probably present the year round, but definite records are noted only for June and July 1959, September and October 1962.

The back is brownish olive, the head a richer brown; the wings are margined with rufous on the flight feathers; slightly less than half of the inner web of each tail feather is brightened with pinkish cinnamon, conspicuous only when the tail is spread; the throat and breast are rather dark gray, the belly yellow; the bill and legs are black, the eyes brown. The mouth lining is orange.

The song is a long, plaintive, whistled *wheeeeee,* very gradually rising in pitch, and similar to that of *M. tuberculifer,* except that it does not fall off again. It may last as long as two seconds. It may be shown graphically as (1), (2).

REFERENCES:
(1) Condor 62:5:341–350, voice (Lanyon).
(2) Slud 1964.

Myiarchus tuberculifer platyrhynchus Ridgway

Dusky-capped Flycatcher   Mosquero Común

Arizona, Mid. Am., and S. Am.
Resident   6½ in. (5¾ to 7)   18 gr.   Plate 24

Fairly common. In general, it is found in clearings with scattered trees, second-growth woods, and the edges of heavier forests, where it forages from ground level to moderate heights. To many it is known as the Olivaceous Flycatcher (A.O.U. 1957). At Tikal it is widespread but not abundant, and more likely to be seen at lower elevations than on the high ridges.

It is the smallest of the *Myiarchus* group at Tikal. The head is slightly darker than the back (not rich brown), with a brownish patch over the ears; its tail feathers lack the bright cinnamon webs (some individuals have a narrow margin of rusty color, but on the *outer* instead of the inner webs).

The back is greenish brown, the wing feathers have pale rufous edges, the tail is gray-brown, the throat and upper breast are very pale gray merging into pale yellow on the lower breast, which becomes deeper yellow on the belly. The bill, rather broad and flat, is very dark brown, almost black; legs are blackish, eyes dark brown. The mouth lining is orange.

It utters a variety of whistles. One series is described as a short sharp whistled *whit,* followed by a long-drawn-out plaintive whistled *wheeeu,* and closing with a whistled short cut-off *whe-du,* not always in the same sequence, and given as a dawn song lasting for some twenty minutes before sunrise; it is usually heard only from February through June (1), (3). Compared with *M. yucatanensis,* the long whistle may be shown graphically as

(2).

It nests in cavities in trees and stumps, often less than ten feet above ground but also at much higher levels. The cavity is partly filled and lined with soft vegetation, cotton, hair, feathers, and such. Four dull white eggs are the usual clutch, heavily blotched and spotted with dark brown (1).

Near its nest it appears to be unafraid of humans; it may perch within arm's length and intently watch the activities of a careful observer.

REFERENCES: Peterson 1960, p. 160, picture in color.

(1) P.C.A. 34:396–399, life history (Skutch); p. 397, picture in black and white.

(2) Condor 62:5:341–350, voice (Lanyon).

(3) Mexican Bird Songs, recordings by L. Irby Davis.

Nuttallornis borealis (Swainson)

Olive-sided Flycatcher   Mosquero Boreal

N. Am. and mts. n.w. Mexico (Baja Calif.); migrates through Mid. Am.; winters chiefly S. Am., occasionally n. to Costa Rica

Transient   7½ in.   34 gr.

Uncommon. It has been recorded only twice, in October 1962, during a heavy influx of migratory birds which occurred throughout September and October. It inhabits semi-open country with scattered trees, but is also found in marshy openings within heavy forest.

It is similar in appearance to the Coues' or Greater Pewee (*Contopus pertinax*) and the smaller Wood Pewees; the former is more uniformly gray below and lacks a white throat, the latter have prominent wing bars.

It is grayish olive on the back, darker on the crown; the dusky wings show pale streaks but no clear wing bars; white may be seen at each side of the lower back, and sometimes white tufts show from under the wings. The throat is white, and white continues down the breast (rather dingy) and the middle of the belly, heavily flanked on the sides with dark brownish gray. The large broad-based bill is black above, dull yellow below; legs are black and eyes are dark brown.

It perches upright on some fairly high, exposed bare branch, from which it makes long sallies after insects and to which it usually returns.

Its voice is rarely heard while migrating. It is a spirited whistle symbolized as

a higher whee and a down-slurred pee

a sharp whip,

often referred to as saying "quick-three beers" (1). Other one-, or two-, or three-syllable notes and emphatic *pip*'s and *tsee*'s are also given (2).

REFERENCES: Peterson 1960, p. 161, picture in color. Austin 1961, end papers, picture of egg in color.
(1) Bent, No. 179.   (2) Slud 1964.

Contopus virens (Linnaeus)

Eastern Wood Pewee   Mosquero Norteño

E. N. Am.; migrates through Mid. Am. (not reported El Salvador); winters from Nicaragua but chiefly to n.w. S. Am.

Transient   6 in.   15 gr. (12 to 16)

Common spring and fall migrant. It is known to be present here from 31 August to the end of September (or later), and from 17 March (or earlier) to 19 May, overlapping only in the spring the breeding months (April through July) of the very similar resident Tropical Pewee (*C. cinereus*).

It is interesting to note that not a single Western Wood Pewee (*C. sordidulus*) has been recorded at Tikal.

The Eastern Wood Pewee is found in light forests, open country with scattered trees, and partially cleared agricultural land; at times it may spread out into open areas within heavier forests. It forages from low to moderate heights, selecting various exposed perches from which to make round-trip sallies after insects.

It is olive-brown above, of a slightly greener tone than the Tropical Pewee and a grayer tone than the smaller flycatchers

LINEATED WOODPECKER p. 124.

MALE: 12 inches (northern Pileated is over 17 inches); conspicuous red crest, crown, forehead, and mustache; white neckline runs down to breast (not down back as on Pale-billed); upperparts black with some white on shoulders; underparts black on breast, barred black and pale buff on lower breast and belly.

FEMALE: similar to male, but lacks red on forehead and lacks red mustache. (See female Pale-billed.)

PALE-BILLED WOODPECKER p. 128.

MALE: 13½ inches; entire head and crest conspicuously red; white neckline runs down back, upperparts otherwise black; underparts black on breast, coarsely barred black and pale yellow on lower breast and belly.

FEMALE: similar to male, but black on forehead, top of crown, and chin (face remains red which distinguishes it from the Lineated).

SMOKY-BROWN WOODPECKER p. 128.

MALE: 6½ inches, smallest of resident woodpeckers; upper and lower parts dull brown, tinged with orange-red on back, and with dark red spots on crown.

FEMALE: similar to male, but lacks red on crown.

PLATE 21

WOODPECKERS

LINEATED

♂

♀

PALE-
BILLED

♂

♂

♀

SMOKY-
BROWN

♂

♀

inches 3
cms 7

BUFF-THROATED FOLIAGE-GLEANER p. 137

7½ inches. Sexes alike; upperparts dark brown, the rump and tail ruddy colored; a pale line above the eye, a dark line back of the eye; underparts are pale buff on throat, blending to dark brown on the belly; the substantial bill is yellow below.

SCALY-THROATED LEAFSCRAPER p. 139

7½ inches; primarily a ground feeder. Sexes alike; darker brown above and below than Buff-throated Foliage-gleaner, but with conspicuous white (and black) scaly-appearing throat; tail is largely black; bill long and slender.

BARRED ANTSHRIKE p. 140

6½ inches. Sexes differ greatly.

MALE: conspicuously barred black and white (more streaked than barred effect on cheeks and throat); the elongated crown feathers sometimes erected crest-like. Eyes yellowish white for both sexes.

FEMALE: upperparts rich ruddy brown, the crown darker chestnut; a pale collar at the nape; sides of throat and cheeks paler buff, streaked narrowly with black; underparts buff, palest on throat.

RUSSET ANTSHRIKE p. 141

6 inches, inconspicuous, usually fairly high in trees. Sexes very similar; upperparts brown, the rump and tail ruddier; cheeks and underparts paler, yellow-brown, graying at sides and belly. Males sometimes display a concealed pale patch on the back.

Could be confused with larger Buff-throated Foliage-gleaner.

DOT-WINGED ANTWREN p. 142

4¼ inches. Sexes differ materially, but both have conspicuous white spots on the wings and tail, and a large usually concealed white patch on the back.

MALE: mainly glossy black, becoming dark gray on the sides and belly.

FEMALE: dark slate gray above, rich ruddy brown below.

DUSKY ANTBIRD p. 143

6 inches. Sexes differ, but both have pale brown eyes and a usually concealed white patch on the back.

MALE: dark gray above and below, nearly black on crown and on wing tips; two narrow obscure wing bars.

FEMALE: dull olive above, somewhat ruddier on wings; face and underparts tawny, becoming grayish olive on sides.

PLATE 22

BUFF-THROATED
FOLIAGE-GLEANER

SCALY-THROATED
LEAFSCRAPER

BARRED ANTSHRIKE

♀

RUSSET
ANTSHRIKE

♀

DOT-WINGED ANTWREN

♂

DUSKY ANTBIRD

♀

0 inches 2
0 cms 5

PLATE 23

CINNAMON BECARD

GRAY-COLLARED BECARD

♀

♂

ROSE-THROATED BECARD

♀

♂

Immature

♂

0   1 inches 2   3
0 1 2 3 cms 5 6 7

CINNAMON BECARD p. 149.

5½ inches. Sexes alike; upperparts a bright ruddy brown, darkest on the crown (note pair of pale and dark lines from eye to bill); underparts buff, very pale on the chin.

Two larger Becards (not illustrated) are very similar in both color and pattern; size and voice are best guides; see the Rufous Mourner (8 inches) and the Rufous Piha (10 inches).

GRAY-COLLARED BECARD p. 150.

6 inches. Sexes differ materially.

ADULT MALE: distinctively patterned, with blue-black crown, back, and tail; blue-tinged gray collar, cheeks, neck and underparts; white bars and streaks on the wings; white tips on the graduated tail feathers.

ADULT FEMALE: patterned like the male but with rich brown back and rump instead of black; pale tawny collar, cheeks, neck, and underparts instead of gray; the crown is black flecked with brown, the nape solid black; the tail also retains some black with bright tawny tips instead of white.

Female may be confused with female and immature Rose-throated Becards which, however, have all-black crowns and lack this bird's distinctive pattern.

ROSE-THROATED BECARD p. 151.

6½ inches. Sexes differ.

ADULT MALE: the Tikal race is very dark brownish black above, somewhat paler or grayish below; the rosy throat is inconspicuous, often entirely lacking; the back has a concealed white patch which is sometimes displayed in the presence of the female.

FEMALE: upperparts ruddy brown, the crown and nape black; underparts paler brown with dull brown smudges on breast and belly.

IMMATURE MALE: similar to adult female, but darker brown, and with dark gray cheeks; also has the male's usually concealed white shoulder patch.

of the similar *Empidonax* group. From the latter it is also distinguished by its lack of eye-rings. Its relatively long wings have two wing bars which are not always conspicuous. Underparts are whitish all down the middle, sometimes tinged with pale yellow, and bordered on the sides with light gray. The bill is dark brown above, orange-yellow below (the resident pewee is lighter yellow below); legs are black; eyes dark brown.

The voice continues in limited use during migration but is usually silent during the winter. It is a clear, sweet, plaintive whistle, a characteristic   pee   wee   most frequently

oo

heard mornings and evenings. The bird also utters a coarse *chip* (1).

REFERENCES: Peterson 1960, p. 161, picture in color. Austin 1961, p. 207, picture in color. Murphy and Amadon, plate 72, color photograph, with nest.

(1) Slud 1964.

Contopus cinereus brachytarsus (Sclater)

Tropical Pewee   Mosquero Tropical

Trop. Mid. Am. and S. Am.
Resident   5¼ in.   11½ gr.

Uncommon. It is found mainly in open country with scattered trees or tall shrubs, in forest edges and clearings; it avoids closed woodland; reported to be inexplicably rare in some areas. Only three records have been noted for Tikal: 29 June and 5 August 1959 and 4 September 1962, whereas the Eastern Wood Pewee (*C. virens*) has been found to be common during spring and fall.

It is gray-olive above, lacking any eye-ring but with a light gray area before the eye; the wings have two obscure bars; the throat is a dull white which continues down the middle breast and belly, tinged with yellow and flanked with pale gray at the sides. The bill is blackish above, yellowish below with a dark tip; legs are black, eyes dark brown. The mouth lining is bright yellow. (In the hand it is separable from the

Eastern Wood Pewee by noting that the tenth or outermost primary is shorter than the sixth.)

Its voice, heard usually in the early morning, is a sharp, high-pitched repetitive *weet weet weet,* relieved from time to time by low musical two-syllable notes, or an occasional low warble. At the nest it also utters a sharp *peet* and a trilled *cheee* (1). Eisenmann says the call note is a slightly burred or trilled *pee-ee,* usually given from a low perch, or from dead trees and dry bushes (2).

The nest may be saddled on a horizontal branch like that of the Wood Pewee, or placed in a vertical fork of a bush or tree, located from seven to thirty-five feet up (sometimes higher). It is a broad, shallow open cup, compactly made of lichens, fibers, tendrils, and such, bound together with much cobweb, and lined with finer material (1).

Two, more often three eggs are laid. They are dull white, blotched and spotted with bright brown and lilac (1).

REFERENCES:
(1) P.C.A. 34:322–327, life history (Skutch); p. 322, picture in black and white.
(2) Condor 59:4:255 (Eisenmann).

* Contopus pertinax subsp.

Greater Pewee   Mosquero
                                                     Tengofrío

Highlands Arizona, and Mid. Am. s. to n. Nicaragua
Visitor?   7½ in.   25 gr.

Mention only is included of this flycatcher on the strength of sight reports made at Tikal by C. Russell Mason and Margaret H. Hundley on 15 March 1963. No other Petén records are known to me. The nearest breeding areas are some eighty miles to the southeast, in the Mountain Pine Ridge of British Honduras (Russell 1964). To many it is known as Coues' Flycatcher (A.O.U. 1957).

Compared with the Olive-sided Flycatcher (*Nuttallornis borealis*), which it most closely resembles, it is a more uniformly grayish bird, lacks the narrow white strip down the middle of the breast, and lacks the white marks on the lower back and white tufts at the sides of the wings.

The voice is a loud, characteristic, frequently uttered imitation of José María, with the *ría* drawn out and emphasized; and a simple phrase incessantly repeated at dawn which sounds like *Fred-rick fear, Fred-rick fear* (1).

Nests are located both high and low, usually in conifers, supported between horizontal forks. They are neat, rather deep cups, substantially constructed of plant material securely bound with cobwebs, and smoothly lined with fine grasses. Eggs, about three in number, are dull white, sparingly marked with small spots (1).

REFERENCES: Peterson 1960, p. 161, picture in color.
(1) Bent, No. 179 (Skutch Ms.).

Empidonax flaviventris (Baird and Baird)

Yellow-bellied Flycatcher   Mosquerito

N.w. Canada (e. of Rocky Mts.), and n.e. N. Am.; winters
    through Mid. Am.
Winter Resident?   5 in.   10½ gr.

Uncommon. It has been recorded during September, October, and February, and may winter through, but more field experience is needed to be certain of its status. It is found in the thickets along roadsides and in the heavy brush along the northern edge of the airstrip.

It is dark green above, a browner tinge on the crown, with yellow eye-rings and two olive-yellow wing bars; underparts are pale yellow, with a light wash of gray across the chest and sides. The bill is black above, light brown to yellow below; legs black; eyes dark brown. In the fall other *Empidonax* flycatchers may be tinged with yellow, but not as bright.

Its voice may be heard to a limited degree during the winter: variations of peeping notes, such as a high, sharp *peeer,* a spiritless, two-syllable *per* wee and also a harsh *chip* (1), (2).

REFERENCES:
(1) Peterson 1960, p. 161, picture in color (of *E. difficilis*). Murphy and Amadon 1953, plate 81, color photograph (with nest).
(2) Slud 1964.

Empidonax traillii traillii (Audubon)

Traill's Flycatcher   Mosquerito
                                            Mosquerito Pálido

N. Am.; winters Mid. Am. (unreported Brit. Honduras) to S. Am.

Winter Resident?   5½ in.   11¾ gr. (10 to 13½)

Common fall migrant. It is usually found in low, dense, brushy woodland areas, with streams or lake shores included. At Tikal it occurred from about a quarter mile west of Aguada Tikal to a half mile east of Aguada Dimick, a comparatively low-level area, and was not present on the higher ridges. It was first recorded with certainty on 13 September 1962, during a substantial influx of the species which continued through October. Twenty-four birds were captured, many in mist nets, along with three *E. flaviventris* and one *E. minimus,* which gives a rough idea of the relative numbers of *Empidonaces* present during the period. The great preponderance of Traill's Flycatchers was difficult for me to accept at the time, as they had never been found previously in any part of the Yucatán Peninsula, so far as I knew. None have been found here during the spring migrations.

To many the race is known as the Alder Flycatcher.

It is olive-colored above, with a slightly brown tone (immatures are still browner), with whitish eye-rings (sometimes obscure) and pale wing bars (usually conspicuous). Underparts are dull white, palest on the chin and throat, grayish at the chest and sides, the belly occasionally tinged with yellow. The bill is black above, light brown to yellow below; legs are black; eyes, brown.

The characteristic song is a buzzy, three-syllable whistle

the phrase repeated with short intervals between (1), (2).

Visitants regularly utter a recognizable, thrush-like *whit,* and other notes (3).

REFERENCES:

(1) Peterson 1960, p. 161, picture in color. Murphy and Amadon 1953, plate 73, color photograph (with nest).

(2) Proc. Am. Phil. Soc., 107:1:21–50, relationship of song and species recognition (Stein). (Includes list of important references.)

(3) Slud 1964.

Empidonax minimus (Baird and Baird)

Least Flycatcher   Mosquerito Chebéc

N.w. Canada (e. of Rocky Mts.) and n.e. N. Am.; winters
   through Mid. Am. to cent. Panama
Winter Resident   5 in.   10¼ gr.

Fairly common. It has been found—based mainly on sight records—year after year since 1956 from early February until 7 May, and also reported for the fall, when a specimen was taken 23 October 1962. The presence of many Traill's Flycatchers (*E. traillii*) in the fall of 1962, some of which when first seen were thought to be Least Flycatchers, suggests that sight records of these species should be carefully weighed before they are accepted as facts.

It is the smallest of the three *Empidonaces* found here, only slightly smaller than the Yellow-bellied Flycatcher, from which it is readily distinguished. It is olive-colored above with a grayish tone, conspicuous white eye-rings, and two whitish wing bars. Underparts are dull white, palest on the chin and throat, pale gray on the chest and sides. The bill is black above, brown below (paler brown basally); legs are black; eyes brown.

Its characteristic song is the only one of its kind, a simple, emphatic, two-syllable _te $\diagup^{\text{dick}}$ or *che-béc,* unmusical, repeated over and over. However, it is seldom heard during migration or in the winter, when it may utter a short sharp *pwit,* stronger than the similar note of *E. traillii* (1), (2).

REFERENCES: Murphy and Amadon 1953, plate 76, color photograph (with nest).
(1) Saunders 1951.   (2) Slud 1964.

Terenotriccus erythrurus fulvigularis (Salvin and Godman)

Ruddy-tailed Flycatcher   Mosquerito

Mexico (Tabasco), Guatemala, Honduras, Brit. Honduras,
   Nicaragua, Costa Rica, Panama, and S. Am.
Resident   4 in.   7 gr.

Rare. It is usually found within humid forests and in adjoining semi-open areas with scattered trees. It forages from eye level to the tops of the understory, flitting from a perch after insects and usually coming to rest on a different perch.

It is gray-olive on the head and back, shading to buff on the lower back and then to a ruddy tail; the dark brown wings have the flight feathers broadly margined with rufous; underparts, including the underside of the wings, are ochre buff, paler on the throat and chin. The bill is black above, flesh color below; legs are red-brown; eyes are very dark brown. The base of the bill is surrounded by heavy bristles.

Its voice is a low, weak, two-syllable whistle, with a short interval between the two notes, the first syllable sometimes higher in pitch (1); also a thin *tseé-oo-tee* (2); or a high, thin *cheé-twit* (3).

The nest is the pensile type (see appendix D), attached to a drooping slender twig or vine, ranging from five to fifteen feet above ground. It is made of fibers, dead leaves, stems, and such vegetation, entangled and bound together like a mass of felt (not woven). The nest chamber is located in the lower third of the pyramid-like structure, with the entrance hole at one side, near the bottom. There is a visor-like projection or shield over the entrance. Two white eggs are deposited, blotched with brown. The bird sits on the nest with its reddish tail projecting out of the entrance (1).

REFERENCES:
(1) P.C.A. 34:534–538, life history (Skutch); fpc., picture in color; p. 535, picture of nest.
(2) Eisenmann 1952.   (3) Condor 59:2:96 (Howell).

Myiobius barbatus sulphureipygius (Sclater)
[*Myiobius sulphureipygius*]

Sulphur-rumped Flycatcher   Mosquerito de Barbas

Trop. Mid. Am. (except El Salvador) and n.w. S. Am.
Resident   5 in.   11 gr. (10 to 12½)

Common. It inhabits the moderately heavy understory and
thickets within the humid forest, more rarely well-shaded
second growth and forest edges.

It is green-olive on the back and shoulders and on the head,
the last with a partly concealed yellow patch. The rump is
bright yellow, which is conspicuously displayed whenever the
dark wings are allowed to droop and the blackish tail is
fanned out, characteristic habits of the Sulphur-rumped Flycatcher. Underparts are also largely yellow, palest on the
throat, but with a broad area of brown or tawny across the
chest, up onto the neck, and down the side of the breast and
belly. Its bill is broad, usually blackish above, largely flesh-
colored below; stiff down-curved bristles extend far out to the
tip or beyond; legs are brown-gray; the dark brown eyes are
noticeably large.

Its usual utterance is a low, sharp, even, explosive *chwit*
or *psit*. Rarely it sings a weak, musical *cheu-cheu-cheu-cheu*
(1), (2).

Its nest is often built low, only six feet above ground, but
may also range thirty feet up. While it is of the freely swinging
pensile type, attached to a slender drooping twig or vine
tendril, it is also of very individual design (see appendix D
and reference [1] for complete details). First, a body of
matted fibrous material is built up on the twig or tendril; then
the mass is spread apart from below to form it into a hollow
cone or bell, one side of which is left thick; the thick side is
then worked inward to form a shelf part way across the bottom of the bell; the shelf is next formed into a nesting cup in

which the eggs are laid; the thin side of the bell is left in position as a protective apron beyond the cup, thereby leaving an opening in the bottom of the structure for the entry of the bird. It may take three or four weeks to complete a nest (1).

Two white eggs are deposited, finely speckled with brown. The bird sits with its tail over the entrance and under the apron (1).

REFERENCES:
(1) P.C.A. 34:539–551, life history (Skutch); fpc. picture in color; pp. 541, 542, pictures of nest in process of construction.
(2) Slud 1964.

Onychorhynchus coronatus mexicanus (Sclater)

Royal Flycatcher   Mosquero Resplandor
                                         Mosquero Real

Trop. Mid. Am., n. Colombia, and n.w. Venezuela
Resident   6½ in.   19 gr. (16½ to 21)

Fairly common. It is found in humid forests (usually reported in connection with streams, which are lacking at Tikal), where it forages in the understory. We see it here flying across wide roads and trails, or perched on some bare branch at low to moderate heights.

It is largely brown-olive above, shading to yellow-brown on the rump and a tawny tail; the tail is somewhat rust-colored below, and dark tipped; the wings have small but conspicuous light buff spots; underparts are largely tawny, pale on the throat, darker and somewhat barred across the breast and sides, tinged with yellow on the belly. It has a crest which is usually seen flattened to a ridge over the crown and projecting back over the nape; taken together with the large bill it gives the bird a hammerhead effect. In this position it shows no color, but when the crest is raised it becomes a spectacular fan across the crown, on the male a rich, flaming scarlet, on the female yellow-orange, both bordered with rich violet and black spots. The bill is wide and long, blackish above, varying from brown to yellow below; legs are yellow-ish; eyes, brown. The mouth lining is yellow.

It utters a loud, clear, hollow-sounding whistle, given singly; also a higher, sharper, wiry note, repeated many times (1).

Its nest is located from eight to twenty feet high. Although of the matted pensile type, attached to a slender, drooping branchlet or vine, it has some very individual features (see appendix D). It is more loosely contructed, but still not woven, from two to six feet long, looking more like some wind-blown hanging mass of vegetation than a nest. Below its bulky central area a shallow niche is opened up in which the eggs are deposited, the incubating bird sitting on them with most all its tail sticking out into the open air (1).

The two eggs which are laid are unusual for flycatchers, being dark red-brown at the large end, buff-colored at the other end (1).

REFERENCES: Austin 1961, p. 207, picture in color. de Schauensee 1964, p. 304, picture in color.

(1) P.C.A. 34:516–533, life history (Skutch); p. 517, pictures in black and white.

Platyrinchus mystaceus timothei Paynter

White-throated Spadebill   Mosquerito Pico de Zapato

Trop. Mid. Am. and S. Am.
Resident   4 in.   9½ gr. (8 to 12)

Common. It is found in the undergrowth within the forest or at its edges, and near trails and small clearings, where it forages within ten feet of the ground.

It is brown-olive over the head and back; somewhat rusty on the very short, stubby tail; the wings have a small dark brown patch near the base of the flight feathers; an indistinct greenish yellow or buff ring surrounds the eye and extends forward to the bill; the throat is white, the rest of the under-parts mainly pale yellow tinged with buff across the breast. The crown of males usually has a large but partly concealed patch of yellow, often exposed when the bird is calling (1).

The bill is short and flat, extremely broad, spade-like. It is black above, varying from flesh color to yellow below; legs are pinkish flesh color; eyes brown.

Its voice is an unmusical trill, explosive at the end; it also utters a short, sharp arresting *squick* (1), and a frequently repeated buzzy, two-syllable call (3).

Its nest is not the pensile type so common to many other small flycatchers here. One in Costa Rica was a compact, V-shaped, open cup, built into the upright crotch of a shrub, forty inches above ground. The light-colored vegetable fibers of the body contrast sharply with the lining of fine black filaments. The exterior is covered with papery bits of decaying leaves and scraps of snakeskin. The egg is white with a yellow tinge and barely visible rufous markings on the larger end (Skutch, in litt.). In Venezuela, two eggs are deposited, café-au-lait in color (2).

REFERENCES: Blake 1953, p. 359, picture in black and white. Sutton 1951, p. 230, picture in black and white (of bill).
(1) Slud 1964.
(2) K. de Phelps 1953, p. 56, picture in color.
(3) Russell 1964.

Tolmomyias sulphurescens cinereiceps (Sclater)

Yellow-olive Flycatcher   Mosquerito Pico Plano

Trop. Mid. Am. and S. Am.
Resident   5½ in.   14½ gr.   Plate 25

Fairly common. It avoids dense forest, but is found in the thin understory below tall, thick-canopied trees, a condition present in much of the Tikal area; it also inhabits forest edges and even clearings, provided shady trees are near by.

It is slate gray on the head and nape, shading to bright olive-green on the back and rump; the flight feathers and also the dark tail feathers are edged with yellow-green; the throat and chest are pale gray shading to pale sulfur yellow on the belly. The bill is short and fairly broad, black above and gray below; legs are gray with a reddish brown cast; eyes are white (sometimes pale yellow-white); they are surrounded by a ring of grayish white which extends from near the top of the eye-ring to the bill.

It is a comparatively quiet bird, its voice usually a thin, weak, hissing whistle, *ss-ss-ss-ss,* which, if rapidly repeated, becomes more and more insistent (1), (2).

The nest is located about six to twenty feet up, of the freely swinging pensile type (see appendix D), attached to a slender, drooping twig or vine. However, it includes an interesting feature which is said to be shared only with the Eye-ringed Flatbill (*Rhynchocyclus brevirostris*). The entrance hole in the side of the hanging nest chamber does not open directly to the outside, but communicates with it through a downwardly directed tube or spout. The flycatcher skillfully shoots vertically up into the hole at the bottom of the spout and so into the nest chamber. When sitting on the nest the bird's head is above the tube; when leaving the nest she dives downward through the tube and out into the air (1).

Sets of two or three eggs are usually laid; the eggs are whitish or creamy white, sparingly speckled with shades of brown (1).

REFERENCES:
(1) P.C.A. 34:496–507, life history (Skutch); pp. 497, 499, pictures in black and white.
(2) Slud 1964.

Rhynchocyclus brevirostris brevirostris (Cabanis)

Eye-ringed Flatbill   Mosquero Pico Chato

Trop. Mid. Am. and n.w. S. Am.
Resident   6 in.   22 gr.   Plate 27

Common. It inhabits the forests and taller shady second growth, where it forages below the canopy, from about twenty to fifty feet up, sometimes close to ground level. It avoids open country.

The plumage is largely a uniform olive-green above and below, becoming pale yellow on the lower breast and belly;

the dusky wing and tail feathers are edged with olive-green; the heavy bill is short and very broad, second in that regard only to the Spade-bill (*Platyrinchus mystaceus*), black above, flesh-colored below; legs are gray; eyes are large, brown to dark brown, with a conspicuous white eye-ring.

Its usual note is a weak, harsh, often spluttering whistle; other simple calls are given occasionally (1).

The nest is the pensile type which includes a tubular spout-like entrance (see *Tolmomyias sulphurescens* and appendix D for details); it is located from about eight to thirty feet above ground. Two pale red-brown eggs are deposited, somewhat speckled with darker brown (1).

REFERENCES:
(1) P.C.A. 34:508–515, life history (Skutch); pp. 509, 513, pictures in black and white.

Oncostoma cinereigulare cinereigulare (Sclater)

Northern Bentbill   Mosquerito
                                                        Sordina

Trop. Mid. Am. to cent. Panama
Resident   4 in. (or less)   6¾ gr. (5 to 8)

Not uncommon. It may be more numerous than is readily apparent. Though not at all shy, it is so inconspicuously plumaged as to be easily overlooked. Though a forest bird, it is found at no great distance inside the edges—where it inhabits dense underbrush—and in thickets and tangles beside trails, roads, and other cuts through the woodland; it is seldom seen above eye level.

The head is slate gray, some individual birds tinged with green; the rest of the upperparts are mainly olive-green, which is also the color of the margins of the wing and tail feathers; underparts are light gray on the throat and upper breast, shading to sulfur yellow on the belly. The short bill is distinctive, with a high, sharply down-curved ridge, black above, light-colored below. Legs are pinkish flesh; eyes white or pale yellow-white.

The female is said to be silent, the male heard mainly in

April, May, and June. He has a strong voice for so small a bird, unmusical, but diagnostic, an odd-sounding, harsh, guttural gargle, or growl, as *grrrrr* or *awwwrp*. Sometimes short whistles and throaty trills are heard (1), (2), (3).

The nest is the pensile type (see appendix D), with the entrance hole in the side partly shielded by a visor-like projection above it. It is often located within two feet of the ground within brushy growth. Two eggs, probably white, are deposited (1).

REFERENCES: Blake 1953, p. 262, picture in black and white.
(1) P.C.A. 34:555–560, life history (Skutch); pp. 556, 559, pictures in black and white.
(2) Slud 1964.
(3) Mexican Bird Songs, recordings by L. Irby Davis.

Elaenia viridicata placens Sclater
[*Myiopagis viridicata*]

Greenish Elaenia   Mosquerito de Corona Amarilla

Trop. Mid. Am. and S. Am.
Resident   5 in.   12½ gr.   Plate 25

Not uncommon. It inhabits semi-open country and thin woodlands with fairly heavy undergrowth. It was first found at Tikal on 14 May 1959; perhaps it was only recently attracted by the brushy cover which quickly followed the opening of park-like areas, roads, and trails.

It is gray-olive on the crown, which has a partly concealed (usually visible) patch of bright yellow; the face is gray, with a line of lighter gray from over the eye to the bill and sometimes an obscure eye-ring; upperparts are otherwise mainly dull olive-green, the darker tail feathers with filmy bright green margins; underparts are light gray on the throat, darker on the chest, then gradually shading to bright yellow on the belly. The bill is comparatively short, black above, variably gray, brown, and black below; legs are dark gray; eyes brown.

From time to time it utters a simple, buzzy, placidly given call, slightly variable, as *rees* or *cheez;* also *cheez weez* (1). Skutch (in litt.) describes the call, in Costa Rica, as a low harsh whistle; and a dawn song as *peer-pee, peer-pee, peer-pèer-pee,* persistently given, over and over in a high thin voice, continuing for many minutes.

The nest is a little open cup, less than two inches across, so small that the head and tail of the sitting bird project over the rim. It is sometimes located some twenty feet above ground in the upperstory of tall shrubs, not saddled on a branch, but attached to a group of small ones by cobweb. It is made entirely of short twigs, so openly woven that the contents are visible through the bottom. Two eggs are deposited, heavily marked with lilac and brown (2).

REFERENCES:
(1) Slud 1964.
(2) Condor 64:4:256–257, nest described, with picture (Rowley).

Camptostoma imberbe imberbe Sclater

Northern Beardless Tyrannulet   Mosquerito Silvador

S.w. U. S. and Mid. Am. to n.w. Costa Rica
Resident   4 in.   7½ gr.   Plate 26

Rare. It is said to inhabit drier regions; also thickets and scrub in coastal areas, avoiding forest interiors. One was found at Tikal 5 October, another 16 October 1962, both between ten and fifteen feet up in the same tree, located at the edge of the forest adjoining a large milpa.

This very small flycatcher is gray-olive above, with somewhat obscure buff wing bars; underparts are pale gray on the throat and chest, shading gradually to very pale yellow on the belly. The bill is small and narrow, dark brown above, light brown and orange (basally) below; legs are black; eyes brown.

The song is a series of gentle, refined *ee-ee-éé-ee-ee* notes, stronger in the mid-portion. Its call note is a one-syllable, thin, piercing *peeeéuk,* perhaps the note most often heard (1), (2). A six-syllable song given at sunrise in April and May is *chew-did-ee, chew-did-see,* the whole repeated some thirty or more times (4).

Four similar flycatchers of the genus *Myiarchus* are illustrated, together with a "fifth" tail feather of each. The birds are shown with their bills aligned vertically (not in normal perching attitudes), to permit closer comparison. A wing and the tail of the Great-crested are shown to indicate the rufous areas as seen from below, when the bird is in flight. Less color is visible on the upper surface of the tail, when the less colorful outer webs are exposed.

BROWN-CRESTED FLYCATCHER p. 172.

9 inches, the largest of this group; also known as Wied's Flycatcher. Compared with the Great-crested, the head is paler brown, the back is browner (less greenish olive), and underparts are paler gray and paler yellow. The bill is black below as well as above; the mouth lining is pale ochre-buff (the other three are orange).

GREAT-CRESTED FLYCATCHER p. 173.

8½ inches, and somewhat less bulky than the Brown-crested. Upperparts are olive-green, the head darker and browner; the throat and upper breast are gray, the lower breast and belly a brilliant yellow (especially in spring). The bill is usually brown below, palest at the base.

YUCATÁN FLYCATCHER p. 174.

7 inches, a much smaller bird than the two crested flycatchers. Upperparts are brown-olive, the head dark brown; underparts are the darkest gray and dullest yellow of the group. The tail flashes less rufous than the two larger birds, partly because the tail feathers have smaller areas of color and also because the color is pinker in tone. The bill is black.

DUSKY-CAPPED FLYCATCHER p. 175.

6½ inches, the smallest of this group; also known as Olivaceous Flycatcher. Upperparts are dark brown-olive, the head decidedly dusky brown; the throat is palest gray of the group, merging through yellow-gray to pale yellow, finally richer yellow on the belly. There is very little rufous flash in the tail, as only the very edges are ruddy. The bill is dark brown below.

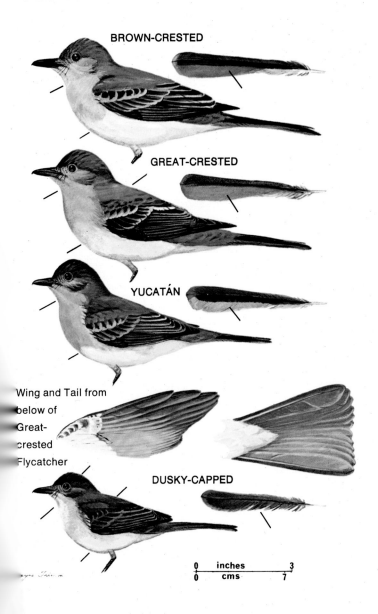

PLATE 24   FLYCATCHERS of MYIARCHUS GROUP

BROWN-CRESTED

GREAT-CRESTED

YUCATÁN

Wing and Tail from below of Great-crested Flycatcher

DUSKY-CAPPED

inches   3
cms   7

These birds have been illustrated together because they are readily confused. For example, the brownish female Plain Antvireo resembles the Tawny-crowned Greenlet (despite the latter's white eyes) and the Sepia-capped Flycatcher (despite its longer tail).

PLAIN ANTVIREO   p. 141
4½ inches. Sexes differ materially, both are heavy billed and stubby tailed. MALE: gray, darkest on crown and cheeks, palest on yellow-tinged belly; two obscure white wing bars and obscure white tail tips. FEMALE: brown on forehead, crown, nape, wings, tail; back dull olive-gray; below whitish throat, brown-gray breast, pale yellow belly; two obscure buff wing bars and buff tail tips.

TAWNY-CROWNED GREENLET   p. 230
4½ inches. Differs from female Plain Antvireo by slender bill, browner above, yellowish white eyes, ruddy legs, yellow patch at bend of wing with dark brown patch below it. Cheeks gray; underparts gray on throat, tawny on breast, olive on belly.

SEPIA-CAPPED FLYCATCHER   p. 199
5 inches. Sexes alike; longer tail, two buff wing bars, *dark* brown head, olive-green back distinguish it from the two preceding birds. Gray on throat, olive-green on breast, yellowish on belly.

GREENISH ELAENIA   p. 192
5 inches. Sexes alike; a small-billed bird with a bright yellow crown patch (partly concealed). Above olive-green, darkest on the crown and with obscure spectacles; underparts are light gray throat, darker gray breast, bright yellow belly.

OCHRE-BELLIED FLYCATCHER   p. 200
5 inches. Sexes alike; told by its ochraceous buff lower breast and belly (similar color at base of lower bill), and by its wing-twitching, first one wing then the other. The head, throat, and chest are dusky gray, the back and tail green-olive.

YELLOW-OLIVE FLYCATCHER   p. 189
5 inches. Sexes alike; white eyes, white eye-ring and flat bill. Slate gray head, olive-green upperparts; wing and tail feathers conspicuously edged with yellow; pale gray throat and chest, sulfur yellow lower breast and belly.

GRAY-HEADED GREENLET   p. 231
4 inches. Sexes alike; this little vireo not too difficult to identify, although gray head, olive-green upperparts, pale gray underparts, and yellow crissum describe other species also. Its short tail, clear eye-rings (or partial spectacles), and vireo-like bill separate it from the Tennessee Warbler with which it is sometimes seen, along with Bananaquits, Euphonias, and Red-eyed Vireos.

PLATE 25

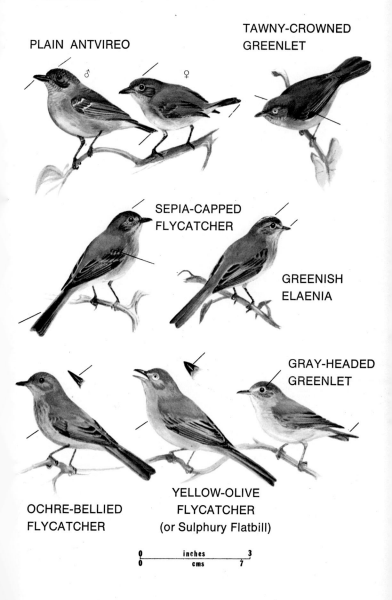

PLAIN ANTVIREO

TAWNY-CROWNED GREENLET

SEPIA-CAPPED FLYCATCHER

GREENISH ELAENIA

GRAY-HEADED GREENLET

OCHRE-BELLIED FLYCATCHER

YELLOW-OLIVE FLYCATCHER
(or Sulphury Flatbill)

inches 3
cms 7

PLATE 26

SCRUB EUPHONIA

YELLOW-BELLIED
TYRANNULET

PALTRY
TYRANNULET

YELLOW-
THROATED
EUPHONIA

BANANAQU

OLIVE-BACKED
EUPHONIA

| 0 | inches | 3 |
| 0 | cms | 7 |

NORTHERN BEARDLESS
TYRANNULET

SCRUB EUPHONIA *p. 271*

3¾ inches. Sexes differ materially.

MALE: blue-black above, and on head, face, throat, and chest; bright yellow on forecrown and forehead; bright yellow on other underparts. White patches on tail and wings are conspicuous in flight, when seen from below.

FEMALE: dull olive-green above, much grayer in tone than the female Yellow-throated Euphonia; underparts olive-yellow, grayish in tone, becoming clear yellow at lower tail coverts.

YELLOW-THROATED EUPHONIA *p. 272.*

4 inches. Sexes differ materially.

MALE: much like Scrub Euphonia, but slightly larger, a little less yellow on forehead and forecrown, yellow (not blue-black) on throat and chest, and yellow of underparts has an orange tinge.

FEMALE: olive-green above (greener than Scrub Euphonia); underparts gray on throat, greenish yellow and white on breast, flanks, and belly, becoming clear yellow at lower tail coverts. A brighter bird than the female Scrub Euphonia.

OLIVE-BACKED EUPHONIA *p. 273.*

4 inches. Sexes differ.

MALE: olive-green above, with yellow forehead; head has bluish iridescence, back has bronze iridescence; underparts have conspicuous dark tawny down middle of breast and belly, and on under tail coverts, otherwise dull olive-green with yellowish markings.

FEMALE: dull olive-green above, the forehead ruddy brown instead of yellow; underparts greenish yellow, the tawny color paler and limited to lower belly and coverts.

YELLOW-BELLIED TYRANNULET *p. 198.*

3½ inches. Sexes alike; crown slate gray with *clear white* border on forehead and sides; cheeks dark; back and rump green-olive; underparts pale yellow. Tail is stubby.

PLATE 26 (*continued*)

PALTRY TYRANNULET
p. 197.

4½ inches. Sexes alike; crown gray with *dull* whitish border on forehead and sides; back and rump green-olive; wing and tail feathers margined with green-yellow; underparts gray with wide dusky streaks, pale yellow on belly. Tail is long and often held tipped up.

BANANAQUIT
p. 234.

4¼ inches. Sexes alike; head black with conspicuous white stripe over the eye; back gray, rump dingy yellow; underparts gray on throat and chest, yellow on breast, dingy white on belly. A small white patch on side of wing is usually visible. The bill is rather long, down-curved, and needle sharp. Tail is short and obscurely white-tipped.

NORTHERN BEARDLESS TYRANNULET
p. 193.

4 inches. Sexes alike; a small, slim-tailed, gray-toned bird, slightly darker gray on crown, decidedly paler gray below; pale yellowish white on belly. The buff on the wings forms indefinite wing bars. The small narrow bill is pale orange below.

The nest is a globular mass lodged between the stems of a palm or within a pendant clump of vegetation such as moss, mistletoe, or epiphyte, the entrance hole at the side. If located in a palmetto it may be only five or ten feet up; if in a tree, as high as forty feet. Two white eggs, finely speckled with red-brown, are the usual set (1), (2), (3).

REFERENCES:
(1) Peterson 1960, p. 161, picture in color.
(2) Slud 1964.   (3) Bent, No. 179.
(4) Auk 59:1:23, voice (Sutton and Pettingill).

* *Tyranniscus vilissimus* subsp.

Paltry Tyrannulet   Mosquerito Vil

Trop. Mid. Am. (from Chiapas south, except Brit. Honduras) and S. Am.
Resident?   4½ in.   Plate 26

Uncommon. It was first identified by Margaret H. Hundley and C. Russell Mason in March 1963, and again in March 1964. It is found at the edges but not far inside humid forests, along roads and trails cut through the forest, and in semi-open areas with shady scattered trees. It forages in well-foliaged crowns of small and medium-sized trees, where it feeds not only on insects but also on small berries.

It has a dark gray crown which contrasts with a dull white forehead, a dull white line over the eye, and green-olive upperparts; wings have no clear wing bars, but the feathers are margined with pale yellow; the long narrow gray-brown tail feathers are margined with green (the tail is often held tilted upward in characteristic fashion); underparts are pale gray on the throat and breast, shading to a yellow-tinged white belly; sides are pale green-yellow. The bill is black, very short and narrow; legs are black (and so long and stiffly held as to give an additional characteristic effect).

The following descriptions of voice may be helpful to observers, although they probably relate to the Lesser Paltry Flycatcher (*T. v. parvus*): a frequently uttered *pee-ee-yíp* or *chee-yíp* (2); a low, full, plaintive whistle, repeated over and over (1). An early morning "dawn" song is a sad-sounding, weakly whispered *yer-de-dee,* several times repeated and followed by three or four quavering *pe-pe-pe* notes, the whole series repeated for many minutes. It is sung regularly from February through July, occasionally through October (1).

The nest is an enclosed, egg-shaped structure with an entrance hole at one side, often built inside a pendant tuft of mosses or lichens, or in the midst of dangling epiphytes such as orchids, bromeliads, or ferns. It is made of a variety of mosses, fibers, and rootlets all bound together with much cobweb, thickly lined with silky seed-down (1).

Two eggs are deposited, dull white, blotched and speckled with shades of light brown (1).

REFERENCES:
(1) P.C.A. 34:465–474, life history (Skutch); p. 466, picture in black and white; p. 467, picture of nest.
(2) Eisenmann 1952.

Ornithion semiflavum semiflavum (Sclater and Salvin)

Yellow-bellied Tyrannulet   Mosquerito
Pequeñin

Trop. Mexico, Guatemala, Brit. Honduras, Honduras, Nicaragua, and Pac. slope of Costa Rica

Resident	3½ in.	7¼ gr.	Plate 26

Not uncommon, but localized in the sunny borders and along the wide roads close to Aguada Tikal. It is usually found in the edges of forest areas but not in the interiors; it forages in small trees, shrubs, and thickets, and up into medium-sized trees.

It is slate gray on the crown, with a clear white line over the eye and a dark mask through the eye; upperparts are olive-green; the tail is short, the feathers margined green; underparts are bright yellow. The bill is black, with a sharply bent ridge; legs are black; eyes very dark brown (appear black).

Its call is not distinctive: a series of three to five *dee*'s, in the same pitch and a minor key (1).

REFERENCES:
(1) Slud 1964.

Leptopogon amaurocephalus pileatus Cabanis

Sepia-capped Flycatcher   Mosquerito de Cabeza Parda

Trop. Mid. Am. (except El Salvador) and S. Am.
Resident   5 in.   11 gr.   Plate 25

Common. It is found mainly in the brushy understory within the forest. Rather quiet and not conspicuously plumaged, it is not readily seen; so little is known about it that it should be given greater attention at Tikal, where it is present in fair numbers.

The crown and nape are dark brown, contrasting with an olive-green back; the dusky wings have two buffy wing bars; a narrow grayish white eye-ring blends into gray-brown cheeks; underparts are gray on the throat, darkening to gray-green on the breast, which in turn shades into yellow on the belly. The bill is slender, black above, dark brown below; legs are gray; eyes vary from light to dark brown.

The call note is loud and harsh, strong enough for a bird three times its size (1).

The nest is of the simpler pensile type (see *Terenotriccus* and appendix D); but all those found have been located in darkish places, such as below the lip of an undercut bank, a deep recess, a shallow cave with overhanging rock, or suspended beneath a log bridging a rivulet. Such a nest at Tikal was swinging free from the thatched roof, inside a large outhouse. It contained two white eggs, but the owner was not identified. A nest in Mexico contained two young birds; another had three pure white, slightly glossy eggs (1).

REFERENCES: de Schauensee 1964, p. 304, picture in color (of *L. a. faustus*).
(1) Condor 46:1:6–8, voice and nests (Robert T. Moore).

Pipromorpha oleaginea assimilis (Sclater)

Ochre-bellied Flycatcher   Mosquero Ocrillo

Trop. Mid. Am. and S. Am.
Resident   5 in.   13 gr.   Plate 25

Common. It is found within the forest, where it forages from the ground up to medium heights. It also inhabits thinned woodland, forest edges, open areas with scattered shady trees, and even coastal scrub.

Upperparts are mainly dull dark green, the head with a slightly grayish tone, the wings and tail feathers with brighter green, fuzzy margins. Underparts are gray on the throat, darker on the chest, which blends into diagnostic shades of ochre buff on the breast and belly. The bill is black, long and slender (see illustration), legs are gray, eyes dark brown. It has a characteristic habit of frequently twitching the wings, first on one side, then on the other, but not both at once.

The female appears to be silent. The male sings unmelodiously but steadily all day long, from early March well into September, usually from a variety of perches scattered over a broad but still-restricted territory, and ranging roughly ten to thirty feet above ground. It opens with some four to ten low, widely spaced, weak notes, as *whip-wit-whip-wit-wit——*, followed by a series of two to twelve rapidly delivered, animated notes, as *chip-chip-chip-chip-chip-chip* (1).

The nest is the pensile type (see appendix D), fastened to a hanging slender vine or branchlet, and with a visor-like shield above the entrance hole. It may not always swing clear in space, but be hung close to a tree trunk or other solid material, usually from four to twelve feet above ground. Three eggs are usually deposited, rarely only two, pure white and unspotted (1).

REFERENCES:
(1) P.C.A. 34:561–570, life history (Skutch); p. 562, picture in black and white.

HIRUNDINIDAE

Progne subis subsp.

Purple Martin Golondrina Azul

N. Am., Mexico, West Indies; the e. N. Am. race winters chiefly in Brazil, with a few records from e. Mexico, Guatemala, Brit. Honduras, Honduras, Nicaragua, and Panama
Transient   8 in.   50 gr.

Uncommon migrant. The sight record of a single male on 24 March 1960 (Raymond A. Paynter, Jr.), is the first report for the Petén. Since then sight records have been reported for 30 September and 26 October 1962, when five to ten were seen among large flocks of other swallows.

The male is glossy blue-black above and below, duller on the wings and tail. The female is dark brown above, with a grayish forehead and often a faint collar around the neck; underparts are gray-brown on the throat and breast, shading to pale gray on the belly. Immature males are much like females, and both are almost indistinguishable from Gray-breasted Martins (*Progne chalybea*), except for the latter's smaller size, dark forehead, and white belly. They fly with quick flaps, alternating with circular glides, and spread their moderately forked tails more frequently than do other swallows.

The call is a rich throaty series of *tchew-wew-wew,* or *pew-pew*-etc. (1).

REFERENCES: Blake 1953, p. 368, pictures in black and white. Austin 1961, p. 217, picture in color.

(1) Peterson 1960, p. 140, pictures in black and white; p. 167, voice.

Progne chalybea chalybea (Gmelin)

Gray-breasted Martin Golondrina Gris

Ah Cuzam (a general term)

Texas, Mid. Am., and S. Am.
Resident   6½ in.   40 gr.

Uncommon, except for one group localized along the air-strip, where they appeared to be nesting in holes some twenty-five feet up in dead palm trees. Perhaps only six or eight in the area in 1959. The species inhabits large clearings and is often found in villages and towns.

The male is bluish black above; underparts are gray-brown on the throat, breast, and sides, contrasting with a white belly. Females and immature males are brownish above, otherwise much like adult males. All Gray-breasted Martins are diffi-cult to distinguish from female Purple Martins (*P. subis*), except for the latter's larger size, pale-appearing forehead, and darker belly. The bill is black; legs are black; eyes, dull dark brown.

The voice is smoother and more musical than that of other swallows, sounding like repeated warbled *choor*'s (*oo* short), given in an irregular up-and-down pattern (1).

Nests are usually placed in holes in trees, preferably bare-limbed, in palm stubs, in old woodpecker holes, and in suit-able openings in buildings. Three or four white, unmarked eggs are usual (2), (3).

REFERENCES: Blake 1953, p. 368, picture in black and white. Austin 1961, p. 217, picture in color.
(1) Slud 1964.   (2) Bent No. 179.
(3) Herklots 1961.

Hirundo rustica erythrogaster Boddaert

Barn Swallow   Golondrina de Tijereta
                                    Golondrina Tijerilla

Old World, N. Am. to cent. Mexico; migrates through Mid.
   Am.; winters in S. Am., occasionally in Mid. Am.
Transient   7 in. (long tail)   16 gr.

Not uncommon (but perhaps erratic) migrant. It is rather
widespread, numerous along shore lines, and also found inland
over open country, farmlands, fields, and marshes.

It was first recorded at Tikal on 7 April 1962 (Jorge A.
Ibarra). In the fall of 1962, I recorded it as follows: on 1,
2, 3, 28 September, and 1, 2 October, only one individual
at a time; on 4 October, eight; 5 October, two; 25 October,
twenty-six or more along with a large flock of perhaps a hundred Rough-winged Swallows (*Stelgidopteryx ruficollis*).

The adult is blue-black above, the wings and tail dull black,
the long deeply forked tail having white spots which form a
band when spread; the forehead is chestnut. Underparts are
chestnut on the chin and throat, a partial collar of blue-black
extending from the neck to the sides of the chest, and contrastingly pale cinnamon buff breast and belly. The bill and
legs are black, eyes dark brown. Immatures are duller, some
with pale foreheads and shorter tails.

The musical twittering commonly heard in the north is
lacking during migrations; here the voice is limited to *krik-
krik* or *swik-swik* notes, and also a metallic *whit* (1).

REFERENCES: Blake 1953, p. 371, picture in black and white.
Austin 1961, p. 216, picture in color; end papers, picture of egg in
color.
   (1) Slud 1964.

Stelgidopteryx ruficollis stuarti Brodkorb

Rough-winged Swallow Golondrina de Pecho Gris

N. Am., Mid. Am., and S. Am.; the northern races winter through Mid. Am.

Resident 5½ in. 16 gr.

Common. The race is found throughout the area, from the airfield, the camp, the adjacent aguadas, on up to the ruins which predominate at higher levels. Flocks of twenty or more frequently forage in and out of temple doorways, where the cool interiors have attracted flying insects. They also fly in still-larger flocks when foraging high in the air above camp. On one such occasion, about four to five in the afternoon, I watched a group of about seventy high in the sky, with some fifty swifts (*Chaetura vauxi*) flying even higher above them. After a period of time the swallows drifted lower and lower over Aguada Tikal, finally surprising me by circling down repeatedly in long, broad streams close over its surface, many of them dipping into the water momentarily at the low point of their sweeps. The swifts remained high in the air.

Upperparts are uniformly darkish brown, the darkest of the numerous "races"; underparts are grayish on the throat, slightly tinged with rufous; the breast is brownish gray shading to light gray on the belly and a white crissum, the last broadly tipped with brownish black. The bill is black, legs are black, eyes very dark brown. The tail is slightly forked.

Soft, clear, singing notes are sometimes uttered and rarely a brief musical trill (1). More usual notes are harsh chirps, an upturned *shrirk* or a *djreet* (2).

Nests are in burrows or tunnels, often preformed by other birds. At Tikal they were found behind crevices inside of ruined temples, in particular in two temples located in the H-Group. Four or five pure white eggs are the usual clutch (1).

REFERENCES: Austin 1961, p. 216, picture in color.
(1) P.C.A. 34:265–274, life history (Skutch); p. 266, picture in black and white.
(2) Slud 1964.

Stelgidopteryx ruficollis fulvipennis (Sclater)

About 22 through 25 October 1962, flocks of Rough-winged Swallows were observed behaving conspicuously different from normal. They perched on horizontal wires near Aguada Tikal, in the company of Barn Swallows which had recently become numerous, giving me the feeling that they were migrants, as the residents had not previously so perched. I also noted, due to the exposure of their under tail coverts while perched, that occasional birds lacked the dark terminals on the crissum of *S. r. stuarti* (1). By good fortune, two birds captured in mist nets proved to be *S. r. fulvipennis* when later identified with the assistance of Raymond A. Paynter, Jr., at the Museum of Comparative Zoology, Harvard College.

REFERENCES:
(1) Condor 59:3:212, 213, subspecies discussed (Paynter).

CORVIDAE

Cissilopha sanblasiana yucatanica (Dubois)

Black-and-blue Jay   Chara de Negro y Azul

Chél

S.w. Mexico (Nayarit to Guerrero, Yucatán Pen. and Tabasco), Guatemala (Petén), and Brit. Honduras
Resident   12 in.   130 gr.

Uncommon, perhaps rare. It was found only in the tintal, in very dense, low, almost impenetrable cover, two and one-half miles east of Aguada Tikal, during May, June, July, and August 1959. Efforts to find it again from August through October 1962 were unsuccessful.

It is conspicuously bright blue on the back, wings, rump, and tail, otherwise mainly solid black. The bill is black, legs yellow-orange, eyes very dark brown. Two immatures, fully developed, replaced the blue plumage almost entirely with white, and had yellow bills, yellow legs, and lighter brown eyes.

It is interesting to know that bones, found in a very ancient cache at Tikal, have been identified as this species.

They nest in trees and shrubs; five eggs are reported for a nest found in a pine tree in British Honduras (1).

REFERENCES: Blake 1953, p. 380, picture in black and white. (1) Russell 1964.

Cyanocorax yncas centralis (van Rossem)
[*Xanthoura yncas*]

Green Jay   Chara Verde

Ses-ib

Texas, Mexico, Brit. Honduras, Guatemala, Honduras, also highlands n. and w. S. Am.
Resident   10½ in.   70 gr.

Uncommon, perhaps rare. It is found in second growth, semi-open woodland, and brushy thickets. It was first recorded 12 June 1957, and again 19 October 1962. The small sizes of the specimens suggest that perhaps they should be assigned to *C. y. maya*.

It is conspicuously colorful: a bright green above except for bright yellow outer tail feathers and a blue head; bright yellow below slightly tinged with green, and a black chest and throat. The bill is black, legs are gray, eyes are yellow (not brown, as in northern races).

Two or more individuals together chatter with a noisy, raucous *cra-cra-cra-cra-cra* of typically jay-like quality. They also utter a variety of throaty and buzzy rattles, squeaky snarls, and snapping noises (2), (3).

The nest (in Texas) is a twiggy bowl in a thicket or small tree; three or four brown-spotted eggs are deposited (2).

REFERENCES: Blake 1953, p. 379, picture in black and white.
(1) Sutton 1951.
(2) Peterson 1960, p. 176, picture in color; p. 168, voice.
(3) Bird Songs, recordings by Paul Schwartz.

Psilorhinus morio cyanogenys Sharpe

Brown Jay

Urraca Chillona
Pea

Paap

E. and s.e. Mexico, Guatemala, Brit. Honduras, Honduras,
Nicaragua, Costa Rica, and n.w. Panama
Resident   17 in.   240 gr.

Common. The Brown Jay is found within the forest as well
as in forest edges, tall second growth, and clearings with
shady trees. It avoids extensive heavy-forest regions, and also
is absent from the tintal.

It is deep brown above and below, except for a creamy
white breast and belly, broadly white-tipped outer tail feathers,
and grayish thighs. The bill, the legs, and the bare skin about
the eyes all vary from black (the most usual but not invari-
able color in adults) to yellow. Other races differ from the
above in details, some lacking entirely the white-tipped tails.

It forages in small, loose flocks which are conspicuous for
their loud, raucous, persistent alarm call, a rapidly repeated
cha · a-cha · a-etc., punctuated by a diagnostic "cork-pulling"
pop which precedes each call. Another call, of more frequent
occurrence during the breeding season, is a drawled, complaining or mournful series of *pee-ah*'s (1), (2).

The nest is a bulky platform made of longish coarse sticks,
which are broken off trees deliberately rather than picked off
the ground, with smaller sticks filling the center portion, and
finally a rather shallow cup lined with coarse roots. It is often
located out near the end of a long slender branch, twenty to
fifty feet up in trees. Two or three eggs are the usual clutch.
The eggs are a pale chalky bluish gray, thickly speckled with
brown (1).

REFERENCES:
(1) P.C.A. 34:231–257, life history (Skutch); p. 232, picture in
black and white.
(2) Mexican Bird Songs, recordings by L. Irby Davis.

TROGLODYTIDAE

Thryothorus ludovicianus albinucha (Cabot)
[*Thryothorus albinucha*]

Carolina Wren   Chinchivirín
White-browed Wren

Yancotíl (wrens in general)

E. U. S., Mexico (s. to San Luis Potosí and in Yucatán Pen.),
   Guatemala (Petén), Nicaragua
Resident   5½ in.   16 gr.

Uncommon, but not rare. It is found in woodlands, under-growth, thickets, and often near habitations. It has been recorded here in the months of February, July, August, and October, always in or near the thickets at the eastern end of the airfield, at Aguada Dimick, and a bit beyond. Regarded by some as a race of the Carolina Wren, by others as a distinct species (*T. albinucha*), then called White-browed Wren.

It is dark brown above, the tail blackish, with gray bars, the outer tail feathers with white bars; underparts are grayish white tinged with brown, lightest on the throat and crissum. A long, conspicuous whitish stripe extends over the eye. The bill is dark brown above, gray-brown below; legs are gray; eyes are brown. It lacks the ruddy effect of the northern race; and is darker above, lighter below.

Northern birds have characteristic (though variable) songs, of two to four explosively clear rich whistled notes, each phrase repeated a number of times (1).

They nest in holes or cavities, or build domed nests in more open situations. Two or three, perhaps four or five eggs are deposited, white or creamy white, irregularly spotted with shades of brown (2). I have no definite data on clutches of local birds.

REFERENCES: Peterson 1960, p. 177, picture in color (of *T. ludovicianus*).
(1) Saunders 1957.   (2) Bent, No. 195.

Thryothorus maculipectus canobrunneus Ridgway

Spot-breasted Wren   Chinchivirín Pinto

Xan-cotí

Trop. Mexico, Guatemala, Brit. Honduras, El Salvador, Honduras, e. Nicaragua
Resident   5½ in.   15 gr. (♂ 16, ♀ 14)

Common. It is found in the forest, forest edges, undergrowth, thickets, and tangles, usually within fifteen feet of the ground, but occasionally thirty feet up in vines.

Upperparts are mostly uniform unstreaked brown, darkest on the crown, a clear white line over the eye, and the tail barred with black; the cheek is streaked with black and white; underparts are whitish, clear on the throat, the lower belly grayish brown, and all between (lower throat, breast, and part of the belly) conspicuously marked with minute but clear black speckles. The bill is brown above, gray below; legs are gray; eyes are brown, often with a reddish cast.

A clear, sweetly whistled, lively song is given as a duet by both the male and female, each singing a part of it, and alternating so closely that it sounds like only one continuous strain (1), (2). Sutton called it an uproarious "squeal, churl, squeal if you will" (3).

The nest is usually a globular affair of fine grasses, weed stems, and the like, with an entrance hole at one side. It is located in tangles within ten feet of the ground, sometimes higher. Two or three white eggs, heavily spotted with light brown, are usual (1).

REFERENCES: Blake 1953, p. 404, picture in black and white. Sutton 1951, p. 126, picture in black and white.
(1) Auk 57:3:308, 309, description (Skutch); fpc., picture in black and white.
(2) Mexican Bird Songs, recordings by L. Irby Davis.
(3) Condor 50:3:103, voice (Sutton).

Henicorhina leucosticta prostheleuca (Sclater)

White-breasted Wood-Wren   Chinchivirín Cantor

Trop. Mid. Am. (except El Salvador) and S. Am.
Resident   4 in. (short tail)   14¾ gr.

Common. It is the most numerous of the four wrens at Tikal, especially conspicuous by reason of its steady singing and chatter. It inhabits the heavy undergrowth of humid lowland forests where it forages on the ground and up to about ten feet above ground, in dense tangles of decaying (and live) vegetation.

A small wren with a very stubby little tail, its upperparts are red-brown (paler in some individuals), its wings and tail more or less barred with black; its crown may be red-brown like its back or may have a grayish tone; the face is streaked conspicuously with black and white and has a long white line above the eye; underparts are clear white on the throat and upper breast, shading to pearl gray on the lower breast and to brown on the belly. The bill is black, legs are gray or dark brown, eyes dark brown.

Both sexes sing, the male giving three rich, full, unhurried whistles, the female responding with up to five weaker, mellower notes, the whole followed by short pauses between repetitions. When complaining or alarmed they utter harsh *churr*'s among other notes (1), (2), (4).

The nest is usually built anywhere from the ground level (rarely on it) to eighteen inches up, a small, roofed-over structure with a side entrance, the enclosed cup about two inches below the lip. It is made of leaf skeletons, rootlets, and fibrous materials; often lined with feathers. A clutch consists of two or three white eggs, often unmarked, sometimes speckled with brown (1), (2), (3).

REFERENCES: Blake 1953, p. 408, picture in black and white.
(1) P.C.A. 34:138–145, life history (Skutch); p. 139, picture in black and white.
(2) Ibis 100:2, p. 219, nest described (Skutch).
(3) Russell 1964.
(4) Mexican Bird Songs, recordings by L. Irby Davis.

Uropsila leucogastra brachyura (Lawrence)

White-bellied Wren Chinchivirín

E. and s.w. Mexico, Brit. Honduras, Guatemala, and n. Honduras
Resident 4 in. 10 gr.

Uncommon but not rare. Here it is found mainly inside the forest, often foraging at rather higher levels than the other three wrens; also found at forest edges, but less frequently. It may be overlooked, as it is very small, not conspicuously patterned, and not a loud singer.

Its tail is short but not stubby as is the Wood-Wren's and is not held cocked up. Upperparts are pale brownish gray, the wings obscurely barred, the tail more clearly barred; a white stripe extends over the eye. Underparts are plain dingy white, tinged with pale brown on the sides and flanks. The bill is dark brown above, gray below; legs are gray, eyes brown.

Its song is musical and rather rhythmical and has also been described as tinkling and bubbling, but so soft as to sound far-off even when close at hand (1), (2). In British Honduras it is a rolling, vireo-like phrase, as *witch-giver* or *whisky-bird,* repeated over and over at intervals of a few seconds; the call is a faint *chup* (Willis, in litt.).

The nest is an oval or ball-shaped retort, with an entrance about two inches long at one side; a smooth, neat structure of loosely woven dead plant stems, leaf skeletons, straw, and such, the exterior brightened by lichens, moss, cobweb. It is said that this wren nests almost exclusively in bull-horn acacias, which are populated by stinging ants; one nest, however, was found three feet from the "paper-nest" of small black hornets. Nests are located, usually, from six to twenty feet above ground, and five to twelve feet out near the end of a drooping branch.

It is interesting to note that it takes much disturbance of the nest to make the wren show itself.

Four unspotted eggs are deposited, pale bluish green and rather glossy (1), (2), (Willis, in litt.).

REFERENCES:
(1) Condor 50:3:101–111, voice and nests, with pictures (Sutton).
(2) Sutton 1957.

MIMIDAE

Dumetella carolinensis (Linnaeus)

Catbird   Pájaro Gato
                                               Maullador

N. Am.; winters through Mid. Am. (except El Salvador) to cent. Panama
Winter Resident   8½ in.   38 gr.

A common fall and spring migrant. It has been noted from 12 to 26 October, but has not been observed again (probably only due to a lack of observers) until 13 February. The latest spring record is 2 May.

It is found in thickets adjacent to cleared areas, open aguadas, and abandoned *chiclero* camps, and also in the ground cover within more open forest.

It is mainly slate gray, darker on the wings and tail, lighter gray below, with a black crown and a red-brown patch below the tail.

Its song is not heard here, but its sharp, cat-like *meaow* is frequently uttered.

REFERENCES: Peterson 1960, p. 192, picture in color. Austin 1961, p. 249, picture in color.

TURDIDAE

Turdus albicollis leucauchen Sclater
[*Turdus assimilis*]

White-throated Robin   Sinsontle

Pichhum (thrushes in general)

Trop. Mid. Am., w. Colombia, and Ecuador
Resident   9 in.   65 gr.

Not uncommon. It is usually found inside the forest, where it forages high and low in the understory; less often near clearings with low tangles and thickets, where it forages close to the ground.

At Tikal it is blacker in appearance than would be expected from most descriptions. Upperparts are nearly black with a slightly brown tone; the whitish throat is almost concealed by black streaks; a whitish collar below the throat contrasts with the grayish brown-tinged breast; the belly is dingy white. The bill is usually all yellow, the upper portion sometimes brown; legs are brownish yellow; eyes are brown, surrounded by a narrow but conspicuous eye-ring of yellow or orange-yellow.

Its halting song, brilliant, thrush-like, and varied, is interrupted by intrusions of high-pitched, "chaffy" notes. It is given mainly from early March through June (1), (3). The bird's presence is often revealed by a monosyllable, *ek* or *ok,* sounding thick and guttural (2).

Its nest, some five to twenty-five feet up in small trees, shrubs, or thickets, is a bulky structure, composed of a variety of plant stems, fibers, and mosses surrounding a thick wall of mud, within which is the open cup lined with softer fibers. Two, more often three eggs are deposited, dull white, heavily mottled all over with red-brown (1).

REFERENCES: Blake 1953, p. 424, picture in black and white.
  (1) P.C.A. 34:83–86, life history (Skutch); p. 84, picture in black and white.

(2) Slud 1964.

(3) Mexican Bird Songs, recordings by L. Irby Davis.

Turdus nudigenis tamaulipensis (Nelson)
[*Turdus grayi*]

Clay-colored Robin   Sinsontle Común
                                          Ruiseñor

Xk'ok'

Trop. Mid. Am. and n. Colombia
Resident   9½ in.   74 gr.

Fairly common. Throughout its wide range it is most abundant where there are habitations, cultivated fields, coffee plantations, and such. To a lesser extent it enters semi-open woodlands. At Tikal it was first seen on 8 May 1959, since when its population has increased along with the increase of dwellings and other man-made alterations of the habitat.

It forages from moderately high in trees down to ground level, where I noted an individual feeding young birds, from 24 to 31 August.

Its general appearance is that of a rather uniformly brown-colored robin, darker and tawny above, lighter and clay-colored below, pale buff on the throat. Its only streaks are on the throat and they are inconspicuous. The bill is greenish yellow, legs are yellowish gray, eyes a soft brown.

Its lilting voice is very similar to the clear, whistled caroling of the American Robin (*T. migratorius*), but smoother, mellower, and so even more pleasant to the ear. It is heard mainly from early February to mid-August. When alarmed it utters a robin-like cackle; also a distinctive upwardly inflected, querulous, mewing *keyooo* (1), (2), (3).

Its nest is built in a great variety of places: out on a branch, in the crotch of a tree, on top of a post or slender stump, on the ridgepole of a shed, and such-like solid bases. It is usually located from five to fifteen feet up, rarely thirty feet or higher. It is an open bowl, much like an American Robin's, with an inner shell of mud mixed with fibrous material, an outer bulky wall of various plant material, a lining of rootlets, softer fibers and grasses. Two, more often three eggs are deposited, pale blue, speckled and mottled all over with red-brown (1).

REFERENCES: Blake 1953, p. 425, picture in black and white.
(1) P.C.A. 34:67–82, life history (Skutch); p. 67, picture in black and white.
(2) Slud 1964.
(3) Mexican Bird Songs, recordings by L. Irby Davis.

Hylocichla mustelina (Gmelin)

Wood Thrush   Tordo Pinto

E. N. Am.; winters through Mid. Am. to cent. Panama
Winter Resident?   8 in.   50 gr.

Not uncommon, but still not numerous. It has not been recorded from 8 November to 20 February, probably because of lack of observers. The latest spring record is 23 April, the earliest fall record 10 October. It is usually found on or near the ground, in the forest understory and in thickets adjoining the forest; also near habitations where numerous shade trees are present.

Somewhat smaller than any of the robins (*Turdus*), it is the largest of the four thrushes (*Hylocichla*) found here. Upperparts are olive-brown, the head and nape a characteristic ruddy brown; underparts are mainly white, with large, round, dark spots scattered conspicuously over the chest and breast. The bill is black above, yellowish below; legs are very pale flesh color; eyes are brown. The mouth lining is orange.

Though the flute-like song is not heard during the winter, characteristic call notes are uttered, among them a sharp, rapid, three or four-syllable *quick-quick-quick*, or *pit-pit-pit-pit* (1), (2). On 4 April 1956 I was close enough to hear one sing its typical three- to five-note song, *ah-lee-o-lay*, not loud and clear, but very softly muted.

REFERENCES: Peterson 1960, p. 193, picture in color. Austin 1961, p. 252, picture in color; end papers, picture of egg in color.

Murphy and Amadon 1953, plate 119, color photograph (with nest). Wilson Bull. 68:3:fpc., five thrushes pictured in color; pp. 171–199, a comparative study (Dilger).

(1) Slud 1964.   (2) Saunders 1951.

Catharus ustulatus swainsoni (Tschudi)
[*Hylocichla ustulata*—AOU 1957]

Swainson's Thrush   Tordo
Olive-backed Thrush   Solitario

N. N. Am.; migrates through Mid. Am.; the eastern race (*swainsoni*) winters from s. Mexico south, chiefly in S. Am.; the western race (*ustulata*), to Costa Rica.
Transient   7 in.   30 gr.

Uncommon. Our only records (all were *swainsoni* at Tikal) began 25 September 1962 and continued to mid-October, during which time they were frequently seen, foraging over a wide area, from the neighborhood of Aguada Tikal up to the higher levels of the Great Plaza. Van Tyne (1935) reported one individual as *ustulata,* for 15 April 1931, at near by Uaxactún, the only other record for the Petén.

In the north it is more arboreal than either the Wood Thrush or the Gray-cheeked Thrush, inhabits mixed conifer and deciduous forests, but requires conifers for nesting. At Tikal it foraged near the ground, as indicated by the number we freed from mist nets.

It is uniformly dull olive-brown above, with buff cheeks and conspicuously buff eye-rings, which distinguish it from the Gray-cheeked Thrush. Underparts are white except for the buff tinge on the throat and chest, and the boldly spotted chest and upper breast. The bill is blackish above; legs are brown toward the front, nearly white toward the rear; eyes are brown.

A quick soft *pwink,* accompanied by a flick of the wings, may be heard (1). Its northern song may become audible in late April: a series of musical phrases spiraling upward and ending in a high-pitched, weak trill (1), (2).

REFERENCES: Peterson 1960, p. 193, picture in color. Murphy and Amadon 1953, plate 120, color photograph (with nest). Wilson Bull. 68:3:fpc., five thrushes pictured in color; pp. 171–199, a comparative study (Dilger).

(1) Slud 1964.　　　(2) Saunders 1951.

Catharus minimus minimus (Lafresnaye)
[*Hylocichla minima*—AOU 1957]

Gray-cheeked Thrush　　　　　　　　　　　　　　Tordo

N. N. Am.; the race *bicknelli* winters in West Indies and n. S. Am.; the race *minima* winters (rarely) in Nicaragua and Costa Rica, chiefly n. S. Am.

Transient　　　　　6½ in.　　　　　27 gr.

Uncommon, perhaps rare. On 9 October 1962 two were found in a roadside mist net. They were the only Gray-cheeked Thrushes clearly identified that fall, and it is probable that the record would not have been made without the aid of nets. Van Tyne (1935) reported one at Uaxactún, 28 April 1931, the only other record for the Petén.

It is uniformly dull olive-brown above, even duller and somewhat grayer than the Swainson's Thrush; grayish cheeks and obscure eye-rings serve further to distinguish it from the buff-faced Swainson's Thrush. Underparts are mainly white, with dusky spots scattered in a streaky effect down the throat and chest and sides of the breast. The bill is black above, brown below; legs are brown toward the front, silver gray toward the rear; eyes are brown.

It is practically voiceless during migration, uttering at most a weak little *wheesp* (1).

REFERENCES: Peterson 1960, p. 193, picture in color. Wilson Bull. 68:3:fpc., five thrushes pictured in color; pp. 171–199, a comparative study (Dilger).

(1) Slud 1964.

Catharus fuscescens fuscescens (Stephens)
[*Hylocichla fuscescens*—AOU 1957]

Veery   Tordo

N. Am.; winters in S. Am.; recorded in migration Mexico
(Yucatán, Veracruz), Brit. Honduras, Guatemala (Petén),
Honduras (Bay Is.), Costa Rica, Panama
Transient   7½ in.   31 gr.

Uncommon, except during the fall migration, when it
seemed for a short time to be the most numerous of the four
migrant thrushes at Tikal. It was first seen 16 September
1962. From 1 to 16 October two to four were seen daily and
more than eight were released from nets during that period.
It foraged on the ground and among edge thickets, from the
north side of the airstrip, through the camp grounds and on
to the western area known as Group E. This is all comparatively low ground; none were found on the higher ridges.

This may be the first time the Veery has been recorded, not
only for the Petén, but for all of Guatemala.

Upperparts are uniformly tawny, only slightly rusty; underparts are white on the throat, lower breast and belly, the
chest and upper breast buff and lightly spotted. The bill is
black above, light brown and yellowish below; legs are brown
or light brown; eyes are brown.

It appears to be silent during migration (1). The song in
the north is a series of four or five buzzy phrases, as *vee-er,
vee-er, vee-er, vee-er,* which roll breezily downward.

REFERENCES: Peterson 1960, p. 193, picture in color. Murphy
and Amadon 1953, plate 121, color photograph (with nest). Wilson
Bull. 68:3:fpc., five thrushes pictured in color; pp. 171–199, a
comparative study (Dilger). Auk 73:3:fpc., pictures in black and
white.

(1) Slud 1964.

SYLVIIDAE

Polioptila plumbea superciliaris Lawrence

Tropical Gnatcatcher   Encinerito

Trop. Mid. Am. (except El Salvador) from s.e. Mexico
(Quintana Roo) s. to S. Am.

Resident   4 in.   6 gr.

Uncommon. It was first noted 7 July 1959. It is usually
found well above ground—including the canopy of semi-open
forest and forest edges—less often in the understory, foraging
at about eye level.

Upperparts are mainly bluish gray, the males only with
glossy blue-black on the crown and hind neck, both sexes
with black middle tail feathers and white outer tail feathers.
The face is white, from above the eyes down and including
the throat. Underparts are mainly white, the breast and sides
tinged with light blue-gray. The tail is long and slim, usually
held cocked up in the air, and is frequently flicked, flashing
the white side feathers. The slender bill is black above, dark
gray below; legs are dark gray to black; eyes dark brown.

The call note is a mewing, nasal *myaaa,* "instantly recognizable" (2); or a fine, thin, nasal *chaaa* (1). The song is a
simple, melodious, slow trill, which begins high-pitched and
thin, descending in pitch to become deeper and fuller toward
the end. It is usually delivered from a treetop from January
through June (1).

Nests have been found in bushes and trees, from six to
twenty-five feet above ground, often saddled well out on a
slender branch. The cup is small and compact, made of fine
fibrous material and lined with plant down; the outer surface
is more or less covered with lichens and mosses, the whole
held together with much cobweb. It may be mistaken for the
nest of a hummingbird. Two or three eggs are deposited,
white, finely speckled all over with brown (1).

REFERENCES:
(1) P.C.A. 34:43–53, life history (Skutch); p. 44, pictures in black and white.
(2) Slud 1964.

Ramphocaenus rufiventris ardeleo Van Tyne and Trautman

Long-billed Gnatwren   José Seco
Pajarito Picudo

Trop. Mid. Am. and n.w. S. Am.
Resident   4¾ in.   9½ gr.

Fairly common. It is found in dense tangles, thickets, and undergrowth in forests and in second-growth woodlands, most numerous when adjacent to openings and edges. It forages from a little above ground level to some thirty feet up in vine tangles, but avoids the high forest canopy. Its presence is often revealed by its song.

Its general appearance is of a small, pale brown, wren-like bird with an exceptionally long, straight bill, and a long, slim tail which is frequently cocked up and down. The crown is olive-brown, the back gray-brown, the face bright cinnamon, becoming white on the chin and throat. The throat is streakily spotted, sometimes obscurely, with dusky. Underparts are shades of buff, lightest on the belly. The graduated outer tail feathers are tipped with white. The bill is brown above, flesh-colored below; legs are gray; eyes brown.

The song is a clear, long-continued, trilled whistle, all on the same key (1), (3), or rising slightly at the end (2). It is repeated all day long and may be heard throughout the year. At times it voices a surprisingly loud, clear, staccato whistle; also a low, dry *churr* when alarmed (1), (3).

The nest is located close to the ground, sometimes only six inches up, well hidden in a bushy shrub or other low cover. It is a thick-walled, open cup about four inches in outside diameter, made of small twigs, many dried leaves, and other vegetation, lined with fine fibers or grasses, all held together with cobweb. Two eggs are deposited, white, lightly sprinkled over with fine pale cinnamon spots (1), (4), (5).

REFERENCES:

(1) P.C.A. 34:54–61, life history (Skutch); p. 55, picture in black and white.
(2) Slud 1964.
(3) Mexican Bird Songs, recordings by L. Irby Davis.
(4) Condor 59:2:100, nests (Howell).
(5) Auk 70:3:369, nest (Eisenmann).

BOMBYCILLIDAE

* Bombycilla cedrorum Vieillot

Cedar Waxwing   Capuchino

N. Am.; winters through Mid. Am. to cent. Panama
Transient   7 in.   30 gr.

Not uncommon as a spring migrant. It frequents semi-open forests, forest edges, and open areas with scattered trees. It travels in compact flocks which perch in trees, usually in the crowns, foraging for small fruits, sallying flycatcher-like after insects, and sometimes sitting quietly for long periods. Occasionally it feeds on the ground.

The first time it was seen here—and probably the first record for the Petén—was on 16 February 1958, when about twelve were noted; on the twenty-eighth, twenty-eight were counted. Late visits were recorded on 8 May 1959 (only two were seen).

It is a notably sleek, smooth, well-groomed-looking bird, largely velvety brown or fawn-colored above and below, with a conspicuous, stiffly held crest, a black facial mask, and a yellow band at the end of the tail. The secondary wing feathers are often tipped with scarlet waxy droplets; the wings, rump, and tail are grayish; the belly is yellowish, the under tail coverts are white. Immatures are gray instead of brown, and heavily streaked below.

The only note, usually given in flight, is a weak, coarsely sibilant *sss* (2), or a high, thin lisp like *zeee* (1).

REFERENCES: Blake 1953, p. 441, picture in black and white. Murphy and Amadon 1953, plate 126, color photograph (with nest).

(1) Peterson 1960, p. 192, picture in color; p. 191, voice.
(2) Slud 1964.

VIREOLANIIDAE

Smaragdolanius pulchellus pulchellus (Sclater and Salvin)

Green Shrike-Vireo   Verdino

S.e. Mexico (Veracruz and Chiapas), Guatemala, Brit. Honduras, Honduras, Costa Rica, Panama

Resident   5½ in.   25 gr.   Plate 27

Uncommon, perhaps rare. It usually keeps to the canopy inside the tall forest, where it is difficult to see it; it is also found in second growth, semi-open situations, and plantations with scattered trees, where it forages at lower levels, and then appears less rare. The first record obtained with certainty was made 23 February 1958, and this may also be a new record for the Petén. A sight record dates back to March 1957.

Upperparts are rich, glossy green, with a cerulean blue crown and nape; underparts are yellow-green, clear yellow on the throat and under tail coverts. The bill is conspicuously heavy, black above, blue-gray below; legs are blue-gray.

Its presence is best revealed by its song, sung from February through July. It is very like that of the Tufted Titmouse (*Parus bicolor*), *peer-peer-peer*, the penetrating, whistled notes monotonously repeated every two or three seconds for long periods (Willis, in litt.); also described as a rapid, musical three-noted *cheéur-cheéur-cheéur*, sounding like *cheery*, whistled all on a level pitch (2), (3).

REFERENCES:
(1) Russell 1964, p. 145.   (2) Slud 1964.
(3) Mexican Bird Songs, recordings by L. Irby Davis.

VIREONIDAE

Vireo griseus griseus (Boddaert)

White-eyed Vireo   Vireo Ojo Blanco

E. U. S. and n.e. Mexico (to San Luis Potosí and Hidalgo); winters U. S. to Mexico, Brit. Honduras, Honduras, and Nicaragua

Winter Resident?   5 in.   11 gr.

Uncommon. It was not found at Uaxactún by Van Tyne (1935). It was first recorded at Tikal on 6 and 14 February 1958, again on 18 October 1962, and seems to be rather rare, whereas the much yellower resident race (*V. griseus semiflavus*) is common. It inhabits dense, shrubby undergrowth and young second growth primarily; sometimes adjacent to forest edges.

Upperparts are grayish olive with two pale wing bars and yellow eye spectacles; underparts are mainly white with a wash of pale yellow on the sides and partly on the breast. The bill is black above, gray below; legs are gray; the eyes are clear white. Immatures tend to have even less yellow spectacles and generally duller plumage.

The song, as heard in the north from April through September, is a very characteristic series of about five to seven emphatic, sharply separated, rather musical notes, sometimes written as *chick-a-per-weeoo-chick,* the *weeoo* a long, loud whistle. It sings many variations, but the quality is usually recognizable (1), (2), (3). The alarm note is a short *clinck* (3).

REFERENCES:
(1) Peterson 1960, p. 208, picture in color.
(2) Bent, No. 197.   (3) Saunders 1951.

Vireo griseus semiflavus Salvin
[*Vireo pallens*]

White-eyed Vireo (resident race)   Vireo Manglero
Mangrove Vireo

Trop. Mid. Am. from Yucatán Pen. and Sonora s. to n.w.
  Costa Rica
Resident   4¾ in.   10½ gr.

Common, but localized. Like the northern migrant White-
eye, it is found in thick, shrubby undergrowth, sometimes
mixed with young second growth or near forest edges. At
Tikal it was rarely seen around camp and Aguada Tikal, but
ranged throughout the wetter grounds to the east, at Aguada
Dimick, the brush east of the airfield, along the forest edges
at the milpa beyond the airfield, and most conspicuously in
the low tintal, another mile farther east and beyond the inter-
vening forest, where it was heard often, singing and calling
(between the Aguadas Pucte and Terminos). It seems strange
that no White-eyes of any sort were reported at Uaxactún by
Van Tyne (1935), who collected there from 26 March to 15
May 1931.

While much like *V. griseus griseus,* it is considered by many
as specifically distinct; it seems to be smaller, and is a much
yellower bird; its spectacles are brighter yellow, and it is pale
yellow on the chin and throat, even on wing bars and belly.
Its eyes are not as pure a white; half the birds recorded were
noted as having eyes of a light brown tinge, one of them a
male with gonads very enlarged.

The song as heard at Gallon Jug, British Honduras, is a
repeated nasal *duréé-duree-duree-duree-duree;* the scolding
call is a nasal *d'reeeeeee* (Willis, in litt.). Of two nests found
in British Honduras, one held two eggs, the other three (1).

REFERENCES:
(1) Russell 1964.

Vireo flavifrons Vieillot

Yellow-throated Vireo   Vireo Pecho Amarillo

E. N. Am.; winters through Mid. Am. to Colombia
Transient   5½ in.   17 gr.

Uncommon. It is included on the strength of a sight report made by Howard Rich, of Newton, Massachusetts, on 17 March 1964, who showed it to other members of the party, including Margaret H. Hundley; all agreed that the voice and field marks were perfect for this species. I have found no other record for the Petén.

It inhabits open forest and forest edges; it is also found in shade trees in residential areas, foraging usually well up in the crowns.

About the most brilliantly colored of the vireos, the upperparts are deep olive-green, shading to gray on the rump, the wings and tail dusky; excellent field marks include yellow spectacles, two conspicuous white wing bars, bright yellow on the throat and breast, and a clear white belly.

The song, which may continue during migration (1), is a series of short phrases with pauses between; rather similar to the songs of the Red-eyed Vireo (*V. olivaceus*), but slower, lower in pitch, the notes and phrases all slurred, one into the other (2). Another, perhaps more usual winter call, is a distinctive, harsh, rapidly descending *zhuh-zhuh-zhuh-zhuh-zhuh* (3).

REFERENCES: Peterson 1960, p. 208, 220, pictures in color. Austin 1961, p. 281, picture in color. Murphy and Amadon 1953, plate 133, color photograph (with nest).

(1) Bent, No. 197, p. 284 (Skutch Ms.).
(2) Saunders 1951.   (3) Slud 1964.

These birds have been illustrated together because there is a preponderance of green in their plumage, greens of various shades from slightly green-toned browns to brilliant emerald.

The honeycreepers belong to an exclusively American family. They feed largely on the nectar of flowers, which is carried into the bill through a highly modified tubular tongue. The males of many nectar-feeding birds, such as the honeycreepers and hummingbirds, are brilliantly colored. The two species of honeycreeper illustrated on this plate are no exception.

The shrike-vireos are a small New World family of only three or four species. As the name implies, they resemble both shrikes and vireos. Probably they are related to the vireos rather than to the shrikes.

The manakins are another family of birds restricted to the tropics of the New World. In most species of these small birds the males are brilliantly or conspicuously colored, as in two of the three species shown on this plate. The male manakins display their bright plumages during remarkable courtship dances, in which they hop or fly about in distinctive fashion. Snapping noises are often made with the shafts of the wing feathers, which are thickened in some species. These displays attract mates. The females are then left to build nests and raise the young entirely unaided by the males.

GREEN HONEYCREEPER *p. 232.*

5½ inches. Sexes differ.

MALE: a "bottle green" bird with a jet black crown and cheeks, dusky flight feathers and tail. The bill is long, slightly down-curved, black above, conspicuously yellow below.

FEMALE: emerald green with a yellowish tone below, lacking the black head of the male. The lower bill is more brownish yellow.

IMMATURE MALE: much like adult female but showing some of the male's blue-green plumage with scattered black spots on the head.

RED-LEGGED HONEYCREEPER *p. 233.*

5 inches. Sexes differ greatly.

MALE: conspicuously smalt blue, contrasting with black upper back, wings and tail, and black eye-stripe; crown conspicuous pale turquoise; legs are bright red; wings display canary yellow in flight, seen mainly from below. Bill more slender than Green Honeycreeper's and *all* black.

PLATE 27

GREEN HONEYCREEPER

♂

♀

♂ Immature

♂

GREEN SHRIKE-VIREO

♀

RED-LEGGED HONEYCREEPER

♂

♀

EYE-RINGED FLATBILL

RED-CAPPED MANAKIN

WHITE-COLLARED MANAKIN

♂

♀

THRUSH-LIKE MANAKIN

0   inches   3
0   cms   7

PLATE 27 *(continued)*

FEMALE: green-olive above; green-yellow below with dull olive streaks on throat and breast; flight feathers and tail dark brown; legs dull red-brown.

IMMATURE MALE: not illustrated; similar to female, developing black wings and tail before the blue colors of adult male.

GREEN SHRIKE-VIREO   *p. 222*

5½ inches. Sexes alike; cerulean blue crown and nape, not conspicuous at a distance; upperparts, including wings and tail, bright grass green; underparts yellow on throat and under tail coverts; wings display yellow in flight. Bill is heavy, bulbous below, gray-blue.

RED-CAPPED MANAKIN   *p. 154*

4½ inches. Sexes differ greatly. Note small bill, short tail.

MALE: conspicuous scarlet head, nape, upper back, contrasting with mainly black plumage elsewhere; yellow on chin (and lower bill) and on thighs (displayed in presence of female); wings display pale yellow linings when in flight. Eyes are white (females usually brown). The unique dancing and wing-snapping activities in presence of female should be watched for.

FEMALE: green-olive above, duller than on Red-legged Honeycreeper; underparts dull olive-green becoming yellower on the belly; wings show yellow below in flight. Eyes brown (usually).

IMMATURE MALE: not illustrated, but strikingly like female *even when in breeding condition.* Eyes white (usually).

WHITE-COLLARED MANAKIN   *p. 155*

4¾ inches. Sexes differ greatly.

MALE: pure white across upper back, nape, neck, throat, and breast contrasting sharply with black crown, black wings and tail, and yellow belly; green lower back and rump not conspicuous; legs are bright orange; wings display pale yellow linings in flight. The unique dancing and wing-snapping activities in presence of female should be watched for.

FEMALE: dull green above, brownish on flight feathers; greenish on throat and breast, streaked with dusky, the lower breast and belly yellow-green (almost lemon yellow); legs bright orange similar to male.

PLATE 27 *(continued)*

EYE-RINGED FLATBILL (flycatcher)   *p. 190*

6 inches. Sexes alike; upperparts green-olive; underparts similar but paling to yellow on belly and under tail coverts eyes are brown surrounded by white eye-ring, conspicuously big-eyed; bill is notably broad and flat.

THRUSH-LIKE MANAKIN   *p. 156*

6½ inches. Sexes alike; the largest and brownest bird of this group, but still has greenish tone both above and below, palest on the chin and on under tail coverts. Tail feathers and flight feathers are edged rusty brown.

PLATE 28

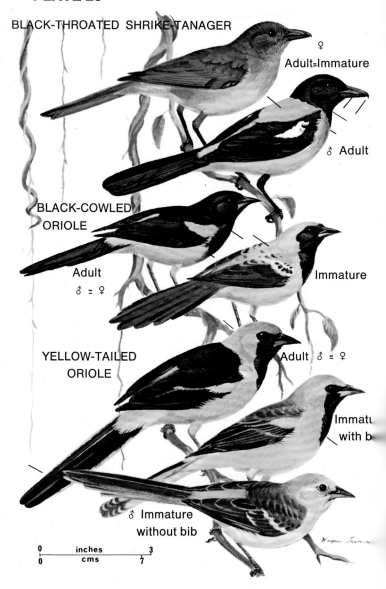

BLACK-THROATED SHRIKE-TANAGER

♀ Adult=Immature

♂ Adult

BLACK-COWLED
ORIOLE

Adult

♂ = ♀

Immature

YELLOW-TAILED
ORIOLE

Adult ♂ = ♀

Immature
with b

♂ Immature
without bib

0   inches   3
0   cms   7

BLACK-THROATED SHRIKE-TANAGER

p. 281.

8 inches. Sexes differ materially, but both have very large non-oriole-like bills, all-black, strongly hooked at the tip, and with a "tooth" at the middle of the upper bill (this last not obvious from a distance).

ADULT MALE: in addition to the diagnostic bill, the all-black head distinguishes it from the orioles, except the Black-cowled and the Baltimore, but note its yellow back. The black throat has a brown crescent below it, similar to that of the Black-cowled Oriole, but the latter has an *extensive* black bib. The rump and underparts are yellow. The wing has a white patch near the shoulder (usually yellow on orioles).

ADULT FEMALE: dull-plumaged, with grayish head, brownish back and tail, olive (orange-tinged) rump, yellowish underparts. Immature much like female, but male may be more confusing when approaching adult plumage.

BLACK-COWLED ORIOLE

p. 266.

7½ inches. Sexes alike, immature differs.

ADULT: black on head, neck, upper back, throat, extensive chest bib, and tail; black wing has bright yellow epaulet; lower back, rump, rest of underparts bright yellow except for brown crescent below the black bib.

IMMATURE: we frequently found them much like adults except for very yellowish upper backs. Younger birds have yellow also on crown and nape and neck, retaining a black facial mask similar to many other orioles. The yellow is pale with a greenish tinge.

Superficially similar Orange Orioles are much more brilliantly plumaged; Yellow-backed Orioles are also more colorful and in addition are decidedly larger (about 9 inches long).

YELLOW-TAILED ORIOLE

p. 268.

8½ inches. Sexes alike, immature differs; a large oriole, with a slow labored flight; the tail is pumped up and down.

ADULT: conspicuously yellow outer tail feathers on black tail, appearing all yellow from below; crown and nape rich orange-yellow; lower back, rump, breast, and belly bright yellow; black on wings with yellow patch, and black facial area and bib.

IMMATURE: patterned like adult, but much duller yellows, the black tinged with olive. Some, of both sexes, *lack the black face and bib,* and have horn instead of gray on lower bill.

Vireo olivaceus olivaceus (Linnaeus)
[*Vireo olivaceus*—AOU 1957]

Red-eyed Vireo　　　　　　　　　Vireo de Ojo Rojo

N. Am. and n. Mexico (n.e. Coahuila); migrates through
　Mid. Am.; winters in n. S. Am.
Transient　　　　6 in.　　　　17 gr.

Common in migration. Early arrivals in the fall overlap—
for a short time only—the departures of the resident race, the
Yellow-green Vireo (*V. o. flavoviridis*). It is of interest to
report that one individual of each race was taken on the same
day and in the same place: 7 August 1959 at Aguada Dimick.
In the late summer of 1962 all specimens taken after 14
September were Red-eyed Vireos and no Yellow-green singers
had been in evidence even during the previous thirty days.
We have no clear evidence of a similar overlap in the spring,
but sight records indicate that both races are present by (or
before) the middle of March. By the middle of April the
Red-eyed Vireo seems to be absent and the Yellow-green is
busily singing; all specimens taken from 16 May to 7 August
1959 (with the exception of the one individual noted above)
were Yellow-green Vireos.

It is usually found near openings in the forest, in tall but
light forest and forest borders, and in fairly open country
well supplied with scattered trees, where it forages well above
ground, hidden by the foliage.

It is olive-green above (yellow-green on the resident race),
with a clear gray cap; a white stripe above the eye, bordered
above by a sharp black, is a good field mark (both are much
duller on the resident race); underparts are mostly white
(strongly washed with pale yellow on the Yellow-green resident). The bill is black above, gray below; legs are bluish
gray; eyes are bright red (the resident race sometimes is
brownish red). The mouth lining is pinkish.

It is usually silent during migration, but may begin to sing
during its return to the north; there it sings short abrupt
phrases separated by deliberate pauses, sounding like an
upward-inflected question followed by a downward-inflected

response, and frequently repeated throughout the day. It also utters a nasal, whining *chway* (1).

REFERENCES: Blake 1953, p. 452, picture in black and white. (1) Peterson 1960, p. 208, picture in color. Austin 1961, p. 281, picture in color. Murphy and Amadon 1953, plate 132, color photograph (with nest).

Vireo olivaceus flavoviridis (Cassin)
[*Vireo flavoviridis*–AOU 1957]

Yellow-green Vireo   Vireo Cabeza Gris

Texas and Mid. Am.; winters in n. S. Am.
Summer Resident   6½ in.   18 gr.

Common. This is one of the few species breeding in Central America and wintering in South America. It arrives in the Petén early in April and departs by the end of September. Here in Tikal it has not been noted before the middle of March and may depart before the middle of August. (See notes on Red-eyed Vireo, *V. o. olivaceus*.) It is of interest to recall that Van Tyne (1935) found neither of these two closely related vireos during his work at nearby Uaxactún, from 26 March to 15 May 1931.

It is found in light, thinned-out forest, in open country with scattered shady trees, in coffee plantations which combine shrubs and shade trees, and in the proximity of habitations with shrubs and trees, where it forages at lower levels than does the substantially smaller Red-eyed Vireo.

For plumage differences see the notes on the Red-eye.

The song also resembles the Red-eye's, but is still distinctive. It is given less clearly, and uses shorter phrases with appreciably longer pauses between them; a series of liquid, two-syllable notes is occasionally interrupted by a sharp single syllable, as in *viree-viree-viree-fée-viree-viree-vireo*. It also utters a scolding, high-pitched, nasal *chaaa* (1).

The nest is a deep cup hung in a horizontal fork near the end of a slender branch in a bush or tree, usually well concealed by surrounding foliage. Most often it is only six to twelve feet above ground, but may occur forty feet up. Two, more frequently three eggs are deposited, white, lightly marked with brown spots.

REFERENCES: Peterson 1960, p. 208, picture in color.
(1) P.C.A. 34:11–28, life history (Skutch); p. 13, picture in black and white.

Vireo philadelphicus (Cassin)

Philadelphia Vireo   Vireo Gris-oliva

E. N. Am.; winters in Mid. Am. to w. Panama
Transient   5 in.   12 gr.

Uncommon, perhaps rare. Only one individual has been found, taken in a mist net near camp on 23 October 1962; probably a new record for the Petén. Many Tennessee Warblers (*Vermivora peregrina*) were feeding close by, in a Cedrillo (*Guarea excelsa*).

It occurs in thinned woodlands, young second growth, and open areas mixed with thickets and scattered trees, where it forages both high and low.

It is grayish olive-green above, grayest on the crown, with an obscure white line above the eye and a dusky streak through the eye (similar to the facial marks of a fall Tennessee Warbler); underparts are mainly pale yellow with a greenish tone, lightest on the belly (the fall Tennessee Warbler is mostly white below, with some pale yellow on the sides).

Usually silent during migration.

REFERENCES: Peterson 1960, pp. 208, 221, pictures in color.

Hylophilus ochraceiceps ochraceiceps Sclater

Tawny-crowned Greenlet   Pajarito de Corona Ocre

Trop. Mid. Am. (except El Salvador) and S. Am.
Resident   4¼ in.   11 gr.   Plate 25

Common and rather numerous. It is found mainly in the shaded undergrowth of the forest, where it forages at only moderate heights, along with other small forest birds.

This "greenlet" is not green at all (see illustration). It is rich olive-brown above, shading to russet on the tail and to a golden tawny color on the crown; underparts are gray on the throat, ochre tawny on the breast, yellowish olive on the belly. There is a dark brown patch at the base of the primaries and a bit of yellow at the bend of the wing which help to distinguish it from the somewhat similar *female,* Plain Antvireo (*Dysithamnus mentalis*). The bill (heavier on the antvireo) is long and slender, dark above, gray below; legs are ruddy; eyes white (some with yellowish tone).

Its presence may be revealed by an incessantly repeated loud, rather harsh, nasal, one-syllable note, as *doy-doy-doy.* It seems not to have a genuine song (1). However, various other notes have been described, too numerous to include here (2).

The nest is a sturdy open cup, hung in the fork of a horizontal branchlet, partly concealed by the overhanging foliage, and ranging from six to twenty-five feet above ground. It is composed of seed-down and plant fibers, held together with cobweb. Two eggs are deposited; their color and marks seem not to have been described (1).

REFERENCES:
(1) P.C.A. 34:35–38, life history (Skutch); p. 36, picture in black and white.
(2) Slud 1964.

Hylophilus decurtatus decurtatus (Bonaparte)

Gray-headed Greenlet   Pajarito Cabeza Gris

Trop. Mid. Am. to cent. Panama
Resident   4 in.   8½ gr.   Plate 25

Common and rather numerous. It is found within the forest where it forages high and is difficult to see, but seems more numerous at lower levels in the young trees and shrubs bordering the roads and trails, and in thinned-out parts of the woods. Away from Tikal it is also found in shaded coffee fincas and pastures.

The general effect is of a perky, short-tailed, bright gray, little bird, with a white eye-ring. Upperparts are bright olive-green, with a gray crown and nape; underparts are grayish white, lightest on the belly, but with a wash of pale yellow on the sides and clear yellow below the tail. The bill is black above, gray below, sometimes light brown; legs are gray; eyes brown.

The voice is soft, clear, and melodious, but so weak that it is easily overpowered by other singers; a somewhat chirping phrase is written *chichi-cher cher cher cher chichi-cher* (1). A common and distinctive utterance is a harsh *chchrch-chchrch-chchrch* (2); other calls are described by Eisenmann (3).

The nest is a deep, pouch-like cup hanging down about four inches (more than twelve inches, per Hundley, in litt.) between the forks of a branchlet, located some fifteen feet above ground. It is composed largely of dead leaves bound together with fibers and much cobweb. Two eggs are deposited, white, spotted and blotched with pale brown (1).

REFERENCES:
(1) P.C.A. 34:29–34, life history (Skutch); p. 30, picture in black and white. Austin 1961, p. 282, picture in color.
(2) Slud 1964.
(3) Condor 59:4:256, voice (Eisenmann).

COEREBIDAE

Chlorophanes spiza guatemalensis Sclater

Green Honeycreeper   Pajarito Verde
                                          Chipe Gorrión Verde

Trop. Mid. Am. (except El Salvador) from Chiapas to S. Am.
Resident   5½ in.   21 gr.   Plate 27

Uncommon. An individual was collected on 8 October 1962, when it was feeding from ten to thirty feet up in trees bordering the main road, west of Aguada Tikal. It frequents the tops of flowering trees in the humid forest, the forest edges, thickets, and openings; also clearings with scattered trees and shrubs. It feeds on fruits, both soft and hard, as well as insects.

The male is bright glossy bluish "bottle green," all over except the head, which is black on the crown and face. The female lacks the black on the head, is yellow-green above, and still more yellow below. Immature males also lack black head-color. The long, sharp, decurved bill is mostly black above, bright yellow below; legs are gray with a greenish tone, eyes are red or red-brown. The mouth lining is yellow.

About the only utterances are warbler-like *chips* (1), or tirelessly repeated *tsip*'s, rapidly given (2), or a short, nasal grunt, *uhr* (3).

The nest is a shallow, open cup, built on a thick base of dry leaves, located from ten to thirty feet up in well-foliaged trees. Two eggs are deposited, white, with a wreath of brown spots at the large end (1).

REFERENCES:
(1) Condor 64:2:92–98, life history (Skutch). K. de Phelps 1953, p. 66, picture in color.
(2) Slud 1964.   (3) Eisenmann 1953.

Cyanerpes cyaneus carneipes (Sclater)

Red-legged Honeycreeper   Chipe Gorrión Azul

Trop. Mid. Am., S. Am., and Cuba
Resident   5 in.   13 gr.   Plate 27

Common. It forages, often in small bands, through the crowns of forest trees and in the company of other small birds; also found in forest edges, thinned woodland, and in open country if supplied with tall shady trees (as in coffee fincas). It occasionally comes down to moderate levels in the trees around Aguada Tikal.

To some it is better known as the Blue Honeycreeper.

The male is a rich, shining, blue-violet above and below, strongly accented by a turquoise crown, jet black wings and tail, and bright red legs. In flight, the wings show brilliant flashes of canary yellow. The female is olive-green above with dull brown wings and tail, a dark line through the eye (a pale one above it), dull greenish yellow underparts, and obscure breast streaks. Her legs are red-brown. Bills, long, slender, down-curved, are jet black, eyes very dark brown. The male goes through a molt, when its blue plumage becomes largely green, as is the case with immatures, which then look like the dull-plumaged females.

The song is a simple, unmusical series of clear but rather weak notes, as *tsip-tsip,* sometimes interrupted by a thin mewing *chaaa,* which is also the more frequently heard call note (1).

The nest is a slight, open, shallow cup, located ten to forty-five feet up in a bush or tree. It is made of plant fibers, rootlets, and grasses, held together and to the supporting branchlet with cobweb. Two white eggs are deposited, speckled with brown (1).

REFERENCES: Blake 1953, p. 458, pictures in black and white. Austin 1961, p. 294, picture in color. Bond 1961, plate 7, pictures in color (male and female, Cuban race).

(1) P.C.A. 31:387–403, life history (Skutch); p. 388, pictures in black and white. Condor 64:2:106–111, additional history (Skutch).

Coereba flaveola mexicana (Sclater)

Bananaquit
Pajarito Amarillo
Reinita Amarilla

Bahamas, West Indies, trop. Mid. Am. (not reported El Salvador), and S. Am., casual in Fla.

Visitor?   4¼ in.   9 gr.   Plate 26

Uncommon, perhaps rare. It was first seen on 22 September 1962, feeding with two or three others of its kind, together with warblers, vireos, and euphonias, in the trees bordering the road west of Aguada Tikal. It has been reported only once before, at Remate, 10 August 1923 (Van Tyne 1935).

It frequents humid forests if not too extensive and solid, forest edges, thinned woods, and many varieties of open country, often adjacent to habitations.

It is patterned (in miniature) like some of the very much larger flycatchers (see the Kiskadee); dark gray and blackish above, bright yellow below; a gray throat and chest, and a very conspicuous white stripe over the eye. A small white patch on the wing is rather conspicuous. The rump is dingy yellow, the belly dingy white. The bill is needle-sharp, down-curved, and black; legs are dark gray; eyes are dark brown.

Throughout the year it persistently sings a wheezy little trill, high-pitched and buzzy, almost insect-like in thinness and lack of volume (1).

The nest differs from that of every other Central American bird (1). It is a thick-walled, closed globe, not pensile, but built on some branch or cluster with a little, round, downward-facing opening at one side. The sitting bird faces the opening. The nest is located both high and low in trees or shrubs. Usually two eggs are deposited, dull white and spotted with brown (1).

REFERENCES:
(1) P.C.A. 31:404–420, life history (Skutch); p. 405, picture in black and white. Gilliard 1958, plate 191, color photograph (with nest).

PARULIDAE

Mniotilta varia (Linnaeus)

Black-and-white Warbler   Pepino
                                       Chipe Rayado

E. N. Am.; winters through Mid. Am. to n. S. Am.
Winter Resident   5 in.   10 gr. (8 to 13)

Fairly common. It has been recorded as early as 31 August in the fall, as late as 7 April in spring, and some probably remain through the winter. It is found in trees at moderate heights throughout the forest where not too extensive or dense, and in light undergrowth. It creeps *up* tree trunks (never down) and along branches (sometimes even on the under-side), foraging for insects.

It is striped black and white above and below, including a broad white central crown stripe; the belly, however, is pure white. The female lacks most of the stripes on the underparts. Spring birds weighed less (8.0 to 9.5 gr.) than fall birds (10.2 to 13.2 gr.).

It is practically silent; the northern song is a thin, insect-like *wee-see wee-see,* given repeatedly seven or more times.

REFERENCES: Peterson 1960, p. 212, picture in color. Dick 1957, plate 2, pictures in color.

Protonotaria citrea (Boddaert)

Prothonotary Warbler   Chipe

S.e. U. S.; recorded from Mexico (Yucatán Pen. and Cozumel I.), Guatemala, Brit. Honduras, Honduras; winters in Nicaragua, Costa Rica, Panama, and n. S. Am.
Transient   5½ in.   12 gr. (9.5 to 15.5)

Uncommon. It was first seen on 27 August 1962, foraging slowly and deliberately both on the ground and in low, thinned undergrowth at Aguada Tikal. Positive records were obtained in September and October, but none in the spring. It is primarily a bird of moist woods, near slow streams and swamps.

The entire head, nape, and breast are golden yellow, the head with an orange tone in spring; the back is yellow-green, the wings gray with a bluish tone in spring; the tail is dark gray disclosing white inner webs on the outside feathers when spread. The female is duller, and the olive-green tone of the back extends into the crown.

It is practically silent; in the north it voices a series of simple, emphatic, whistling notes, all on the same high pitch, as *tweet-tweet-tweet-tweet-tweet.*

REFERENCES: Peterson 1960, pp. 213, 221, pictures in color. Dick 1957, plate 1, pictures in color. Murphy and Amadon 1953, plate 160, color photograph (with nest hole).

Helmitheros vermivorus (Gmelin)

Worm-eating Warbler   Chipe Come Gusano
                                       Pulgonero

E. U. S.; winters in Mid. Am. to e. Panama
Transient   5½ in.   12½ gr. (11 to 14)

Not uncommon. It was first recorded on 20 March 1957; on 17 March 1963, five were reported in one day. The earliest fall record is 20 September.

It is found in woodlands and undergrowth, preferably not far from water; largely but not exclusively terrestrial, it forages in a deliberate manner, much like an Ovenbird (*Seiurus aurocapillus*).

It is mostly dull olive-green above, conspicuously marked with bold black stripes on the buff head; underparts are rich buff, palest on the throat and belly.

Here it seems to be silent; its northern song is a thin, buzzy, insect-like, long-continued trill, as

trrrrrrrrrrrrrrrrrrrr

REFERENCES: Peterson 1960, p. 209, picture in color. Dick 1957, plate 2, picture in color.

Vermivora pinus (Linnaeus)

Blue-winged Warbler   Chipe
                                       Gusanero Aliazul

E. U. S.; winters s.e. Mexico, Guatemala, Brit. Honduras, Honduras, e. Nicaragua, Costa Rica, Panama, and casually to Colombia
Transient   4½ in.   9 gr.

Uncommon. It was first recorded 2 October 1962; has not been seen in the winter or spring. It is found in woodland openings, in brushy borders, and in open situations which are overgrown with weedy plants and shrubs, where it forages rather deliberately from the ground up to moderate heights.

It is a bright yellow little warbler with gray or blue-gray

wings; the wings have two white bars, the yellow face has a sharp, narrow, black stripe through the eye. The back is greenish or bright olive-green; the inner webs of the tail feathers are extensively white, seen only when the tail is spread.

In migration it sometimes utters a squeaky *skwik* (1). Its northern song has a wheezy, insect-like quality and has been described as an "inhaled and exhaled" *beeee-bzzz*.

REFERENCES: Peterson 1960, p. 213, picture in color. Dick 1957, plate 4, pictures in color. Wilson Bull. 63:1:fpc., pictures in color (includes hybrids); pp. 5–15, discussion of hybrids (Parkes). Gilliard 1958, plate 188, color photograph (with nest).
(1) Slud 1964.

Vermivora peregrina (Wilson)

Tennessee Warbler   Chipe de Tennessee
                                         Gusanero Verdillo

E. N. Am.; winters Mid. Am. to n. S. Am.
Winter Resident   4½ in.   9¼ gr.

Common, both spring and fall. It was first recorded 22 February 1958, has been seen as late as 28 March and as early as 22 September. Early in October 1962 a flock of more than twenty were observed feeding in a Cedrillo (*Guarea excelsa*), together with bananaquits, vireos, and euphonias.

In migration it is found in a wide variety of habitat (except extensive, heavy forest), foraging at all levels, from low shrubs to high in tall trees.

The male in spring plumage has a gray head with a clear white stripe above the eye, greenish upperparts with dusky wings and tail, and plain white underparts. In the autumn the gray is tinged with olive-green like the back, the white becomes tinged with pale yellow. The female and immatures are even duller, less contrasting, the head and back more uniformly greenish, the stripe over the eye yellowish, the underparts dingy yellow. Fall birds often develop a single obscure pale bar on the wing.

Migrants frequently repeat weak chirps, as *tsit* (1). The northern song, also heard occasionally during migration, is a long series of loud, staccato notes, loudest at the end; one example is: *tizip-tizip-tizip-tizip-tizip-tizip, zitzitzitzit, zizizizizi* (2).

REFERENCES:
(1) Slud 1964.
(2) Peterson 1960, pp. 209, 221, pictures in color. Dick 1957, plate 6, pictures in color.

Dendroica petechia subsp.

Yellow Warbler   Chipe Amarillo

N. Am., n. and cent. Mexico, West Indies, coasts of Mid. Am. and n. S. Am., to Peru and Galápagos Islands. Some authors consider tropical and West Indies birds separate species and call the northern group *D. aestiva*.

Transient   5 in.   9½ gr.

Fairly common. It was first recorded 19 February 1958, since when it has been noted as late as 28 March, and as early in autumn as 18 September. A series of seven specimens was taken during September and October 1962, which included two or more "races."

It avoids extensive heavy forest, usually inhabiting thickets and shrubs, especially when close to water. The park-like grounds and roads near Aguada Tikal seem to attract it, as they do numerous other species.

It is nearly all bright yellow, with a slightly greenish tone on the upperparts, the dusky wings brightened by yellowish margins and the dusky tail with diagnostic yellow spots which are visible when spread; the breast and sides are streaked with chestnut red, (obscure on fall birds and sometimes lacking on females). The immature Alaska Yellow Warbler (*D. p. rubiginosa*) may be very greenish; shades of yellow are quite variable in other subspecies, but the yellow tail spots are still present.

All Yellow Warblers taken at Tikal were migrants from

North America, mainly the northeastern race *D. p. aestiva,* possibly one of the Alaskan *rubiginosa;* other migrant sub-species may occur, but separating migrants at Tikal, especially in full plumage, is usually not practical.

Migrants regularly utter a strong *chip,* or weak *tsit*'s, or a still weaker *tsint* (2), (4). The northern song (which may be given in winter also) is a musical, clear, sibilant whistle, very cheery, described as: *tsee-tsee-tsee-tsee, ti-ti, wee;* another variation is: *weet-weet-weet-weet, tsee, tsee, tsay,* which falls down the scale at the end (1), (3).

REFERENCES:
(1) Peterson 1960, pp. 213, 220, pictures in color. Dick 1957, plate 10, pictures in color.
(2) Slud 1964.   (3) Saunders 1951.
(4) Bent, No. 203, pp. 176–178 (Skutch Ms.).

Dendroica magnolia (Wilson)

Magnolia Warbler   Chipe
                                        Chipe Pechirayado

N. Am.; winters through Mid. Am. to cent. Panama
Winter Resident   4½ in.   8½ gr.

Fairly common. It was first noted on 10 March 1957; since then it has been recorded as late as 8 May (collected), and as early as 12 October. It is found here in semi-open areas, along the wider roads, at milpas and such places, where it forages among plants, small trees, and shrubs at low levels.

Above it is blackish and white, with a gray head, a yellow rump, and a broad white band midway across the black tail; below it is yellow with a white belly, and heavy black streaks down the breast and sides. The face has a dark cheek with a white line above it. In the fall the breast streaks are mostly lacking, the black upperparts acquire a greenish tone, but the wide white tail-band remains. From below, the tail appears all white except for the black terminal band; frequently fanned open and displayed, in the fashion of the American Redstart (*Setophaga ruticilla*).

It utters an arresting metallic call note while migrating (2). The northern song has either a rising last note, as

weeteé,   wheeta-wheeta   weeto

wheeta-wheeta /   or a falling   (1).

REFERENCES:

(1) Peterson 1960, pp. 212, 220, pictures in color. Dick 1957, plate 11, pictures in color. Austin 1961, p. 286, picture in color. Murphy and Amadon 1953, plate 161, color photograph (with nest).   (2) Slud 1964.

Dendroica coronata coronata (Linnaeus)

Myrtle Warbler   Chipe Coronado

N. N. Am.; winters from U. S. through Mid. Am., casually
   to Colombia
Winter Resident   5½ in.   11 gr. (9 to 13)

Common. It was first noted on 15 March 1957; this is a new record for the Petén, strangely enough in view of its present obvious prevalence. It arrives late in the fall and was not seen in 1962 until 27 October, when six individuals suddenly appeared. Records of 16 December and 6 February confirm its status as a winter visitant. It feeds on the lawns, and in shrubs and low trees throughout the camp and village grounds.

In all plumages the bright yellow rump and the white throat, taken together, are distinctive field marks.

It also has a yellow crown-patch and yellow at the sides of the breast, brighter in spring than in autumn. In spring the male is blue-gray above with black streaks, the female brownish; the wing has two white wing bars; the dark tail has partly concealed white spots near the tips of the three outer feathers; underparts are white (dingy in fall), the male with an inverted black chest crescent which streaks on down each side, the female with fewer and somewhat lighter streaks. Immature birds and fall-plumaged adults are brown and sparrow-like.

During migration it may sing a jumbled series of about a

dozen notes, rapid, weak, and varying irregularly in pitch
(1). On its wintering grounds it gives its call note, a loud,
harsh, distinctive *tchip* (1), (2).

REFERENCES: Peterson 1960, pp. 212, 220, pictures in color.
Dick 1957, plate 14, pictures in color.
(1) Pough 1953.   (2) Slud 1964.

* *Dendroica townsendi* (Townsend)

Townsend's Warbler   Chipe

Mts. n.w. N. Am.; winters to Mexico, Guatemala, El Salvador,
Honduras, Nicaragua
Accidental?, Transient   4½ in.

Rare. It is included on the strength of two sight reports,
one on 28 March 1960, the other on 17 March 1964. The latter
is credited to C. Russell Mason, Director of the Florida Audubon Society, who saw an individual bird near the Jungle
Lodge, "at close range for several minutes."

The male is distinguished by a black crown, cheek, throat,
and upper chest, patterned against a yellow ground-color (including a yellow breast). The female has yellow, not black,
on the throat and chest, replaces the other black markings of
the male with a greenish gray pattern, but the dark cheek
patch is still a distinctive mark. Both sexes are otherwise more
or less streaked on the sides, the upperparts yellowish olive-
green, the belly white. Fall and immature plumages tend to
brownish and obscure markings.

REFERENCES: Peterson 1960, p. 224, pictures in color. Dick
1957, plate 16, pictures in color. Bent, No. 203, p. 288, winter
residents in Guatemala (Skutch Ms.).

Dendroica virens virens (Gmelin)

Black-throated Green Warbler   Chipe Garganta Negro

E. N. Am.; winters through Mid. Am. to Colombia
Winter Resident   4½ in.   8 gr.

Uncommon. It was first seen on 12 March 1957. One individual, collected on 8 February, tends to confirm it as a visi-

tant, although it usually winters at higher elevations. I found none in the fall of 1962 although I watched for it until 27 October, which indicates that it may arrive even later than the Myrtle Warblers. It is usually found in tall trees in the forest, but also in clearings supplied with scattered trees and shrubs where it sometimes forages at much lower levels.

The male in spring plumage is clearly marked: bright olive-green above, with two white wing bars; a bright lemon yellow face, bordered below by a solid black throat and chest; white breast and belly with black streaks down the sides. The tail, blackish above, appears largely white from below. Females and immatures are duller, lack most all of the black throat and chest, and instead may have a wash of pale yellow; they still retain the yellow-cheek effect.

It is rather limited in winter to a call note, *tsick,* but may on occasion be heard to voice its northern song, one of the sweetest, most musical, and distinctive, of a drowsy quality; *zee-zee-zee-zoo-zee* is one variation which has been phrased as "trees, trees, murmuring trees" (1), (2).

REFERENCES:
(1) Peterson 1960, pp. 212, 220, pictures in color. Dick 1957, plate 18, pictures in color. Murphy and Amadon 1953, plate 152, color photograph (with nest).
(2) Bent, No. 203, pp. 302–304, migrants described (Skutch Ms.).

Dendroica cerulea (Wilson)

Cerulean Warbler Chipe Ceruléo

E. N. Am.; migrates through Mid. Am. (unrecorded El Salvador); winters in n. S. Am.
Transient 4½ in. 9 gr.

Rare. Only one has been seen, a male collected on 29 September 1962. It was foraging in the low, heavily foliaged orange trees close by Aguada Tikal. It usually inhabits open woodlands and tall trees within swamps or rich bottomlands where, foraging high, it is difficult to observe.

The male is a bland, pale blue above, the back streaked with black, the dusky wings with two white bars; below it is white with a distinctive *narrow* band of black across the chest. The female lacks the chest band and the black streaks but retains the wing bars; upperparts are more grayish blue and greenish, underparts dingy white or tinged pale yellow on the breast; there is a distinctive white stripe above the eye.

The winter note is a kissing *tsip* (3). The song is a series of even-pitched *zray*'s followed by a higher pitched trill, as *zreeeee* (1), (2).

REFERENCES:
(1) Peterson 1960, p. 209, pictures in color. Dick 1957, plate 17, pictures in color.
(2) Saunders 1951.   (3) Slud 1964.

Dendroica fusca (Muller)

Blackburnian Warbler   Chipe Garganta Anaranjada

E. N. Am.; migrates through Mid. Am., winters from Costa Rica to n.w. S. Am.
Transient   5 in.   10½ gr.

Uncommon, perhaps rare. A male in spring plumage was seen on 30 March 1956 near Aguada Tikal. None were again reported until 21 September 1962, when two were taken together during an impressive "wave" of arrivals of a variety of species, which continued from the twentieth to the twenty-fourth. It is usually found in coniferous forests, but also inhabits mixed forest, forest edges, and scattered tall trees.

The male is characterized by its flaming orange and black patterned head and brilliant burnt-orange throat and chest; some of the rich color is retained even in the fall. Upperparts are black with white stripes on the back and a wide patch of white on the wings; the breast and belly are pale yellow with black side streaks. The female retains some of the orange on the throat, the rest replaced by deep yellow; upperparts are more greenish, with white streaks and the male's white wing patch is separated into two white bars. The immatures and some fall-plumaged adults, are decidedly duller, brownish above, but still retain yellow throats, white streaks on the back, and white wing bars.

Its usual winter note is like its call note, *tseek;* it may occasionally give one of its northern songs, such as a two-toned

| zip | zip | zip | zip |
| tzi | tzi | tzi | tzi |

followed by a wiry, very high-pitched *ze-ze-ze-ze-ze,* inaudible to some ears (1), (2).

REFERENCES:
(1) Peterson 1960, pp. 209, 220, pictures in color. Dick 1957, plate 17, pictures in color. Gilliard 1958, plate 189, color photograph (with nest).
(2) Saunders 1951.

Dendroica pensylvanica (Linnaeus)

Chestnut-sided Warbler   Chipe

E. N. Am.; migrates through Mid. Am. (unrecorded El Salvador); winters Honduras and Nicaragua through Panama, recorded in Colombia and Venezuela

Transient   5 in.   9½ gr.

Fairly common. It was first seen on 6 February 1958, when a female still in winter plumage was collected. This early date may indicate visitants here as well as transients. Another was taken on 14 February. In the fall of 1962 the earliest notation was made on 13 September. It avoids the high forest except near the edges, and is usually found among medium-sized trees, shrubs, and brushy cover.

In its spring plumage it is readily identified by the yellow, black-bordered crown, solid chestnut sides, and white underparts. Upperparts are yellow-green with numerous black streaks and two yellow wing bars; the sides of the neck are white. Fall plumages and especially immatures are very nondescript. Then the lemon-colored shade of green above, a small white eye-ring, two yellow wing bars and dingy white underparts are marks to look for. Adults may still retain some chestnut.

In winter it frequently utters a sharp *chip,* like its call note *tsick.* It may sing also, especially when migrating north (2). Its song then is loud, not unmusical, but chatter-like, beginning with a half dozen or so two-note phrases at a moderate pitch, followed by a very high-pitched note and a final low-pitched note, dropping abruptly. It has been phrased "I wish, to see, Miss Beecher," the Beecher emphatic (1), (3).

REFERENCES:
(1) Peterson 1960, pp. 212, 220, pictures in color. Dick 1957, plate 20, pictures in color. Gilliard 1958, plate 184, color photograph (with nest).
(2) Slud 1964.   (3) Saunders 1951.

Seiurus aurocapillus (Linnaeus)

Ovenbird   Chipe-tordo

E. N. Am.; winters through Mid. Am. to Colombia and Venezuela
Winter Resident   6 in.   20 gr.

Fairly common. First recorded on 3 April 1957, it has been seen as early as 19 February, and 23 September in autumn. It may winter here. It is usually found in moist forest understory, walking deliberately over the ground under the cover of light or moderately heavy brush.

It resembles a small thrush rather than a warbler. Upperparts are olive-brown, the head with a conspicuous black-bordered, brown-orange crown, and a pale eye-ring; underparts are pale buff on the breast, nearly white on the throat and belly, the breast and sides boldly streaked with black. Legs are pink or reddish brown.

In migration it is limited to its call note, a sharp *tsick* (2).

The northern song sounds like a series of two-syllable phrases, *teach-er-teach-er-teach-er,* louder with each repetition, a most diagnostic crescendo (1).

REFERENCES:
(1) Peterson 1960, p. 209, picture in color. Dick 1957, plate 23, picture in color. Murphy and Amadon 1953, plate 165, color photograph (with nest).
(2) Slud 1964.

SPECIAL NOTE

The three waterthrushes at Tikal are so similar in appearance that a direct comparison of their field marks may be more useful than three separate descriptions. In the following outline therefore:

"A" refers to *Seiurus noveboracencis noveboracensis*
    (eastern race)
"B" refers to *Seiurus noveboracencis notabilis*
    (Grinnell's)
"C" refers to *Seiurus motacilla* (Louisiana Waterthrush)

Upperparts are, A, brownish olive; B, the same; C, grayish olive in tone.

The conspicuous light-colored stripe above the eye is, A, yellowish or buffy yellow; B, paler yellow, or nearly white; C, pure white.

The chin and throat are, A, narrowly streaked with black; B, the same; C, clear unspotted white, except for a single, thin, whisker-like stripe each side of the throat.

Underparts are, A, pale yellow or buff; B, paler yellow, often nearly white; C, usually white, but it still has a buffy tinge at the sides.

The breast and belly are, A, heavily streaked with black, except for a *narrow* clear area down the middle; B, the same; C, more lightly streaked with brown, with a *broad* middle area clear, especially on the belly.

In size, A is the smallest, B is only slightly larger, C is definitely the largest.

* *Seiurus noveboracensis noveboracensis* (Gmelin)

Northern Waterthrush   Chipe de Agua
(Small-billed, eastern race)   Chipe Tordo

N. N. Am.; winters in West Indies, through Mid. Am. and
   n. S. Am.
Transient?   5½ in.   17 gr.

Rare. It is included here because so many sight records
have been ascribed to this *race* that it is difficult to believe it
is not present at all. However, not a single one of the dozen
or so waterthrushes collected, in both spring and fall, has
proven to be *S. n. noveboracensis;* nor did Van Tyne (1935)
find any at Uaxactún. All were the race *notabilis,* or else the
species *S. motacilla.*

Like all waterthrushes, it looks more like a small thrush
than a warbler, and also bears a close resemblance to the
spotted sandpiper because of its habit of constantly teetering
as it walks over the ground. For details of field marks see
SPECIAL NOTE on preceding page.

Its alarm note continues in winter, a loud *tsick*. Its northern
song is not likely to be heard: a vigorous, rapid series as
twit-twit-twit, twee-twee-twee, chew, chew, chew, falling in
pitch at the end (1), (2).

REFERENCES:
(1) Peterson 1960, p. 209, picture in color. Murphy and Amadon 1953, plate 163, color photograph.
(2) Slud 1964.

Seiurus noveboracensis notabilis Ridgway

Northern Waterthrush   Chipe de Agua
(Grinnell's, northwestern race)   Chipe Tordo

N. N. Am.; winters in West Indies, through Mid. Am. and
   n. S. Am.
Winter Resident   5½ in.   17 gr. (13¼ to 19)

Fairly common. It has been recorded as late as 8 May in
the spring, returning as early as 10 August in 1959, but not

until 17 September in 1962. The earliest wintering date, probably due to a lack of observers, is 5 February.

It is usually found in wooded swamps and along the edges of sluggish streams. In Tikal it is present at most any aguada rather than on the steep roads up to the ridges, along which the Louisiana Waterthrush (*S. motacilla*) seemed more prevalent. This pale race of the Northern Waterthrush rather closely resembles the Louisiana, and is distinguished from it by its smaller size, its streaked throat, and its song (which is no help at Tikal). Their call notes are much the same, a loud *tsick*. See *S. n. noveboracensis* for comparisons and references.

Seiurus motacilla (Vieillot)

Louisiana Waterthrush   Chipe de Agua
                                                   Chipe Tordo

E. U. S.; winters in West Indies, and through Mid. Am. to Colombia

Winter Resident?   6 in.   19 gr. (17½ to 21)

Not uncommon. It has been recorded as late as 23 April in the spring, returning at the very early date of 1 August in 1959. In 1962 it returned on 23 August and disappeared about 9 October, after reaching a peak early in September. The earliest winter date, perhaps due to a lack of observers, is 12 February.

It is usually found in forest ravines and the borders of streams swifter than those frequented by the Northern Waterthrush, but is also found in wooded swamps. At Tikal it foraged along the sides and even directly on the wide shady roads leading up to the higher ridges, more frequently than at the aguadas.

It is the largest and also the palest of the waterthrushes, grayish olive above, with a white stripe above the eye; the chin and throat are clear, unstreaked white except for a single thin line at each side; its legs tend to a straw color lighter than the others.

The call note is a loud *tsick*. The northern song, rarely heard during migration, begins with three or four slow, ringing

whistles, each upwardly slurred, followed by a hurried jumble
of emphatic notes, twittering and falling at the close (1), (2).

REFERENCES:
(1) Peterson 1960, p. 209, picture in color. Murphy and Amadon
1953, plate 162, color photograph (with nest).
(2) Slud 1964.

Oporonis formosus (Wilson)

Kentucky Warbler   Chipe

E. U. S.; winters through Mid. Am. to n. Colombia
Winter Resident   5½ in.   13 gr.

Common, rather numerous in February and early March,
and again in September and October. It is seen here as late as
15 April and returns in the fall about 21 August, after which
some remain for the winter. It is usually found well inside the
humid forest, where it forages through the underbrush and
on the ground; also in thinned woodland and forest edges,
along roads and trails.

The general effect is of a warbler bright yellow below and
olive-green on the back, with a face conspicuously marked by
bright yellow spectacles, a black *triangular* patch below them
(often called sideburns), and a black forehead and forecrown
above them. The legs are pale flesh color.

During the winter it regularly repeats its distinctive call
note, *chuck* or *stchup* (2). Its northern song is a rapid, rolling, loud chant of two-syllable notes, *tory-tory-tory-tory* or
churry-churry-churry-churry (1).

REFERENCES:
(1) Peterson 1960, p. 213, picture in color. Murphy and Amadon 1953, plate 139, color photograph (with nest).
(2) Slud 1964.

Oporornis philadelphia (Wilson)

Mourning Warbler   Chipe Gemidor

E. N. Am.; migrates through Mid. Am.; winters Nicaragua
s. to n.w. S. Am.
Transient   5¼ in.   11½ gr.

Rare. It was recorded at Uaxactún on 3 May 1931 (Van
Tyne 1935), and at Tikal on 11 May 1959. These are the
only acceptable records known to me for the Petén. It is
usually found in low cover in open situations, such as thickets,
shrubbery, and thickly matted grasses where it may forage
even on the ground.

In spring plumage the male is distinctive, with a large black
bib (or mourning crape) across the throat and chest, an
all-gray face and head, olive-green back, and bright yellow
breast and belly. The female replaces the black with gray. In
autumn, females and immatures acquire *incomplete* eye-rings
(broken in front of the eye) and could be mistaken for Con-
necticut Warblers (*O. agilis*), which have complete eye-rings.
The smaller Nashville Warbler is also similar, but has not
only complete eye-rings but also an all-yellow throat and
underparts.

Migrants utter their alarm notes, clear *tseet*'s or *chips*. The
northern song is too variable to include here (1), (2).

REFERENCES: Peterson 1960, pp. 213, 221, pictures in color.
Dick 1957, plate 25, pictures in color. Murphy and Amadon 1953,
plate 141, color photograph (with nest).
(1) Saunders 1951.   (2) Slud 1964.

Geothlypis trichas brachidactylus (Swainson)

Common Yellowthroat   Chipe Cara Negra
                                                Antifacito

N. Am. and Mexico (to Veracruz and Oaxaca); winters s.
U. S., West Indies, through Mid. Am. to w. Panama, casu-
ally to Colombia
Winter Resident   5 in.   9½ gr. (8 to 11½)

Fairly common. It has been recorded as late as 18 May in

the spring, returning about 5 October or earlier in the fall; some probably winter through. It is found in both wet and dry situations, provided there is rather heavy cover in the form of thickets, tangles, and bushes, close to the ground.

The male has a distinctive black mask or "domino" bordered with pale gray, crossing the face from forehead to neck; upperparts are greenish olive; the throat and breast are bright yellow, the belly white. Females and immature fall birds lack the black mask, the face being olive-green as are the upperparts; underparts are rich yellow on the throat, yellow on the breast, the sides tinged buff, and the belly white; the white belly is a helpful field mark.

It is silent in winter except for an occasional husky *tchep;* on the return to the north it may weakly sing its song; *witchity witchity witchity witch* (1), (2), (3).

REFERENCES:
(1) Peterson 1960, pp. 213, 221, pictures in color. Dick 1957, plate 26, pictures in color.
(2) Slud 1964.   (3) Bent, No. 203, p. 561 (Skutch Ms.).

Icteria virens virens (Linnaeus)

Yellow-breasted Chat   Chipe Grande

N. Am. and n. Mexico; winters through Mid. Am. to w. Panama
Winter Resident   7¼ in.   27 gr. (23 to 30)

Common, especially in the fall. It was first noted 28 March 1956. The latest spring date is 4 April, the earliest fall date is 25 September. It is found in dense forest edges, in thickets, vine and briar tangles, heavy shrubbery and such, where it forages usually below eye level.

Its very large size, two or three times the bulk of most of the warblers, when combined with its clear field marks, make it easy to identify. Upperparts are olive-green including the head and face, the face marked with conspicuous white spectacles; underparts are bright yellow on throat and breast, the belly white.

The alarm note is often heard here, a loud, distinctive,

harsh *tsuck*. The song, which quiets down in the winter, is a long-continued complication of repeated whistles both high and low, mixed with harsh *tsuck*'s, soft crow-like *ka-ka-ka*'s and gurgles; a strange, diagnostic medley (1), (2), (3).

REFERENCES:
(1) Peterson 1960, p. 209, picture in color. Dick 1957, plate 27, pictures in color. Murphy and Amadon 1953, plate 166, color photograph (with nest).
(2) Saunders 1951.
(3) Bent, No. 203, p. 595 (Skutch Ms.).

Granatellus sallaei boucardi Ridgway

Gray-throated Chat   Granatela Gargantigris
                                Chipe

E. Mexico (Veracruz to Oaxaca and Yucatán Pen.), Guate-
    mala, and Brit. Honduras
Resident   5 in.   10¾ gr.

Common but localized. It is found almost exclusively within the tintal, some two miles east of the airstrip, between Aguadas Pucté and Términos, a low forest which loses most all of its foliage during the long dry season (see Map B). It was first recorded there on 26 February 1958, which is also the first time recorded for the Petén.

The male is mainly pale gray above, including the face and continuing around the throat; the crown is bordered at the sides by a black streak, below which a conspicuous white patch extends back from the eye; the breast is conspicuously vermilion red, which extends to the mid-section of the belly and sometimes recurs under the tail; the belly is otherwise white, flanked by pale gray; the blackish tail is white-tipped. The bill is black above, gray below; legs are gray, sometimes with a reddish tone; eyes are dark brown.

The female lacks the vermilion. She is light gray above, the streak behind the eye creamy buff, the face and underparts various shades of buff and buff-gray.

REFERENCES: Dick 1957, plate 31, picture in color (male only). Ridgway, Vol. II, p. 703, description.

Wilsonia citrina (Boddaert)

Hooded Warbler Chipe Careto

E. U. S.; winters in West Indies and through Mid. Am. to
cent. Panama

Winter Resident 5¼ in. 9½ gr.

Common. It was first noted 11 February 1958. The latest
spring date is 6 April, the earliest fall date is 10 August. It
is abundant in late February and early March, again in September and October. It is found in overgrown, moist or humid
forest borders rather than within the heavy forest, and in
dense undergrowth and shrubbery, where it forages at low
levels. The male is distinctive, with a clear yellow face and
forecrown encircled by a black hood which continues as a bib
across the throat and chest; upperparts are olive-green; underparts are clear bright yellow; the inner webs of the outer tail
feathers are extensively white, frequently displayed. Females
in the fall and immatures lack the black hoods and throat,
and appear much like fall Wilson Warblers (*Wilsonia pusilla*);
then the white tail spots of the Hooded assure its identity.

The call note, occasionally heard, is a ringing, metallic
chink. The northern song, omitted in fall or winter, is a clear
ringing, high-pitched whistle: *weeta-weeta-wee-téé-o*, the
slurred *téé-o* especially characteristic (1), (2), (3).

REFERENCES:
(1) Peterson 1960, pp. 213, 221, pictures in color. Dick 1957,
plate 24, pictures in color. Austin 1961, p. 285, picture in color.
(2) Slud 1964. (3) Saunders 1951.

Wilsonia pusilla subsp.

Wilson's Warbler Chipe
Pileolated Warbler

N. Am.; winters through Mid. Am.

Transient 4½ in. 6¾ gr.

Uncommon. It was first noted on 10 March 1957, a new
record for the Petén. The latest spring record is 28 March,

the earliest in autumn is 13 October. Farther south, however, where it winters abundantly, it may linger until May and return early in September.

It avoids heavy forest; found usually in wet, boggy areas and along streams, when well supplied with low thickets and shrubs. Aguada Tikal was more attractive before the brush was cleared away; now the wet grounds and the milpa east of the airstrip provide better habitat.

This is one of the smallest of all the warblers. The male gives the general impression of being all yellow, with a conspicuous round black cap; upperparts are usually described as bright olive-green. Females may retain a gray ghost of the cap, but in autumn, along with immatures, even that is lacking. They may then be identified by the *lack of tail spots;* the similar fall Hooded Warbler still displays white tail spots and the similar fall Yellow Warbler has yellow tail spots.

Its call note is an emphatic nasal *chip*. The northern song may be heard in late winter, a rapidly repeated series of loud, chatter-like notes, dropping in pitch at the end:

chi · chi · chi · chi · chi · chi · chi-chet-chet (1), (2), (3).

REFERENCES:
(1) Peterson 1960, pp. 213, 221, pictures in color. Dick 1957, plate 28, pictures in color. Murphy and Amadon 1953, plate 158, color photograph (with nest).
(2) Bent, No. 203, p. 633 (Skutch Ms.).
(3) Saunders 1951.

Setophaga ruticilla (Linnaeus)

American Redstart   Rey Chipe

N. Am.; winters through West Indies, Mid. Am., and n. S. Am.
Winter Resident   5 in.   8 gr.

Common. It is found in a wide variety of habitat provided it includes trees (excepting dense forest), where it forages up to moderate heights; also in tall thickets and shrubby borders of ponds and streams. It is constantly on the move, frequently flitting about with drooping wings and spreading tail. It is still present as late as 23 April (once recorded on 7 May), and returns by 4 September or earlier.

The male is largely jet black, including the throat and chest, but with conspicuously contrasting, large patches of orange-red on the wings, tail, sides of the breast, and under wing coverts; the lower breast and belly are white. Females replace the orange-red throughout with pale yellow; the black of the throat and chest is replaced with white, the black of the head with gray, and the black of the back with olive-brown.

Migrants may utter a strong *chip* or a clear *tseet*. They seem not to voice any of the northern songs, thin, high-pitched and sibilant, as:

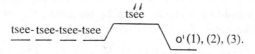

tsee-tsee-tsee-tsee ⟋ tsee ⟍ ♂ (1), (2), (3).

REFERENCES:
(1) Peterson 1960, p. 209, pictures in color. Dick 1957, plate 30, pictures in color. Murphy and Amadon, plate 157, color photograph (with nest).
(2) Slud 1964.   (3) Saunders 1951.

Basileuterus culicivorus culicivorus (W. Deppe)

Golden-crowned Warbler   Chipe
                                               Larvitero

Mid. Am. (chiefly highlands) and S. Am.
Resident   5 in.   9½ gr.

Common. It is numerous within the humid forest, at forest edges, along roads and trails, but seldom beyond into the open. It forages actively through the trees and understory, usually at low levels, occasionally on the ground itself.

Upperparts are grayish, sometimes with a slightly greenish tone, the crown conspicuously marked with a central stripe of yellow or yellow-orange, bordered at the sides by two stripes, the first a long black one, the second a short dull yellow one just above the eye; the cheek is grayish; underparts are rich yellow, tinged with green at the sides. The bill is dark brown above, lighter below; legs are straw yellow; eyes dark brown.

Most usually heard is a sweet little song, beginning with two or three notes warbled on the same pitch, followed by a higher, strongly accented, warbled flourish, as:

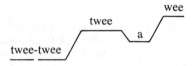

The sharply rising final syllable gives the song its special character (1), (2).

The nest is an almost globular affair, about five inches in diameter, located in a small depression on sloping ground, and with a wide entrance facing downhill. It is composed largely of rootlets, strips of dead leaves, and finely branched liverworts, the inner cup made of very fine brownish fibers densely matted together. Three white eggs are deposited, heavily blotched at the larger end and spotted elsewhere (Skutch, in litt., from a single Costa Rica record).

REFERENCES: Peterson 1960, p. 224, picture in color (of similar *B. c. brasheri*). Dick 1957, plate 34, picture in color.
(1) Slud 1964.
(2) Mexican Bird Songs, recordings by L. Irby Davis.

9 inches, a very large oriole. Sexes alike, but immature differs.

ADULT: two color tones are illustrated; one, a male, bright orange and rich yellow; the other, a female, with strong tones of brown. There is some question whether this color difference is dependent on sex.

IMMATURE: usually lacks black facial mask and bib, as is also the case with some Yellow-tailed immatures; otherwise dull olive-yellow above, and lemon yellow below.

ORANGE ORIOLE

7½ inches, about same size as Black-cowled Oriole. Sexes differ.

MALE: brilliant flaming orange and rich yellow above and below, except for black face, throat, bib, tail, and wings; wing has *both white and yellow* patches on shoulder and white edges on flight feathers. Lacks black forehead.

FEMALE: *patterned* like male, but much duller above, strongly tinged with olive, especially on the back; underparts orange-yellow.

NOTE: It is doubtful that either of these two orioles has been seen at Tikal.

PLATE 29

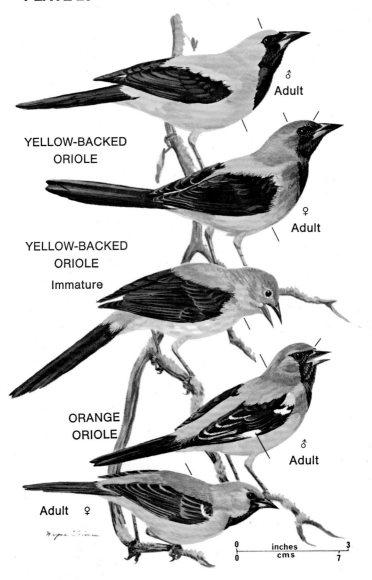

♂
Adult

YELLOW-BACKED
ORIOLE

♀
Adult

YELLOW-BACKED
ORIOLE
Immature

ORANGE
ORIOLE

♂
Adult

Adult ♀

inches
0   3
0   7
cms

YELLOW-WINGED TANAGER *p. 278*

7½ inches. Sexes alike; deep blue and gray-blue on head, nape, throat, and chest, blending to gray-olive above and below; wings are black, with gray-blue shoulders, and bright yellow patches, which are visible below as well as above when in flight; a small clear lozenge of yellow still visible when perched.

RED-CROWNED ANT-TANAGER *p. 278*

Where Red-crowned and Red-throated Ant-Tanagers occur together, the Red-crowned forages at higher levels and in denser cover, while the larger Red-throated prefers the lower levels and thinner understory and also forest edges and semi-open situations. The Red-crowned is misnamed Ant-Tanager as, unlike the Red-throated, it seldom follows army ants.

7 inches long. Sexes differ materially.

MALE: compared with the Red-throated a duller, browner bird, though still strongly washed with red; a usually concealed crown-patch is scarlet, bordered by contrasting dark brown stripes (the other bird's scarlet patch is blurred with brown and lacks this contrasting margin); throat pinkish red blending to dull red on chest and breast, and a grayish belly (the other bird has bright red throat, continuing bright red down the chest and breast and on the sides, blending duller hue only on the belly); the upper bill with distinctive "tooth" effect (lacking on Red-throated Ant-Tanager).

FEMALE: compared with the Red-throated more green-olive (the other bird more decidedly brown in tone); has an ochraceous orange partly concealed crown-patch which, when revealed, contrasts with the olive-brown head (the other bird lacks definite crown-patch); throat an obscure buff which blends into a dull olive breast (the other bird has *clear yellow* throat which contrasts with the adjacent brown plumage).

RED-THROATED ANT-TANAGER *p. 280*

8 inches, substantially larger than the Red-crowned. Sexes differ materially. In general the male is redder, the female browner than the sympatric Red-crowned; see above for comparisons.

ROSE-THROATED TANAGER *p. 277*

6 inches. Sexes differ. MALE: mouse gray above; the crown red, but at Tikal much duller red than other races (sometimes nearly lost); throat rose red; wings and tail feathers edged with dull red; underparts mainly pale gray, buff on under tail coverts.

FEMALE: similarly patterned and gray, but crown and edges of flight and tail feathers olive or yellow-green instead of red; throat clear pale yellow; belly yellow-buff.

PLATE 30

YELLOW-WINGED
TANAGER

RED-CROWNED
ANT-TANAGER

♂

♀

♂

♀

RED-THROATED
ANT-TANAGER

♂

ROSE-THROATED
TANAGER

♀

| 0 | inches | 3 |
| 0 | cms | 7 |

PLATE 31

BLUE GROSBEAK

♂ ♀ ♂ Immature

BLUE-BLACK
GROSBEAK

♂ ♀

BLUE BUNTING

♂ ♀ ♂ Immature

INDIGO BUNTING

♂ ♀ ♂ Immature

Wayne Trimm

```
0        inches        3
0         cms          7
```

BLUE GROSBEAK

p. 287.

6½ inches. Sexes differ materially.

MALE: rich dark blue, brightest on crown; black chin, lores, and some black on wings and tail; wing has two conspicuous rusty tan bars, one wide, one narrow. Bill is large, but less bulbous than Blue-black Grosbeak's. Winter plumage has blue obscured by buff edges on many feathers.

FEMALE: brown above, buff below, pale on throat and belly; wing bars as on male, but paler; rump may have bluish tinge.

IMMATURE: much like female, but blue of male present in varying amounts.

BLUE-BLACK GROSBEAK

p. 287.

6¾ inches, only slightly larger than Blue Grosbeak, but looks stockier and has a very large, more cone-shaped bill. Sexes differ.

MALE: dark blue, almost blue-black; a bright blue line above the eye and on forehead; much black in wings and tail.

FEMALE: distinctively rich dark chocolate brown above, only slightly paler below.

BLUE BUNTING

p. 289.

5 inches, same size as Indigo Bunting, but with bill visibly heavier. Sexes differ materially.

MALE: rich dark blue, nearly as dark as Blue-black Grosbeak, but brightened with *more* shining blue areas, on forehead, forecrown, cheeks, sides of neck and chin, and on rump.

FEMALE: brown with a golden hue above, paler cinnamon below, still paler on throat and belly.

IMMATURE: we illustrate one near adult male plumage, still with much dark brown showing.

INDIGO BUNTING

p. 289.

5 inches. Sexes differ materially. Bill smallest of this group.

MALE: rich deep blue on head, nape, throat, and down middle of breast; brighter cerulean blue on rump, wing shoulders, and rest of underparts; wings and tail black, the feathers liberally edged with greenish blue. In winter the blue plumage may become obscured by brown feather-edges.

FEMALE: olive-brown above; paler brown below, somewhat smudged with broad streaks of darker brown.

IMMATURE: much like female, but brown plumage variably mixed with blue.

ICTERIDAE

Gymnostinops montezuma (Lesson)

Montezuma Oropéndola
Oropéndola
Zacua Gigante

Xhom Bzan

Trop. Mid. Am. (except El Salvador) to cent. Panama
Resident   ♂ 22 in. ♀ 17 in.   ♂ 450 gr. ♀ 212 gr.

Fairly common. It is found in both heavy, humid forest and lightly wooded, agricultural regions, even fairly close to inhabited areas if supplied with scattered tall trees.

The head, nape, throat, and chest are black, the rest of the body a rich chestnut; the outer tail feathers are yellow, the tail appearing all yellow from below. The bill is long and sharp, black except for a conspicuously orange tip which extends for nearly a third of its length. The upper bill continues back over the forehead as a shield. The face has a large, conspicuous patch of bare skin on the cheek, white with a bluish tinge, and reaching up close to the dark brown eye. The male has an additional patch of bare skin well below the cheek, orange in color; also an obscure yellow-orange area on the forehead. The legs are a shiny black. The female is conspicuously smaller.

The voice is a most melodious, long-drawn-out, rapidly ascending liquid gurgle, sounding like the lively flow of water bubbling over a stony brook. Only when nearby are the squeaky, rusty-hinge notes heard. A harsh, stentorian *cack* is the usual alarm call (1), (2).

It is a colonial nester. Groups, or clusters, of elaborately woven pouches, two to four feet long, are suspended some forty feet or more above ground, in a tall tree. The entrance hole is near the top, not far below where the pouch is fastened to the slender tip-end of a branch. Two white or buffy white eggs are deposited at the bottom.

Although oropéndolas have been present from the very beginning of work here in 1956, a nesting tree was not found until 1963, when one was located at the Corriental reservoir; a new colony was started in 1964 in Group E, not far from the village cottages; still later, another at Aguada Tikal itself.

REFERENCES: Austin 1961, p. 288, picture in color (with pink rather than blue-white cheeks). Blake 1953, p. 506, picture in black and white.
(1) P.C.A. 31:287–304, life history (Skutch).
(2) Mexican Bird Songs, recordings by L. Irby Davis.

Psomocolax oryzivorus impacifus Peters

Giant Cowbird   Pájaro Vaquero Grande

Trop. Mid. Am. (except El Salvador) and S. Am.
Resident   ♂ 14 in. ♀ 12 in.   ♂ 210 gr.

Not uncommon, but localized. It was absent until 1963, when a male was taken on 27 April. Since then a small number have been present regularly, usually found foraging on the ground at the near end of the airstrip. It can also be expected near the recently found colonies of oropéndolas.

The male is glossy black with some purplish iridescence, and a distinct ruff or cape about the nape. The bill is short, heavy, and black; legs are black; eyes are red. The female is smaller, a duller black, and lacks the ruff. Immatures have yellow bills and whitish eyes.

The flight is distinctive: direct, but periodically dropping as the bird folds its wings momentarily after each five or six wingbeats.

In general, it is silent. In flight or when alarmed it utters spluttering, piercing screeches, sometimes harsh, nasal whistles and rattles.

It parasitizes oropéndolas and caciques, perhaps exclusively. Even though repeatedly driven away, it finally succeeds in depositing one or two eggs in the host's nest. The total number of eggs involved is not known, but may be as high as six or more. Eggs are pale blue, almost white, with obscure brown, scratchy marks; some are spotless white.

REFERENCES: P.C.A. 31:317–320, life history (Skutch).

Cassidix mexicanus subsp.

Great-tailed Grackle   Clarinero

K'au

S. U. S., Mid. Am., Colombia, Venezuela, and Peru
Visitor   ♂ 16½ in. ♀ 12½ in.   ♂ 200 gr. ♀ 130 gr.

Rare at Tikal. It is included here on the strength of a sight record in March 1960, confirmed by other sight records made later.

It avoids the forest, but is often found (usually in large flocks) in low, wet areas, especially near salt water. Inland it frequents rivers and lagoons. It seems to like towns and villages well supplied with shade trees in which to roost at night, and surrounded by fields and pastures in which to forage by day.

The sexes differ materially. The male is glossy black with purple, blue, and green iridescence. It has an excessively long wedge-shaped tail which is often folded together, upward, in flight. The bill and legs are black, the eyes are yellowish white. The female is much smaller, dark brown above, tawny colored below, with a pale throat and a pale brown stripe above the eye. The eyes are brown.

The voice includes a wide variety of guttural, creaky, or squeaky whistles and chuckles, sometimes overpoweringly harsh and loud, sometimes blended with sweet notes (1), (2).

It is a colonial nester, often building in trees and bushes near water, or among the reeds and grasses which border lakes and lagoons. The nest is a deep cup, plastered with mud and lined with fine fibrous material. Usually three eggs are deposited, less often only two. The eggs are glossy, colored light blue or blue-gray, and marked with dots, blotches, and scrawls of black and brown (1).

REFERENCES: Peterson 1960, p. 225, picture in color. Austin 1961, p. 290, picture in color; end papers, egg in color.
(1) P.C.A. 31:321–334, life history (Skutch).
(2) Mexican Bird Songs, recordings by L. Irby Davis.

Dolichonyx oryzivorus (Linnaeus)

Bobolink

N. Am.; migrates chiefly through West Indies, but also recorded migrating through Mexico (Yucatán Pen. and Cozumel I.) and Mid. Am. (except El Salvador); winters in S. Am.
Transient   7 in.   32 gr.

Uncommon, perhaps rare. Two were taken on 5 October 1962 among the tall grasses at the near end of the airstrip. Sight records of others, one a male still in black plumage, were reported for early October 1964. It is a bird of fields and marshes, and the weedy portions of the airstrip are no doubt attractive. No other Petén records are known to me.

In autumn the male usually looks much like the female and immatures: upperparts yellowish buff, lighter on the head, the face, and underparts, with a heavy dark stripe at the side of the crown, and numerous dark sparrow-like streaks above, a few along the sides below. The tail is black, with diagnostic, sharply pointed feathers. The bill is sparrow-like, light brown above, yellowish below; legs are brown, silvery toward the rear; eyes are brown. The male in spring plumage is distinctively different: all black below and black on the face, head, tail, and wings (except for a large white wing patch); across the nape is a conspicuous collar of yellowish buff; the lower back and rump are white.

It utters its clear, metallic *pink* note in migration. Its northern song is a rather long, bubbling series of irregular up-and-down notes, of metallic, sometimes reedy quality. Toward the end it becomes higher and faster, giving an excited effect (1), (2).

REFERENCES: Peterson 1960, p. 241, pictures in color. Austin 1961, p. 290, picture in color (of male). Murphy and Amadon 1953, plate 169, color photograph (of female).
(1) Saunders 1951.   (2) Pough 1953.

Dives dives dives (W. Deppe)

Melodious Blackbird   Tordo Cantor

Pichh

E. Mexico, Brit. Honduras, Guatemala, Honduras, and Nicaragua
Resident   10–11 in.   ♂ 98 gr. ♀ 85 gr.

Common, but localized. It is found in cultivated country and clearings supplied with scattered trees and thickets, along brushy streams, and often in the neighborhood of habitations. It is conspicuously present among the citrus trees at Aguada Tikal, but avoids the heavy forest and dark aguadas within the forest.

It is glossy black above and below, even the dark brown eyes appearing black. The female is slightly smaller and of a duller black than the male.

It voices a wide variety of melodious songs, given in a wide range of clear, somewhat piercing whistles, often of a liquid quality, as *whit-wheer, whit-whit-whit-wheer;* and *chuck-whéeo;* the flight note is a clear silvery *tink-tink-tink;* the female occasionally sings while sitting in the nest (1), (2). (See page 40 for description of a duet with a Laughing Falcon.)

It nests singly, not in colonies as with some other related birds, and usually in citrus trees, from six to twenty feet up. The nest is a deep woven cup, the interior plastered with mud and then lined with rootlets and fine fibers. Three eggs are the usual set; they are colored light blue, marked with scattered large and small black dots (1).

REFERENCES:
(1) P.C.A. 31:276–280, life history (Skutch); p. 277, picture in black and white. Blake 1953, p. 510, picture in black and white.
(2) Mexican Bird Songs, recordings by L. Irby Davis.

Icterus spurius (Linnaeus)

Orchard Oriole   Chorcha Café

E. U. S.; winters through Mid. Am. to n. S. Am.
Transient   6½ in.   20 gr. (18 to 23½)

Common. It is found in shrubby fields, orchards, and the borders of light woodlands. At Tikal it has been numerous. Flocks of over thirty have been noted in February and March; over a hundred were counted on 23 April 1959, after which the quantity fell rapidly, only two still present on 3 May. In the fall the earliest date is 25 August. Only one in ten or more spring birds is in adult male plumage. One individual in the fall, on 17 October, was recorded as in full adult male plumage.

The adult male is largely black except for rich rusty chestnut on the lower breast, belly, and rump, and a chestnut epaulet on the wing. The female is yellow-green above, yellowish below, with two white wing bars. Immatures are like females, except that the male immature usually has a black throat patch. (Two young males taken in August and September 1962 lacked the black throats.)

It may sing after a fashion in fall and early spring during migration (3). Its northern song is more robin-like than oriole-like: a rapid, high-pitched outburst of mixed whistles and guttural notes, ending with a distinctive down-slurred *wheeer* (1), (2). Its call notes are short *chuck*'s and a rattled *chrrrrr* (2).

REFERENCES:
(1) Peterson 1960, p. 240, pictures in color. Murphy and Amadon 1953, plate 174, color photograph (with nest).
(2) Saunders 1951.   (3) Slud 1964.

Icterus prosthemelas prosthemelas (Strickland)

Black-cowled Oriole   Chorcha de Cabeza Negra

Xhom-Xanil

Trop. Mid. Am. (except El Salvador) to n.w. Panama (Bocas
   del Toro)
Resident   7½ in.   ♂ 30½ gr. ♀ 27 gr.   Plate 28

Common. It is the only common resident oriole; widely distributed in thin woodland, forest edges, along roads and trails,
and in clearings with scattered trees and bushes; forages from
tall shrubs up to moderate heights in trees.

Sexes are alike. The adult is mainly black, the upperparts
bright yellow on the rump and lower back, underparts bright
yellow on the belly and breast. A band of brown occurs between the yellow breast and the black chest and a large yellow
epaulet is present on the black wing. The tail is solid black
(no yellow feathers). In this plumage there is a resemblance
to the adult male Black-throated Shrike-Tanager (*Lanio
aurantius*). However, the Shrike-Tanager is larger, has an
entirely different type of bill (see plate 28), is orange-yellow
on the upper back and on the upper part of the breast or chest
(instead of black), and has a white wing patch instead of a
yellow epaulet.

The immature is much yellower than the adult; not only the
rump and lower back but the upper back also is yellow (a
paler yellow, with a greenish tinge), and this yellow continues
up over the nape and crown, down the neck and across the
chest; this leaves black on the forehead (a good field mark),
on the front half of the face, and on downward—forming a
bib on the chest. The wing epaulet is pale yellow; the tail has
a brownish tone. In this plumage there is a strong resemblance
to the Yellow-tailed Oriole (*I. mesomelas*). However, the
Yellow-tailed Oriole is much larger (an inch longer and half
again as bulky), is a brighter, richer yellow, and has diagnostic, conspicuously yellow outer tail feathers.

The immature Black-cowled Oriole is also similar in color pattern to the adult male and female Yellow-backed Oriole (*I. chrysater*) and to the adult and immature (both sexes) Orange Oriole (*I. auratus*). However, the Yellow-backed is much larger (even larger than the Yellow-tailed), and has brighter colors, strongly accented with orange and brown; the Orange Oriole, while small and about equal to the Black-cowled in size, is brilliantly colored in flaming orange (see plate 29).

There are also intermediate plumages which add to the possible confusion. Problems of this sort are not unusual, but are emphasized here because of frequent reports of the presence of Yellow-backed and Orange Orioles which have been unconfirmed by a single specimen, although conscious efforts have been made to obtain confirmation. Detailed and careful description should accompany such reports.

The presence of the Yellow-tailed Oriole has been fully confirmed, but even that probable resident is rare here.

The song is described as a varied whistle, sweet but hurried, and usually too low to be heard very far. It lacks the mellow volume of the Yellow-tailed Oriole's song. It usually includes a definitive final note (1), (2). The usual call note is a metallic bell-like *woink* (2).

The nest is an interesting and individual structure. It is a deep, open cup, thickly woven of fine fibers, suspended from the underside of a broad leaf (such as a banana plant leaf) by means of plant fibers which are passed through perforations which have been deliberately made by the oriole in the leaf tissue; or, in default of some such leaf, the hammock-like cup is suspended under other available protecting cover, such as the eaves of a house.

Three eggs are the usual clutch.

REFERENCES:
(1) P.C.A. 31:266–268, life history (Skutch); p. 267, picture in black and white; p. 268, picture of nest. Blake 1953, p. 513, pictures in black and white.
(2) Slud 1964.

Icterus mesomelas mesomelas (Wagler)

Yellow-tailed Oriole   Chorcha de Cola Amarilla

Yuyum (orioles in general)

Trop. Mid. Am. (except El Salvador) and n. and w. S. Am.
Resident   8½ in.   43 gr. (34 to 48)   Plate 28

Uncommon, perhaps rare. It avoids the forest and is usually found near swamps, rivers, and lagoons, in tangles and thickets, in banana plantations and overgrown, abandoned clearings; given such habitat nearby, it is not averse to habitations. It has been recorded only once, when a male in breeding condition was taken on 30 June 1959.

In all plumages it is mainly bright yellow, adults with a golden tone, the richest coloring on the nape and crown. It is the only resident oriole with yellow outer tail feathers, the tail appearing all yellow from below. The smaller, transient Baltimore Oriole (*I. galbula*) occurs in spring and fall, when its more orange tail spots may cause some confusion. Black is limited to the middle tail feathers, the upper back, the wings (which also have a patch of yellow), and a frontal patch on the cheek, throat, and chest in the form of a bib. The bib effect is common to many other orioles, in varying degrees.

The immature is a paler yellow and a duller black, mixed with greenish olive; some individuals lack the black face and bib effect, a condition which seems to be connected with the degree of immaturity and is independent of the sex (see plate 28).

The flight is slow and labored, the tail rising and falling like a pump handle; the wings on occasion make a distinctive "crashing" sound.

Songs of this superlative singer include a variety of phrases, separately given. First one series of notes is repeated over and over, then a new variety is repeated over and over, and so on. The notes are full and mellow, the phrases spirited and richly whistled. An alarm note, *chup-chup-chup*, is also mellow. Numerous other calls are given (1), (2), (3), (4).

The only nest which I have found described was seven feet above ground in a bush: an open cup not deep enough to be called a pouch, suspended by its rim, and with so open a weave that the eggs were visible through the mesh. Three white eggs are deposited, thickly marked at the large end and sparingly marked elsewhere with shades of brown (1).

REFERENCES:
(1) P.C.A. 31:263–265, life history (Skutch); p. 264, picture in black and white.
(2) Slud 1964.   (3) Mexican Bird Songs, L. Irby Davis.
(4) Condor 59:4:257 (Eisenmann).

Icterus chrysater subsp.

Yellow-backed Oriole   Chiltote

Trop. Mid. Am. and n. S. Am.
Visitor?   9 in.   50 gr.   Plate 29

Rare. It is described on the strength of sight records in the month of March in 1957, 1960, and 1963, and in September 1962, but see discussion under *I. prosthemelas*. It has not been reported elsewhere in the Petén; in British Honduras it is not uncommon, but has been found mainly in the pine ridges (1). Its presence in Tikal is doubtful, but not impossible.

It is a distinctively large bird, even larger than the Yellow-tailed Oriole (*I. mesomelas*), which it resembles in pattern. However, it lacks the latter's yellow tail feathers and black back; it is also more richly colored with deeper orange and brown tones on the breast and over the nape and crown. Two types of color tones, orange and brown, are illustrated in plate 29. The immature is also illustrated, a duller olive-yellow above, lemon yellow below, dusky olive instead of jet black and usually without the black face and bib, not unlike some immature Yellow-tailed Orioles.

The song of the race *I. c. giraudii*, in the Panama Canal Zone, is a series of six to fourteen loud, clear whistles, moving irregularly up and down scale. Another common call is *teea, cheep-cheep-cheep, tee,* the first and last notes whistled, the others nasal (2).

Nests are sometimes suspended from the underside of palmetto leaves, about ten feet above ground (1).

REFERENCES:
(1) Russell 1964.   (2) Eisenmann 1952.

Icterus galbula (Linnaeus)

Baltimore Oriole   Chorcha Amarilla

E. N. Am.; winters through Mid. Am. to Colombia
Transient   7¾ in.   31 gr.

Not uncommon, especially in fall migration. It was first recorded on 12 February 1958, with March sight records following in succeeding years; many were present from 20 September to near the end of October (perhaps later) in 1962. The fall birds were found mainly in the high weeds at the near end of the airfield, in the adjacent rather open-forest edges, and occasionally in the taller trees scattered through the camp, all typical habitat for this migrant.

The male is conspicuously flaming orange on the breast and belly, on the lower half of the back and rump, and with broad patches of orange at the ends of the outer tail feathers; the head, upper back, and throat are solid black; the black wing has an orange epaulet and a single broad white wing bar.

The female is variable; some appear only as faded males, the black flecked with olive-brown; others are yellow-green above, darkest on the crown, brightening on the rump and tail, the underparts yellow with an orange tinge on the throat and breast. The wings have two white wing bars. The immature is much like the female.

It continues to sing through the winter—a song which is simpler than its northern song, consisting of a series of whistles, all about the same but rich and mellow in tone (1).

REFERENCES: Peterson 1960, p. 240, pictures in color. Auk 55:1:fpc., pictures in color (with *I. bullocki* and hybrids). Murphy and Amadon 1953, plate 178, color photograph (with nest).
(1) Slud 1964.

* *Icterus auratus* Bonaparte

Orange Oriole   Chiltote Amarilla

Mexico (Yucatán and Meco I.)
Visitor?   7½ in.   34 gr.   Plate 29

Its presence in Tikal is doubtful, but a description is included as an aid to identification in the future; a single sight
report which was made in the Great Plaza on 8 March 1957
has not been confirmed. It may be found in or near the edges
of abandoned milpas overgrown with heavy second growth.

Compared with the similar and also doubtfully present
Yellow-backed Oriole (*I. chrysater*), the male adult is much
smaller (7½ inches versus 9 inches); lacks black on the forehead; has white and yellow epaulets and white wing markings
(versus all-black wings); is brilliant flaming orange (not
brownish or yellow-orange); has a smaller black face and
chest bib. Females may be duller and immatures are duller
than adult males, show less white in the wings, but usually
have some black on the throat and bib area (lacking on the
immature Yellow-backed Oriole).

REFERENCES: None.

THRAUPIDAE

* *Tanagra affinis* subsp.

Scrub Euphonia   Calandrita de Garganta Negra

Chinchin-bakal

Trop. Mid. Am. from e. Mexico to n.w. Costa Rica (chiefly
in semi-arid areas)
Visitor?   3¾ in.   10½ gr.   Plate 26

Uncommon. It is usually found in drier climates, in low
dense growth, in agricultural areas with scattered low trees
and second growth, where it forages at low levels; less often
in taller, more humid woodlands where it feeds at higher

levels; mistletoe berries are favored. It was first noted on 18 March 1964, along the road near camp and on up to the Great Plaza; it was then as numerous as *T. lauta;* again noted in March 1965 (Margaret Hundley, in litt.).

The male is glossy blue-black above except for a bright yellow forecrown; the black continues across the face and throat, forming a small bib on the chest; the breast and belly are bright yellow; white patches show on the wings when in flight, and on the outer tail feathers when fanned. The bill is short. The female is gray on the crown and nape, yellow-green on the forehead, olive-green on the back and rump; underparts are mainly olive-yellow, becoming yellow on the belly.

It utters a three-syllable whistle, thinly musical, given at a level pitch, a doubled guttural scratchy call note, and a vireo-like *wheet-chichi-chichih* (1). A high-pitched *see-see-see, dewd-see* is sung from a treetop (2).

REFERENCES: Blake 1953, p. 527, pictures in black and white. Sutton 1951, p. 152, pictures in black and white.
(1) Slud 1964.
(2) Auk 59:1:30 (Sutton and Pettingill).

Tanagra lauta lauta Bangs and Penard

Yellow-throated Euphonia   Calandrita de Garganta Amarilla

Chinchin-bakal

Trop. Mid. Am. (chiefly in the highlands) to w. Panama (Chiriquí)

Resident   4 in.   13¼ gr. (12 to 16)   Plate 26

Common. Not a heavy-forest bird, it is usually found in thinned woodland, forest borders, high second growth, and plantation type land with scattered shade trees, where it forages from moderate heights to high in trees. It nests, however, at low levels. Mistletoe and similar berries are favored food.

The male is glossy blue-black above except for a bright yellow forehead patch; the black continues low across the face but not across the throat, which is yellow; the breast and belly are yellow with an orange tinge; white patches show on the wings in flight and on the outer tail feathers when fanned. The bill is black above, blue-gray below; legs dark gray; eyes dark brown. The female is mainly olive-green above, lacking the gray crown of *T. affinis;* the throat is gray, blending with the greenish yellow breast and belly, the middle portions generously mixed with white, becoming clear yellow below the tail. She is conspicuously brighter in general than the female *T. affinis.*

The male utters a short whistle, rapidly repeated two or three times, sometimes clear and bell-like, more rarely plaintive. The female's voice is thinner, chaffy or high-pitched, almost a trill (1). Other unmusical notes are given, occasionally including the typical *bebebebe* of a euphonia (2).

A nest was found in the crotch of a tree near Aguada Tikal, concealed by a large epiphyte, located about ten feet above ground. It was oven-like, roofed over, untidy in appearance, with a small obscure entrance hole at one side. Others are reported, located three to eight feet up, sometimes on the top of a rotting post. Five eggs, a rather large clutch for euphonias, have been reported; they are white, the large end sometimes washed with brown and heavily blotched with dark brown, the rest with scattered spots (1).

REFERENCES:
(1) P.C.A. 31:247–251, life history (Skutch); p. 248, pictures in black and white. Sutton 1951, p. 152, pictures in black and white.
(2) Slud 1964.

Tanagra gouldi gouldi (Sclater)

Olive-backed Euphonia   Calandrita Selvática

Trop. Mid. Am. (except El Salvador) to n.w. Panama (Bocas del Toro)

Resident   4 in.   13 gr.   Plate 26

Not uncommon. It was first recorded on 10 June 1958 (Edwards, in litt.). It is usually found within the tall forest and its heavy understory, but also enters adjoining clearings with scattered shade trees; though often foraging high in trees, it nests at low levels.

The male is mainly olive-green with a bronzy iridescence above, and a bright yellow forecrown which blends into the dark blue-green head; a black line extends before the eye; the throat, breast, and sides are dull yellow-green, with a diagnostic tawny color on the middle breast, belly, and under tail coverts. The bill is black above, dark gray below; legs are blue-gray; eyes dark brown. Although the colors sound bright, the male, in its forest habitat, is inconspicuous. The female is similar, but replaces the yellow forehead with dark brown; underparts are more uniformly greenish yellow, and tawny occurs only below the tail.

The voice is varied but unmusical, including a soft trill, a weak chirp, an unclear euphonia-like whistle, and a long-continued jumble of kissing and other sharp sounds (1).

The nest is a small globular structure with the entrance to one side, sometimes pensile or suspended free from a vine or branchlet, sometimes incorporated into the natural hanging growth, and located some three to fifteen feet above ground (2), (3). One was found suspended from a rootlet in the roof of one of the ruins of the Central Acropolis at Tikal (Edwards, in litt.).

Two to four eggs are deposited (3).

REFERENCES:
(1) Slud 1964.   (2) Russell 1964.
(3) Willis (in litt.).

Tangara nigrocincta larvata (DuBus)

Masked Tanager   Quitrique Careto

Trop. Mid. Am. (except El Salvador) and n.w. S. Am.
Resident   5 in.   18½ gr.

Fairly common. It is usually found high in flowering forest trees, often in semi-leafless trees, where it forages frequently in the company of other birds. It is also found in semi-open woodland, cultivated areas with scattered trees, even close to habitations, where it forages at lower levels.

Predominantly black, it is conspicuously marked with bright colors. A black mask through the eyes and chin is bordered with purple and blue, shading to turquoise near the neck; the crown, nape, and sides of the neck are a shining golden iridescence; the throat is a rich brown. Brilliant blue turquoise occurs on the rump, two-toned blue and turquoise on the wing epaulets, green on the edges of the flight feathers. Underparts are broadly black on the breast, bright blue on the sides, white on the lower breast and belly. Sexes are alike, but the young bird is very different: upperparts are dull green and black; underparts are gray on the throat and breast, white and buff on the belly and below the tail; the entire plumage shot through with indications of adult colors.

Its most common call is a sharp, dry *tick,* and notes of this character, given with a great variety of timing and emphasis, are its only utterances (1). It may voice a rapidly repeated *djit,* having weak but identifiable resonance; or an excited, continuously repeated *tik* or *sik,* mixed with ticking trills (2); or a weak, one-second-long trill, *tsiriririririririt,* weaker and shorter than that of a Chipping Sparrow (*Spizella passerina*), (3).

The nest is a compact, open cup, located anywhere from four to fifty feet up (or even higher) in a bush or tall tree. It is usually placed in any of a great variety of crotches or crannies, or in heavy foliage out on a limb; rarely in an old woodpecker hole. It is made of a great variety of vegetable materials, depending on whatever is available, bound together with cobweb. Two eggs are deposited, dull white or pale gray in color, thickly sprinkled all over with brown flecks (1), (3).

REFERENCES: Blake 1953, p. 528, picture in black and white.
(1) P.C.A. 31:200–213, life history (Skutch); fpc. picture in color.
(2) Slud 1964. (3) Condor 59:4:257 (Eisenmann).

Thraupis abbas (W. Deppe)

Yellow-winged Tanager   Carbonero

Trop. Mid. Am. from Mexico to s.e. Nicaragua
Resident   7½ in.   45 gr. (40 to 55)   Plate 30

Fairly common. It is found in a great variety of semi-open situations, such as forest edges, second growth, and clearings with tall trees, frequently in the vicinity of villages; forages from moderate heights to high in the crowns of trees; avoids the interior of heavy forests.

The head and neck are deep blue with a black area before the eyes, the throat and chest pale gray-blue; the back and rump are gray-olive, strongly marked across the shoulders with black blotches, and with scattered bluish reflections; the breast and sides are yellow-olive, also with bluish reflections; the tail is black; wings are black with bright yellow patches above and a broad yellow area below which are conspicuously visible in flight, but are reduced to only a small lozenge when perched. The bill is black, legs are dark gray; eyes dark brown.

A pair were seen (at Gallon Jug, British Honduras) carrying dead leaves and grass stems to a large cavity, some sixty feet up in a dead tree at the edge of the forest (Willis, in litt.). A clutch may consist of two eggs (1).

The call is a long *seeeeeet* (Willis, in litt.).

REFERENCES:
(1) Russell 1964.

Piranga rubra rubra (Linnaeus)

Summer Tanager   Quitrique
                                               Quitrique Rojo

S. U. S. and n. Mexico; winters through Mid. Am. to S. Am.
Transient   7 in.   29 gr. (27 to 31)

Not uncommon. Arrivals have been recorded as early as 21 September and the species has been seen as late as 28

March, although it can be expected through April. It is found wherever there are trees, excepting only dense forest, and is not averse to habitations.

The male is rose red all over, duller on wings and tail. The bill is brown above, greenish yellow below; legs are gray or gray-brown; eyes brown. The mouth lining has been noted as greenish yellow. The female is dull olive above, yellowish with orange tones below.

Its northern song is robin-like (1).

Its *chik-a-tuk,* alone or repeated, sometimes followed by *chi-kik,* is commonly heard in winter (2).

REFERENCES:
(1) Peterson 1960, p. 240, picture in color.
(2) Slud 1964.

Piranga roseo-gularis tincta Paynter

Rose-throated Tanager   Quitrique

X-Eret

Mexico (Yucatán Pen. and adjacent islands) and Guatemala (Petén)

Resident   6 in.   23¼ gr. (21 to 25)   Plate 30

Not uncommon, but localized. It is found in humid forest edges; at Tikal it appeared to be limited to the low tintal and the low shrubby growth and forest edge at Aguada Dimick.

The male is mouse gray above, with a dull red crown (sometimes very dull), and a reddish tinge on wings and tail; underparts are pale gray with a buffy tinge, very buffy below the tail, and rose red on the throat. The bill is dark brown above, yellow-gray below; legs are gray; eyes brown. The female is similarly patterned, but darker gray above; yellow-green replaces the red on crown, wings, and tail, pale yellow replaces the rose red throat, and the belly and under tail coverts are buff-yellow. The immature is much like the adult female.

REFERENCES: Blake 1953, p. 532, picture in black and white.

Piranga leucoptera leucoptera (Trudeau)

White-winged Tanager   Cardenalito

Chiefly highlands trop. Mid. Am. to w. Panama; also S. Am.
Resident   5½ in.   16 gr.

Uncommon. It is more commonly expected in cool wet, comparatively high altitudes, where it occurs inside forested areas, and along forest borders and breaks, and where it usually forages at moderate heights to high in tall trees. At Tikal it also occurs entirely inside the forest, foraging along the sides of wide forest roads, but only about twenty feet above ground. When feeding at high levels here it is probably overlooked; it may not be as scarce as appears to be the case.

The male is mainly bright red, with a small black mask from the forehead back past the eyes, and with black wings and tail. Each wing is conspicuously marked with two broad white wing bars. The bill is black above, blue-gray below; legs are gray; eyes dark brown. The female replaces the red above with yellow-olive, and below with golden yellow; the black becomes dull brownish black; the pairs of broad white wing bars remain.

It utters a variety of short, sharp, unmusical notes, among which are: a sharp, rising *whirst;* a characterless *stchirp-sr;* a *squick-squick;* a more patterned *squick, squick-squick;* a true song seems to be lacking (1).

REFERENCES: Blake 1953, p. 533, pictures in black and white. (1) Slud 1964.

Habia rubica nelsoni (Ridgway)

Red-crowned Ant-Tanager   Hormiguero
                                    Hormiguero Matorralero

Trop. Mid. Am. and S. Am.
Resident   7 in.   ♂ 33½, ♀ 31½ gr.   Plate 30

Common and numerous. It is found inside the humid forest at both low and moderately high levels, but usually in the understory; at lower levels it forages in habitat much like that used by the larger Red-crowned Ant-Tanager (*H. gutturalis*), but avoids the forest edge and more open areas frequented by that tanager. Neither does it follow army ants to any great degree.

The male is brown above with a strong tinge of rusty red; the crown has a bright scarlet patch (usually concealed but occasionally raised as a vivid crest), bordered on each side by a dark brown stripe (blackish but not black as in some races), which in turn blends into the brown face; the throat is pinkish red blending into red-brown on the chest and breast; the flanks are gray. The bill is dark brown above, lighter brown below; legs vary from yellowish straw to dark brown; eyes are brown. The female is olive-brown above with a green tinge; the crown has a dull but diagnostic patch partly concealed by olive-brown feathers; the throat is dull buff-yellow which blends into paler breast and belly; the under tail coverts are tawny.

The nest is a neat, shallow, open cup, of rootlets and fibers compactly woven and bound together with cobweb; strong enough to be suspended by the rim without support from below, but still so thin that the eggs may be visible through the bottom. It is located in the undergrowth or in slender saplings, seldom more than twelve feet above ground, at the most nineteen feet up (1). Three eggs are usually deposited, rarely two, conspicuously white or very pale blue, lightly sprinkled with cinnamon to form a wreath about the large end (1).

The voice is less harsh than that of the Red-throated, even pleasant, and characterized by rapid chatter, sometimes incessantly given. Scolding calls are a rapid *chit-chit-cheut-cheut-cheut*, varying in pitch and quality. Songs are slower and smoother, a *cheer-cheer-cheer-cheer-*, each with a downward slur; or given with an upward slur as, *purteé-pirteé-pirteé-pirteé,* the two types sometimes combined (3).

A dawn song, *peter-peter-peter*, strictly limited to sunrise although it may be given for nearly an hour, is flute-like and deliberate; also described for Costa Rican birds is a monoto-

nous, incessant chant (1), (3), (4). Singing in general occurs from about early March to early August.

REFERENCES:
(1) P.C.A. 31:176–182, life history (Skutch); p. 177, picture
in black and white. Condor 63:6:479–503, life history (Willis);
p. 482, picture of nest.
(3) Condor 62:2:73–87, voice and behavior (Willis).
(4) Mexican Bird Songs, recordings by L. Irby Davis.

Habia gutturalis peninsularis (Ridgway)

Red-throated Ant-Tanager   Hormiguero

Trop. Mid. Am. and Colombia
Resident   8 in.   ♂ 39½, ♀ 33 gr.   Plate 30

Common and numerous. It is found in thinner forest and
understory, and usually at lower levels than those chosen by
the Red-crowned Ant-Tanager (*H. rubica*), although there
is substantial overlap of the two species. It enters forest edges
and beyond into semi-open situations such as wide woods-
roads, and low as well as high second growth. It forages over
army ants frequently.

Compared with the Red-crowned, the male is brown above,
somewhat more strongly tinged with rusty red; the crown has
a largely concealed, bright red crown patch which is obscurely bordered by red-brown (lacking the other's dark side
stripes); the face is darker brown, rather dusky; the throat
is brighter rose red, deepening to a broad area of rich red on
the chest, sides, and breast; the rest of the underparts are also
tinged with pinkish red. The tail (male only) is distinctly
longer; the bill is black above, dark brown below; legs vary
from dark straw to dark brown; eyes are brown. The female
is uniformly dull brown above, the crown with a slightly
orange tinge but no crown patch; the throat is distinctively a
paler, brighter yellow than that of the Red-crowned, and is
contrastingly bordered by the brown of the face, neck and
upper breast; the belly and under tail coverts are tawny.

The nest is a more loosely woven, open cup, including leaves and other bulky material in addition to rootlets and finer fibers, and requires support from below. It is often located in a fairly exposed situation, at comparatively low elevations (not over twelve feet up), in forest undergrowth and also in low second growth. Three eggs are usually deposited, rarely two or four, conspicuously white, unspeckled (1).

The voice is recognizably slower-paced and harsher. One rough scolding call is *waij-jaij-jaij;* another is a more excited chatter, *scack-ack-ack*. A day song, entirely different from that of the Red-crowned, is a long series of eleven to fifteen whistled notes, as *pur'-tor-pur'-ter-pir'-tir-pee'-tir-pee'*, and so on. A song sung at sunrise but also given during the late afternoon is a distinctive, slow, deliberate chant, a long series of staccato notes, given in groups of three, as *chuk-per-chick, chuk-per-chick, chuk-* and so on. Other variations are recorded (2).

REFERENCES:
(1) Condor 63:6:479–503, life history (Willis); p. 482, picture of nest.
(2) Condor 62:2:73–87, voice and behavior (Willis).

Lanio aurantius aurantius Lafresnaye

Black-throated Shrike-Tanager   Hormiguero Pico Ganchudo

Trop. s. Mexico, Brit. Honduras, Guatemala, and n. Honduras (see NOTE below)

Resident   8 in.   36 gr. (30 to 41½)   Plate 28

Common and numerous. It is found inside the humid forest, where it usually forages at moderate heights.

The male has an all-black head and throat, a black tail, and black wings with a white patch near the bend; otherwise, it is conspicuously yellow, tinged with orange across the back, paler below, and with a tawny brown crescent across the chest. The female is entirely different: the head is gray with an olive tinge on the crown, paler gray on the throat; the rump is bright orange-olive, which contrasts with the brownish back and tail; the breast and sides are yellow-olive,

which blends to yellow on the belly and to buff below the
tail. The male immature is much like the adult female, but
intermediate plumages can be confusing.

This large tanager is illustrated together with four confusingly similar orioles. Its long, heavy-looking, all-black bill,
with an abruptly hooked tip and strong median tooth-notch,
distinguishes it from all the orioles. Additionally, its yellow
back separates it from the adult Black-cowled Oriole (*Icterus
prosthemelas*) and from the Baltimore Oriole (*I. galbula*);
its all-black head distinguishes it from the *young* Black-
cowled Oriole, which lacks much of the adult's black upperparts and crown, and also from three other orioles which
may possibly be seen (*I. mesomelas, I. chrysater,* and *I.
auratus*).

Refer to *I. prosthemelas* for further comparisons.

It is a rather noisy tanager, and its alarm calls arouse other
foraging birds: a *stcheee,* followed by about four rich *chee*'s
each falling slightly in scale, and ending with several more
level *chee*'s. It also utters strong chatters and other notes (1).

NOTE

A southern group, the White-throated Shrike-Tanager (*L.
leucothorax*) is sometimes considered conspecific under the
name *aurantius,* in which case the vernacular name of Great
Shrike-Tanager covers both groups; the range is then Trop.
s. Mexico to w. Panama (2).

REFERENCES: Blake 1953, p. 537, picture in black and white.
(1) Slud 1964.   (2) Eisenmann 1955, p. 100.

Eucometis penicillata pallida Berlepsch

Gray-headed Tanager   Hormiguero de Cabeza Gris

Trop. Mid. Am. (except El Salvador) to Trop. S. Am.
Resident   6¾ in.   27 gr. (23½ to 31½)

Fairly common. It is found in the humid forest, forest
edges, and second growth, and enters adjacent shaded agricultural areas; forages usually in the understory and is fre-

quently seen close to the ground above swarming army ants.

The sexes are alike. The head and neck are gray; elsewhere upperparts are olive, brightest on the rump, and underparts a rich yellow. The bill is black, legs are flesh-colored, eyes are brown.

The song is a long series of musical notes, complex in form, as *whichís-whichís-whicheery-whichís-whichú,* given in a subdued voice (1). It is also described as a rapidly delivered *chitit-ooweé-wee-aweér,* with many more syllables than those indicated; and other notes are uttered, including *chip*'s and high-pitched sibilants (2).

The nest is a thin-walled, open cup, sometimes so slightly built that eggs are visible from below. It is constructed largely of dark rootlets, with a variety of other material added; located from two to six feet above ground, occasionally higher, in the forest understory, or in bushes and small trees outside the heavy forest (1). Two eggs are usually deposited, pale blue-gray, with a heavy overlay of various shades of brown (1).

REFERENCES:
(1) P.C.A. 31:183–188, life history (Skutch); p. 184, picture in black and white.
(2) Slud 1964.

FRINGILLIDAE

Saltator atriceps atriceps (Lesson)

Black-headed Saltator   Chinchigorrión

Tsapin

Trop. Mid. Am. to cent. Panama
Resident   10 in.   80 gr. (75 to 93)

Common, but localized. It is found in the dense forest edges, thickets, and tangles, almost always in the vicinity of the camp and airstrip. It was frequently enmeshed in road-

side mist nets, where its large size and strong bill made its re-
lease difficult.

The head is mainly black, grayish on the sides, with a grayish white line above the eye, and a large whitish throat patch
completely bordered with black; upperparts are otherwise
yellow-green and underparts largely light gray, blending into
brown on the flanks and tawny below the tail. The bill is
black, legs greenish gray, eyes dull brown.

It utters disagreeably harsh, strident *chuck-chuck-chur-
r-r-r-r* calls, given from inside the heavy brush, where it is
well hidden despite its noise. The raucous voice is also described as *uh*-cackle, cackle-*wheep,* the cackles descending the
scale, the *wheep* rising long and penetratingly sharp; its usual
single note is parrot-like (1); and hear (3).

The nest is a bulky structure located at low levels in the
brush. Two eggs are deposited (2).

REFERENCES: Austin 1961, p. 297, picture in color.
(1) Slud 1964.   (2) Russell 1964.
(3) Mexican Bird Songs, recordings by L. Irby Davis.

Caryothraustes poliogaster poliogaster (DuBus)

Black-faced Grosbeak   Semillero Aceitunado

Trop. Mid. Am. (except El Salvador) to cent. Panama
Resident   7¼ in.   42 gr. (39 to 46)

Fairly common. It is found, usually in small bands, in the
heavy brush and understory within the forest, foraging at
moderate heights, and also at high levels in forest trees.
Rarely, it drops closer to the ground.

It has a small black facial patch at the base of the bill
which is much like that of the male Cardinal (*Richmondena
cardinalis*); the head is yellow with a greenish tinge, shading
down the back through olive-green to gray on the rump;
underparts are shades of gray, with yellow-gray on the belly.
The bill is black, the basal area blue-gray; legs are gray; eyes
dark brown.

Members of a foraging group repeatedly utter a short buzz

followed by a whistled *tweet-tweet* (1). In Costa Rica this characteristic call is described as an almost constantly repeated, sharp, short *pwtst,* followed by *chirp-chirp-chirp* (2). The song is an agreeably musical *churtweét-churtweét-churtweétcha,* leisurely delivered (2); and other variations occur.

REFERENCES:
(1) Russell 1964.   (2) Slud 1964.

Richmondena cardinalis flammigera (Peters)

Cardinal   Cardenal

Chak-ts'its'ib

E. and s. U. S., Mexico, Guatemala (Petén), and Brit. Honduras

Resident   8 in.   38½ gr. (33 to 41)

Uncommon and localized. It is found in the low, bushy scrub, and in the thickets adjacent to the forest at the eastern end of the airstrip. When first seen on 17 February 1958 it seemed to be rare, but there was evidence in the fall of 1962 that its numbers had increased. It is much more shy than are the North American races.

Both sexes have conspicuous crests, but otherwise differ materially. The male is a bright vermilion on the crest, head, nape, and underparts, dull red on the upperparts, and with a jet black facial patch at the base of the bill. The bill is red; legs are brown; eyes brown. The female is dull red on the crest, wings, and tail; the facial patch dark gray rather than black; upperparts olive-brown, underparts paler tawny brown.

The song is rich and musical, a series of loud, clear, slurred whistles. Although it is given with many variations, the quality is recognizably distinctive. Two of many versions of the northern songs are written *whit-whit-whit-whooit-whooit-whooit-whooit,* and *birdy-birdy-birdy*-etc. (1), (2). The call note is a short, thin *chip* or a weak *tsink* (1), (2).

The nest is a loose, deep, open cup, located in a bush or thicket (1). Three eggs are usually deposited (3).

REFERENCES:

(1) Peterson 1960, p. 244, pictures in color. Austin 1961, p. 296, picture in color. Murphy and Amadon 1953, plate 187, color photograph (with nest).

(2) Saunders 1951.   (3) Russell 1964.

Pheucticus ludovicianus (Linnaeus)

Rose-breasted Grosbeak   Realejo Rosado

E. N. Am.; winters through Mid. Am. from s. Mexico to Colombia

Winter Resident?   7½ in.   42 gr. (38 to 46)

Uncommon. It is found in light forest, forest edges, thickets, and semi-open situations, foraging from shrub height to moderate heights in trees. It was first recorded on 3 October 1962, and has been noted through November and in March; seems most conspicuous in the fall.

The male is jet black on the head, throat, neck, and upper back; the black wings have white wing bars and epaulets and some white on the flight feathers; the black tail has white on the outer feathers; the chest and upper breast are conspicuously rose red; the lower back, rump, breast, and belly are white. The bill is brown above, variably light brown, yellow, and gray below; legs are gray; eyes dark brown. The female (also young birds and to a great extent adult males in winter) are very different: heavily streaked with brown and dusky on buffy white, with whitish wing bars and a conspicuous, wide, buffy white stripe above the eye. A male taken on 22 October 1962 was still in summer plumage; fall males often retain some red on the chest; males have rose red and females have orange-yellow under wing linings.

The northern song is a series of clear whistles and short rich warbles, robin-like but mellower (1), (2). The call note is heard in winter, a sharp metallic *kick* (1), or *chink* (3), and sometimes a gentle *mew* (3).

REFERENCES:

(1) Peterson 1960, p. 245, pictures in color. Murphy and Amadon 1953, plate 193, color photograph.

(2) Saunders 1951.   (3) Slud 1964.

Guiraca caerulea caerulea (Linnaeus)

Blue Grosbeak   Ruiz Grande

S. U. S. and Mid. Am. (except Brit. Honduras) to n.w. Costa
 Rica; northern birds winter through Mid. Am. to w. Panama
Winter Resident?   6½ in.   26½ gr. (23½ to 30)
                                                    Plate 31

Not uncommon. It is found in forest edges and thickets,
scrubby, weedy fields and roadsides, where it feeds from
ground level to shrub heights, sometimes in small trees. It
was first seen 4 April 1956, but has also been recorded as
early as 13 February; the earliest fall arrival is 5 October.

The male is deep rich blue (ultramarine), brightest on the
crown, with a small black area at the base of the bill and on
the chin, and two conspicuous red-brown wing bars, one
wide, one narrow. In winter the blue plumage may be obscured by buffy feather edges. The bill is thick, black above,
blue-gray below; legs are black; eyes dark brown. The female
is olive-brown above, with a gray tinge on the rump, obscure
bluish edges on the tail feathers, and two buff wing bars;
underparts are buff, deepest on the chest, contrastingly pale
on the throat and belly. The heavy bill is brown above, paler
brown below; legs are brownish gray.

It utters a sibilant call, like *tsink* (2), and sharp *chink*'s (1).

REFERENCES:
(1) Peterson 1960, p. 245, pictures in black and white. Austin
1961, p. 296, picture in color. Murphy and Amadon 1953, plate
195, color photograph (with nest).
(2) Saunders 1951.

Cyanocompsa cyanoides concreta (DuBus)

Blue-black Grosbeak   Realejo Negro

Trop. Mid. Am. (except El Salvador) and S. Am.
Resident   6¾ in.   31 gr. (27 to 33)   Plate 31

Fairy common. It is most usually found in the understory

of the humid forest, but also enters adjacent clearings, milpas, trails, and roadsides.

A short, stocky, heavy-billed grosbeak, the male is a very dark blue (nearly black), only slightly brighter on the forehead and above the eye, with black wings and tail. The bill is larger and more swollen in appearance than that of the Blue Grosbeak (*Guiraca caerulea*), black above and below except for some gray at the base of the lower bill; legs are black; eyes dark brown. The female is rich dark brown above, slightly paler brown below, the wings and tail dull brown with brighter brown edges.

The typical song varies materially in different regions. However, there is general agreement that the tonal quality is similar and recognizable, that it is very melodious, that it is usually composed of two sections which differ greatly one from the other; the first half has five or six deliberately given loud, full, strong, mellow whistles; the second half is a rapid, breezy flourish, or a soft irregular twitter (1), (2). The second portion is heard only when fairly close, may be omitted altogether, and if singing is long continued, may be slurred over (1).

A song heard in northern Honduras consisted of seven or eight flute-like notes, the first four rising in pitch, the last ones falling (1). Call notes are variously described (1), (2), (3).

The nest is often built in some spiny palm within the forest or near forest openings, usually three to six feet above ground, sometimes a bit higher or lower. It is an ample but not bulky, well-woven open cup, made of a variety of vegetation including long strips of fibrous material, lined with soft, hair-like, fungal filaments. Two moderately glossy eggs are deposited, some white, some tinged with blue, and speckled and blotched with shades of brown and pale lilac (1).

REFERENCES:
(1) P.C.A. 31:50–61, life history (Skutch); p. 51, picture in black and white.
(2) Eisenmann 1952.   (3) Slud 1964.

Cyanocompsa parellina parellina (Bonaparte)

Blue Bunting   Ruiz Azul

Trop. Mexico, Guatemala, Brit. Honduras, El Salvador, Honduras, and Nicaragua
Resident   5 in.   15 gr. (13 to 18)   Plate 31

Common and numerous. It is found in the forest under-brush and forest edges, but is more common in brushy fields such as those bordering the airstrip.

The male is nearly as dark a blue as the much larger Blue-black Grosbeak (*C. cyanoides concreta*), but with a shining blue forehead, ultramarine crown, rump, cheeks, and wing coverts; the wings and tail are blackish, edged with blue. The bill is dark brown above, lighter brown below, a little heavier than that of the Indigo Bunting (*Passerina cyanea*); legs are gray-brown; eyes dark brown. The female is golden brown above; paler cinnamon brown below, palest on the throat and belly.

The song, as noted at Gallon Jug, British Honduras, is a whistled *whreet-whreet-wheet-weet-weet* (Willis, in litt.).

Specimens taken at Uaxactún were identified as *C. p. dearborni* (1).

REFERENCES:
(1) Van Tyne 1935.

Passerina cyanea (Linnaeus)

Indigo Bunting   Ruicito

E. N. Am.; winters through Mid. Am. to cent. Panama
Winter Resident   5 in.   14½ gr. (13 to 16)   Plate 31

Common and numerous. It is found in the vicinity of bushy cover, in clearings, and along roads with scrub and high weeds; abundant along the north side of the airstrip.

Fall arrivals were first noted on 12 October, but they prob-ably are present a week or two earlier. In the spring the last of the flocks have left by the end of April, with solitary strag-glers noted as late as 13 May (Van Tyne 1935). An indi-

vidual female banded at Uaxactún on 10 April 1931 was recaptured in the same locality on 16 April 1933 (*op. cit.*). A
similar event occurred in Middlesex, British Honduras, where
two individuals banded in March were recaptured a year
later (Russell 1964).

The male is a dark blue (ultramarine) on the head and
down the center of the throat and breast, brighter blue with
a green tinge elsewhere, the wings and tail partly black. The
finch-like bill, only slightly smaller than that of the Blue
Bunting (*Cyanocompsa parellina*), is brown, paler below at
the base. Legs are black; eyes dark brown. The female is
olive-brown (not golden like the Blue Bunting) above, paler
brown below, very pale (buffy white) on the throat and
belly, the wings dusky with traces of blue and green. Many
fall-plumaged males have the blue largely obscured by brown;
immatures are largely brown, darker than adult females.

The only utterance in the winter is a sharp little *pit* or *tsip*
(1).

REFERENCES: Peterson 1960, p. 245, pictures in color. Murphy and Amadon 1953, plate 183, color photograph (with nest).
(1) Slud 1964.

Passerina ciris ciris (Linnaeus)

Painted Bunting   Cuatrocolores
                                             Mariposa

S. U. S. and n. Mexico; winters through Mid. Am. to w.
Panama

Winter Resident   5¼ in.   18 gr. (15 to 22)

Common. It is found in the scrubby undergrowth and
thickets of open woodland, forest edges, clearings, and roadsides, occasionally foraging at moderate height in trees.

It was present as late as 29 April in the spring of 1959,
but none were seen by me in the fall of 1962, indicating that
they may arrive after 27 October, the day I left Tikal. They
have been reported for November and December.

The male is a gaudily colored little finch. The head (except
the throat) and nape are dark blue with a violet hue; the

PLATE 32   Temple I, or Temple of the Giant Jaguar, partially rebuilt.

PLATE 33   Air view of the Great Plaza, Tikal, showing Temple I at
the east end and Temple II at the west end of the plaza. Pyramids of
the North Acropolis are at the left. Numerous stelae and altars have
been re-erected along the north staircase.

PLATE 34   A jungle scene typical of Tikal.

PLATE 35 An aguada (water hole) at Tikal, partially opened up for use by *chicleros*.

throat and underparts are bright red, the rump dull red; the back and shoulders are yellow-green; wings and tail dusky with areas of blue and green. The bill is dark brown above, yellow-brown below; legs are gray and brown; eyes dark brown with a narrow red eye-ring. The female is dull green above, dull yellow with a green hue below, palest on the throat and belly.

The only note uttered in winter is a sharp *chip* (1).

REFERENCES: Peterson 1960, p. 245, pictures in color. Austin 1961, p. 296, picture in color. Gilliard 1958, plate 208, color photograph.
(1) Slud 1964.

Spiza americana (Gmelin)

Dickcissel   Sabanero

Cent. N. Am.; migrates through Mid. Am.; winters from s. Mexico to n. S. Am.
Transient   6½ in.   27 gr. (20 to 35)

Common, but only for short periods. It is normally a bird of fields and meadows, perching in scattered trees and dropping down into grain fields or weeds to feed. It has been seen from 6 April (in 1957, when a flock of some eighty birds suddenly arrived) to as late as 2 May (in 1959, all having disappeared by the third). None were seen by me during my visit in the fall, from 17 August to 27 October 1962.

The male is largely gray-headed with a pale yellow stripe over the eye, a white chin and upper throat, and a black bib reaching down into the yellow breast; the back is brown and sharply streaked, the wings marked with broad red-brown epaulets; the yellow breast blends to white on the belly, to gray on the sides. The bill is brown above, gray below; legs are greenish gray; eyes brown. The female is rather like the male, browner above, lightly streaked below, and lacks the black chest spot (which is also obscured on males in the fall). The immature is much like the female, but still more sharply streaked on the breast and sides.

It may sing on its way north, its rather sharp, staccato,

variably repeated *dick-ciss-ciss* (1), (2). Otherwise it utters harsh, guttural notes, as *krik* or *gzit,* and a buzzy *tzrr-tzrr-tzrr.* Active flocks give a constant twittering and the sound of fluttering wings (3).

REFERENCES:
(1) Peterson 1960, p. 241, pictures in color.
(2) Russell 1964.   (3) Slud 1964.

SPECIAL NOTE

Most of the Dickcissels seen on 9 April 1957, a very large flock, were heavily stained salmon red on the throat and about the bill, so much so that they looked like some strange new species rather than like Dickcissels. The same phenomenon was recorded for other birds, as follows: 5 April 1957, Golden-olive Woodpecker (*Piculus rubiginosus*); 3 April 1957, Black-cowled Oriole (*Icterus prosthemelas*); 15 March 1957, and 15, 16, 17 March 1963, Myrtle Warblers (*Dendroica coronata*). It would be interesting to trace the source of the stains, perhaps from a fruit or from pollen.

Sporophila torqueola morelleti (Bonaparte)

White-collared Seedeater   Jaulín

S. Texas and Mid. Am. s. to Costa Rica and w. Panama
  (Bocas del Toro)
Resident   4¼ in.   8¼ gr. (7¼ to 9¼)

Common, but confined to the open, weedy growth along the airstrip, the tall coarse grasses in Aguada Tikal, and the scrubby growth at Aguada Dimick.

The male is mainly black above with a buff rump, the black extending down and across the chest, the chest band sometimes strong, sometimes very slight; the throat is white, the white extending up into the hind neck to form a partial collar; the rest of the underparts are pale buffy white. There is much white in the black wings. The bill is diagnostically stubby and swollen, black, with a brown tinge below; legs are dark brownish gray; eyes dark brown. The female is olive-brown above with two buffy white wing bars; pale buff below. The bill is brown, legs are grayish, eyes are brown. Immatures vary greatly, from much like adult females to much like adult males.

The song is given from early March to late September or longer. It is loud, sweetly musical, and of a characteristic pattern, though variably described: one form begins deliberately with low notes gradually increasing in both pitch and tempo to become an excited canary-like song which tapers off to chaffy trills (1); a similar version, of four-second duration and closing with a very canary-like quality, is written as *swee-swee-swee-swee-swee, teéoo-teéoo-teéoo, tew-tew-tew* (3); another is a series of *cheep*'s, first at a high pitch, then at a lower pitch. Also uttered are a sweet (or a harsh vibratory) *peep*, and short, nasal *mew*'s (2). Roosting flocks produce a continued noisy chatter, interrupted by an occasional song (1).

The nest is a slight but beautiful little open cup, usually from three to five feet up (some higher), in a low tree, shrub, or clump of grass. It is fastened to the branchlets with much cobweb, the body is made of rootlets, fibers, and grasses, the lining of very fine material (1).

The usual clutch is two eggs, but a nest found in a slender bush at Aguada Dimick on 8 July 1959 contained three nestlings; another found in an orange tree close to Aguada Tikal on 27 August 1962 had two nestlings. Eggs are bluish white or pearl gray, finely mottled all over with light brown, sometimes forming a wreath at the large end.

REFERENCES: Blake 1953, p. 569, pictures in black and white. Peterson 1960, p. 244, pictures in color (of northern race).

(1) P.C.A. 31:33–37, life history (Skutch); p. 34, pictures in black and white; p. 36, picture of nest.

(2) Slud 1964.   (3) Condor 59:4:259 (Eisenmann).

Oryzoborus funereus Sclater

Thick-billed Seed-Finch   Semillerito Negro

Trop. Mid. Am. (except El Salvador) and n.w. S. Am.
Resident   4½ in.   12.7 gr. (heavier records elsewhere)

Uncommon but not rare. It is found in humid forest edges
and in adjacent clearings if they include tangles of grass,
weeds, and shrubs, such as the areas at the south side of the
airstrip and Aguada Dimick.

The conical bill is diagnostic, very heavy for so small a
finch, with a squarish profile at the tip and a smooth blending
of the ridge into the curve of the crown. The male is glossy
black except for a partly concealed white wing patch above
and white wing linings below. The bill is dull dark brown
or black; legs are black; eyes very dark brown. The female
is olive-brown above, paler on the rump; underparts are light
cinnamon buff, darker on the chest and sides. Her bill is brown
above, paler below.

The song is a sweet warble, clear and musical, but not loud:
a deliberate, slow-paced, uninterrupted series (often eight to
twelve seconds long) of similar, mellow whistles, ending on
a rising querulous note (1), (2). It is usually given from a
conspicuous perch by an adult male, sometimes by a male in
immature plumage. Females remain hidden and are rarely
seen. The call note sounds like *ik* or *ek* (1).

The nest is a thinly woven cup of fine rootlets, grass, and
similar materials, lined with black horsehair (in Costa Rica),
and located about five feet up in a bush or vine tangle. Two
dull white eggs are deposited, heavily mottled with pale brown
and lilac, especially on the larger end (Skutch, in litt.).

REFERENCES: Blake 1953, p. 571, picture in black and white
(head only).
(1) Slud 1964.   (2) Condor 59:4:260 (Eisenmann).

Volatinia jacarina splendens (Vieillot)

Blue-black Grassquit Jaulín Negro

Trop. Mid. Am., S. Am., s. Lesser Antilles (Grenada)
Resident 4 in. 9 gr.

Fairly common. It is found mainly in open country with grassy fields, brush, and low trees, occasionally in humid forest edges, often in the vicinity of habitations. At Tikal the camp, the two aguadas, and the sides of the airstrip are all attractive habitat.

The male is glossy blue-black, dull black on the wings and tail, and with white patches at the sides of the breast which are usually concealed by the wings. The bill is black above, grayish below; legs are dark gray; eyes dark brown. The female is olive-brown above, with gray-brown wings and tail; underparts are buff, pale on the throat and belly, streaked with dusky on the breast and sides. Her bill is also black above, but varies from medium gray to flesh-colored below; legs are gray (not dark).

The male often jumps a foot or more straight up from a perch and straight down close to the same spot; the jump is accompanied by an insect-like buzz at two pitch levels, as *zrrrr-zir* (in one syllable), ending in a buzzy *tsrzz-tskzzz* (1). It is also described, in the Canal Zone, as an explosive *bzeé-eep,* the whole performance repeated every ten or fifteen seconds for half an hour or more (2). The calls are also given without the jumps.

The nest is a flimsy, open cup, usually located less than four feet above ground. Two, rarely three eggs are deposited (2), (3).

REFERENCES: de Schauensee 1964, p. 336, picture in black and white (head only).
(1) Slud 1964. (2) Eisenmann 1952.
(3) Russell 1964.

Arremon aurantiirostris saturatus Cherrie

Orange-billed Sparrow   Pico de Oro

Trop. Mid. Am. (except El Salvador), and n.w. S. Am.
Resident   6½ in.   37 gr. (32 to 38)

Uncommon. It is found inside the tall, humid forest, where it forages on the moist forest floor (hopping, not walking), or in low, dense cover and tangles, seldom rising more than ten feet above ground.

The bold, bright color pattern is exceptionally conspicuous for a bird of dense, shaded habitat, and may partly account for its shy, retiring disposition. The head is largely black with a gray crown stripe, a white stripe above the eye, and a white throat. The rest of the upperparts are olive-green, with bright yellow at the bend of the wing. The white throat contrasts sharply with the black cheeks and chin and a broad black band across the chest. The breast and belly are white down the middle, merging into gray-olive at the sides. The bill is red-orange, legs pale brown, eyes brown. The female has a smaller chest band.

The song (of *A. a. rufidorsalis*) is composed of five very high-pitched, low-volume notes, the first and last two of equal length, the middle note short, a series of slow, thin squeaks. The alarm note is a sharp *tsit* or *tsick* (2).

The nest is located on the ground, usually against a slope of some sort; a very bulky, roofed-over, oven-shaped structure with a wide, round entrance facing down the slope. The base is thick, bringing the entrance well above ground, often built out in front as a platform. Green ferns are frequently included, along with many dried leaves, coarse sedges, and rootlets; the bottom is well lined with finer rootlets. Two eggs are deposited, white, moderately glossy, and marked in widely varying amounts with brown of all shades (1).

REFERENCES:
(1) P.C.A. 31:94–100, life history (Skutch); p. 95, picture in black and white (of similar *A. a. aurantiirostris*). de Schauensee 1964, p. 384, picture in color (of paler *A. a. erythrorhynchus*).
(2) Slud 1964.

Arremonops conirostris chloronotus (Salvin)
[*Arremonops chloronotus chloronotus* (Salvin)], [see (4)]

Green-backed Sparrow

Semillero
Talero

Xpokin

Trop. Mid. Am. (except El Salvador), and n. S. Am.
Resident   6 in.   26¾ gr. (23 to 31)

Fairly common. It is found in the heavy underbrush and tangles where the forest borders on wide trails, roads, and somewhat weedy clearings, and it enters those more open areas; while not averse to scattered habitations, it is very quick to take to cover; avoids the heavy forest itself. It forages at low levels, often hopping along the ground, to satisfy an extremely varied diet of insects, seeds, berries, and soft fruits, even tiny frogs and lizards.

The head is largely gray, with a diagnostic black stripe each side of the crown (a sibling species, *A. rufivirgatus,* not found at Tikal, but present elsewhere in the Petén, has *brown* stripes), and a narrow black stripe through the eye, from bill to neck; the rest of the upperparts are bright olive-green, with conspicuous canary yellow at the bend of the wing; the underparts are largely dull white, with a strong wash of light gray across the chest and on the sides.

The song, usually heard in the early morning, is sweetly musical. Some of the more southern species (as *A. c. striaticeps* and *A. c. richmondi*), while differing in details, have a common pattern and quality: a series of loud clear whistles, at first repeated slowly, then gradually faster and faster, *zeeee, cho, cho, cho, cho-cho, chochocho;* perhaps like a locomotive starting up and gathering speed (1), (2), (3), (5). On the other hand the songs of the species at Tikal have been described as noticeably different: one, a pretty, ringing *ching-ching-ching-ching-ching,* another like that of the Cardinal (1). A study at Tikal of this material difference is desirable; it is a primary factor in the separation of northern and southern birds into different species rather than subspecies (4). The call note is a sharp *pink,* more metallic and less nasal than that of more southern birds (1).

The nest is located in low vegetation, usually less than three feet up, occasionally higher, sometimes practically on the ground: a roofed-over, oven-shaped, bulky mass, with a wide entrance. It is made of long, broad strips of leaves and a variety of other coarse, dead vegetation, whatever is handy; the lining, however, is of fine grass and fibers. Two pure white eggs, unmarked, are the usual clutch (1).

REFERENCES:
(1) P.C.A. 31:101–118, life history (Skutch); p. 103, picture in black and white; p. 105, picture of nest.
(2) Eisenmann 1952.　　(3) Slud 1964.
(4) Occ. Papers No. 28, La. State U. Mus. Zool., 1963 (Burt L. Monroe, Jr.).
(5) Bird Songs, recordings by Paul Schwartz.

Spizella passerina pinetorum Salvin

Chipping Sparrow　　　　　　　　　　　　　　　Semillero

N. Am. s. through highlands (chiefly) Mid. Am. to n.e. Nicaragua
Visitor　　　　5 in.　　　　12 gr.

Rare. It is found in open woodland and cultivated areas, often in the vicinity of habitations. To our east in British Honduras, it is a moderately common resident of the pine-lands (Russell 1964). Included here on the evidence of a male individual taken on 5 April 1931 at nearby Uaxactún, among a flock of Indigo Buntings feeding on grass seeds in a clearing (Van Tyne 1935, p. 42).

The range of this subspecies is given as the tropical pine forests of eastern Guatemala (Petén district), British Honduras, Honduras, and northeastern Nicaragua (2).

The crown is rusty brown, bordered at each side by a pale gray, broad stripe above the eye and a narrow black stripe through the eye; the rest of the head, nape, and underparts are largely unmarked gray, nearly white on the chin, throat, and belly; the back is brown with conspicuous dusky stripes, the rump dark gray. The bill is dark brown or black, legs dull straw, eyes brown.

The voice is a dry chipping rattle, or a rapid trill all on one pitch; the call note a short *chip* (1).

The nest is a compact, tidy little open cup, usually well concealed in the foliage of a bush or tree. Eggs (three to five in North America) are greenish blue, speckled brown on the larger end.

REFERENCES:

(1) Peterson 1960, p. 253, pictures in color. Murphy and Amadon 1953, plate 207, color photograph (with nest).

(2) Cat. of Birds of N. Am., Field Mus. Nat. Hist., Zool. Ser. 13, Part XI (Hellmayr); Pub. No. 430.

APPENDIX A

DAILY RAINFALL, MAXIMUM AND MINIMUM TEMPERATURES

1959

Day of the Month	June			July			August			September		
	mm.	F°	F°	mm.	F°	F°	mm.	F°	F°	mm.	F°	F°
1	18.0	85	73	0.0	85	73	–	–	–	0.0	89	68
2	0.0	83	73	23.0	80	70	0.0	–	–	4.0	84	75
3	2.0	88	76	0.0	80	72	0.0	88	72	4.0	84	74
4	0.0	88	75	0.0	88	73	0.1	88	71	–	–	–
5	0.0	89	75	0.0	88	75	0.0	89	73	5.0	84	74
6	1.0	90	76	0.0	87	73	0.6	89	74	0.0	85	73
7	0.0	90	75	0.0	88	72	4.5	87	72	0.0	87	72
8	10.4	88	76	0.0	85	72	28.4	83	73	0.0	85	72
9	0.0	90	75	0.0	86	72	2.9	85	75	0.0	84	73
10	0.0	90	75	0.0	86	73	0.0	87	74	2.5	84	71
11	0.0	90	75	0.0	85	71	2.0	87	74	0.0	85	72
12	22.0	87	75	3.5	86	71	0.0	88	72	0.0	85	72
13	0.0	80	73	0.0	85	72	0.0	87	73	0.0	86	73
14	39.5	87	74	0.2	87	75	40.0	87	73	24.5	83	73
15	45.0	88	74	0.0	87	74	0.9	88	73	11.0	84	73
16	0.2	84	75	5.0	86	72	0.0	86	76	0.0	87	74
17	27.9	89	75	0.0	86	73	0.0	86	75	9.5	88	74
18	9.4	88	74	0.0	87	73	0.0	86	72	13.0	87	72
19	47.5	88	75	0.0	86	72	0.0	86	72	6.5	78	69
20	39.4	87	23	10.0	85	73	0.0	85	73	30.0	82	63
21	9.0	86	72	0.0	88	72	3.0	87	76	34.0	84	74
22	5.0	85	72	0.0	87	74	12.0	87	74	12.0	82	75
23	0.0	84	73	4.2	88	75	0.1	82	75	1.5	85	74
24	0.0	87	72	0.0	86	74	8.9	82	75	1.5	86	73
25	0.0	88	74	0.0	87	73	0.0	84	74	0.0	86	74
26	0.0	88	73	2.2	87	72	5.5	84	74	0.0	87	73
27	22.6	84	72	1.3	87	73	0.0	84	72	0.0	87	73
28	2.5	80	70	12.0	86	73	0.0	86	74	0.0	86	72
29	0.0	86	72	22.4	87	72	4.9	87	67	0.0	86	72
30	–	86	73	0.0	85	74	0.0	87	67	0.0	87	74
31				39.0	–	–	0.0	89	67			
Monthly Total mm., max. & min. temp.	301.4	90	70	122.6	88	70	113.8	89	67	159.0	89	68

Approximate accumulated total rainfall for each previous twelve (12) months begins at end of May 1960. These totals lack data which was not recorded, especially during the dry months of December and January; the resulting error is probably not great.

									1960					
October			November			December			January			February		
mm.	F°	F°	mm.	F°	F°	mm.	F°	F°	mm.	F°	F°	mm.	F°	F°
0.0	88	75	34.0	86	72	0.0	84	64	0.0	–	–	1.0	82	49
0.0	89	70	10.5	85	72	0.0	75	62	0.0	–	–	0.0	76	52
0.0	88	70	0.0	85	72	0.0	76	59	0.0	–	–	0.0	78	52
0.0	88	71	0.0	86	72	0.0	–	–	0.0	–	–	0.0	88	60
0.0	88	72	0.0	85	71	0.0	–	–	0.0	–	–	0.0	88	60
0.0	88	72	6.0	84	70	0.0	76	59	0.0	–	–	0.0	88	62
0.0	83	74	23.0	81	70	0.0	76	56	0.0	–	–	0.0	88	62
4.5	87	74	0.0	82	71	0.0	77	58	9.0	–	–	0.0	86	60
5.0	86	75	0.0	83	69	0.0	78	60	4.0	82	63	0.0	86	62
2.0	82	75	0.0	–	–	11.0	78	59	0.0	83	63	0.0	88	64
10.0	81	74	1.0	–	–	0.0	80	68	2.0	84	63	0.0	90	64
4.0	86	74	17.0	–	–	0.0	82	69	3.0	80	68	0.0	88	64
0.0	82	75	0.0	–	–	0.0	82	69	0.0	81	68	2.0	68	60
0.0	88	75	0.0	–	–	0.0	81	66	0.0	82	69	0.0	68	58
0.0	88	74	0.0	–	–	0.0	82	67	0.0	83	69	0.0	78	60
7.0	86	73	0.0	86	66	0.0	83	72	0.0	83	69	0.0	82	60
14.5	83	73	0.0	85	65	0.0	–	–	0.0	84	68	0.0	82	60
1.0	83	72	1.0	86	68	0.0	–	–	4.0	80	70	0.0	82	62
0.0	80	72	9.0	80	68	0.0	–	–	0.5	73	64	4.0	64	62
0.0	83	73	0.0	80	62	0.0	–	–	2.0	72	62	3.0	70	64
0.0	85	75	0.0	80	68	0.0	–	–	0.0	71	63	0.0	72	70
5.0	86	72	0.0	80	65	0.0	–	–	1.0	62	64	0.0	74	68
11.0	83	72	0.0	81	64	38.0	–	–	0.0	70	62	0.0	88	68
6.0	82	73	0.5	83	65	1.0	–	–	0.0	72	61	0.0	90	68
8.0	85	75	0.0	82	59	0.0	–	–	0.0	60	58	0.0	84	66
0.5	84	72	0.0	83	60	0.0	–	–	0.0	72	60	0.0	84	66
0.0	86	72	0.0	85	60	5.0	–	–	1.0	78	62	0.0	80	64
0.0	88	73	3.0	84	58	0.0	–	–	4.0	78	62	0.0	80	64
0.0	88	72	0.0	78	57	4.0	–	–	1.0	80	76	0.0	72	70
0.0	87	72	0.0	70	58	0.0	–	–	2.0	82	64			
0.0	86	71				1.0	–	–	1.0	82	52			
78.5	89	70	105.0	86	57	60.0	84	56	34.5	84	52	10.0	90	49

Contd. Daily rainfall, maximum and minimum temperatures

1960

Day of the Month	March			April			May			June		
	mm.	F°	F°	mm.	F°	F°	mm.	F°	F°	mm.	F°	F°
1	0.0	86	70	0.0	94	72	14.0	92	72	40.0	88	74
2	0.0	86	65	0.0	94	75	0.0	90	76	1.0	88	76
3	25.0	88	68	0.0	96	72	0.0	92	76	16.0	88	72
4	10.0	88	66	0.0	72	64	0.0	90	76	5.0	88	72
5	0.0	78	66	0.0	76	60	0.0	94	78	0.0	90	78
6	12.0	76	64	0.0	76	62	0.0	96	79	5.0	92	76
7	0.0	78	62	0.0	80	62	3.0	90	74	8.0	92	75
8	0.0	78	62	0.0	88	74	5.0	86	70	4.0	88	75
9	0.0	86	62	0.0	88	72	0.0	88	70	28.5	86	73
10	0.0	90	62	16.0	88	72	8.0	90	71	1.5	83	73
11	0.0	90	62	0.0	88	68	0.0	90	70	1.0	85	72
12	0.0	86	72	0.0	88	70	0.0	90	68	34.5	88	74
13	0.0	84	64	0.0	90	72	0.0	88	70	5.0	86	76
14	0.0	86	65	0.0	92	72	0.0	88	70	8.0	86	74
15	0.0	72	72	0.0	90	70	0.0	90	68	13.0	84	74
16	0.0	92	72	0.0	88	70	0.0	92	72	0.2	86	75
17	0.0	94	72	0.0	90	72	0.0	92	72	0.0	89	76
18	5.0	78	66	0.0	87	73	0.0	92	72	5.0	84	75
19	0.0	78	64	3.0	93	71	0.0	92	72	10.0	89	74
20	0.0	74	62	66.0	90	72	0.0	94	70	0.5	81	75
21	0.0	74	62	3.0	88	72	0.0	94	72	0.5	85	76
22	0.0	78	58	0.0	90	72	14.0	94	70	0.0	85	75
23	0.0	82	58	0.0	90	73	0.0	94	72	0.0	87	75
24	0.0	86	60	7.0	90	74	0.0	94	72	13.0	84	74
25	0.0	86	60	0.0	90	72	0.0	92	70	0.0	87	75
26	0.0	90	68	0.0	92	72	0.0	94	72	1.3	84	74
27	0.0	90	70	0.0	95	74	40.0	92	74	15.5	82	74
28	0.0	92	72	0.0	95	74	2.0	86	74	4.0	83	73
29	0.0	92	72	0.0	95	78	32.0	82	72	2.0	84	73
30	0.0	94	72	0.0	96	78	2.0	86	74	28.3	83	73
31	0.0	90	72				15.0	86	74			
Monthly Total mm., max. & min. temp.	52.0	94	58	95.0	96	60	135.0	96	68	214.8	92	72
Rainfall, previous 12 months							1267. mm.			1180. mm.		

July			August			September			October			November		
mm.	F°	F°	mm.	F°	F°	mm.	F°	F°	mm.	F°	F°	mm.	F°	F°
18.0	82	73	0.0	86	76	0.5	80	72	3.5	82	72	0.0	84	72
4.5	85	73	0.0	86	74	17.0	80	74	0.0	82	73	0.0	82	68
0.3	84	73	0.0	86	74	6.0	84	74	0.0	84	74	0.0	82	69
2.0	84	74	6.0	88	74	8.5	84	73	13.5	84	72	0.0	81	70
1.7	86	75	31.0	86	74	12.0	85	72	3.0	84	72	38.0	83	70
0.2	87	76	1.0	86	74	37.0	86	73	5.0	84	73	4.0	86	68
1.8	87	73	0.0	87	74	0.0	86	74	1.0	86	74	2.0	–	–
45.0	85	74	0.0	87	76	0.0	87	71	15.0	84	74	0.0	–	–
7.8	82	74	0.0	86	74	0.0	86	74	0.0	84	74	0.0	–	–
0.0	86	76	5.0	84	72	0.0	87	72	2.5	86	75	2.0	–	–
0.0	87	75	2.0	85	74	0.0	88	75	15.0	84	74	32.5	81	70
2.5	87	76	1.0	88	74	5.0	88	74	3.0	84	74	2.0	82	73
0.0	86	72	6.0	84	74	8.7	88	73	7.0	83	75	31.0	81	73
2.0	87	72	10.0	83	75	0.0	88	72	0.0	85	76	16.0	83	72
25.0	84	72	1.5	84	72	0.0	87	73	0.0	86	77	2.0	80	68
0.5	84	74	0.0	86	74	12.0	87	73	1.5	86	75	5.0	81	70
13.0	82	75	38.0	84	74	28.5	80	74	0.0	86	73	0.0	81	70
21.0	87	74	1.5	84	74	12.0	79	72	0.0	84	73	5.0	81	70
2.5	86	74	5.0	86	74	0.0	86	73	0.0	85	73	0.0	83	71
17.0	87	73	0.0	85	73	0.2	86	74	0.0	85	73	1.0	82	70
5.0	87	73	1.5	86	75	5.0	86	74	1.0	85	72	0.0	79	66
0.0	84	72	30.0	86	74	21.0	85	73	4.0	86	72	0.0	81	66
0.0	84	72	0.3	80	75	11.5	85	73	15.0	80	73	6.0	82	70
0.0	84	70	0.0	84	74	0.0	87	74	4.0	–	–	17.5	83	71
0.0	88	76	0.0	88	74	0.0	86	74	2.0	–	–	10.0	83	70
0.0	87	74	0.0	88	72	0.0	86	72	37.0	–	–	2.0	81	68
15.5	88	71	0.0	87	72	4.5	85	73	15.0	–	–	35.0	79	65
6.0	86	72	6.0	88	74	5.5	84	74	3.0	–	–	0.0	81	68
0.5	86	73	6.5	80	74	3.0	81	73	0.0	–	–	18.0	81	72
75.0	88	72	0.0	84	74	3.5	82	72	2.0	86	74	1.0	81	72
0.5	88	77	4.5	86	72				12.0	83	72			
267.8	88	70	156.8	88	72	201.9	88	71	165.0	86	72	230.0	86	65
1325. mm.			1368. mm.			1411. mm.			1498. mm.			1623. mm.		

Contd. Daily rainfall, maximum and minimum temperatures

	1960			1961								
Day of the Month	December			January			February			March		
	mm.	F°	F°	mm.	F°	F°	mm.	F°	F°	mm.	F°	F°
1	0.0	79	64	0.0	–	–	0.0	76	62	4.7	84	72
2	0.0	72	58	0.0	–	–	4.5	82	62	0.0	84	70
3	4.0	75	60	7.0	–	–	2.7	78	70	0.0	82	70
4	9.0	79	62	5.0	–	–	0.0	76	68	0.0	82	72
5	0.0	80	60	11.0	–	–	0.0	82	66	0.0	83	75
6	0.0	80	62	18.0	–	–	0.0	82	66	0.0	83	72
7	0.0	80	65	3.0	–	–	0.0	78	70	0.0	85	70
8	4.0	82	68	0.0	–	–	5.0	72	68	0.0	85	69
9	0.0	82	68	13.0	–	–	0.0	74	66	4.5	73	62
10	0.0	82	67	17.0	–	–	5.7	76	66	0.0	74	60
11	0.0	80	62	0.0	–	–	0.0	70	62	0.0	78	61
12	0.0	79	58	0.0	82	60	12.0	69	64	0.0	84	68
13	1.0	79	60	1.0	82	60	9.0	68	62	0.0	87	71
14	0.0	80	62	0.0	81	61	5.6	76	66	0.0	87	71
15	0.0	82	64	0.0	82	62	16.0	76	72	0.0	85	70
16	1.0	74	63	1.0	78	54	0.0	80	68	0.0	86	70
17	0.0	73	58	14.0	76	66	0.0	82	67	0.0	91	72
18	–	–	–	2.5	72	68	0.0	84	66	0.0	90	74
19	–	–	–	0.0	74	64	0.0	82	73	0.0	86	74
20	–	–	–	0.0	74	64	0.0	82	76	11.9	87	72
21	–	–	–	0.0	72	68	0.0	84	74	0.0	84	72
22	–	–	–	0.0	72	70	3.0	83	74	0.0	85	72
23	–	–	–	4.7	76	68	0.0	84	73	7.2	83	72
24	–	–	–	2.0	76	68	0.0	85	74	0.0	85	72
25	20.0	–	–	0.0	80	70	6.5	85	62	0.0	86	73
26	5.0	–	–	2.0	81	70	1.0	70	66	0.0	87	73
27	15.0	–	–	3.0	78	71	0.0	81	65	0.0	89	73
28	0.0	–	–	0.0	81	68	0.0	84	72	0.0	92	73
29	0.0	–	–	8.0	80	70				0.0	92	73
30	0.0	–	–	0.0	74	66				0.0	94	76
31	0.0	–	–	0.6	72	62				0.0	95	77
Monthly Total mm., max. & min. temp.	59.0	82	58	112.8	82	54	71.0	85	62	28.3	95	60
Rainfall, previous 12 months	1622. mm.			1700. mm.			1761. mm.			1737. mm.		

April			May			June			July			August		
mm.	F°	F°	mm.	F°	F°	mm.	F°	F°	mm.	F°	F°	mm.	F°	F°
1.0	83	72	0.0	89	76	14.0	86	70	0.0	87	74	0.0	88	75
0.0	80	71	0.5	90	76	2.0	86	68	32.5	86	74	0.0	88	75
11.0	88	71	4.5	90	75	5.0	84	68	7.0	87	75	5.0	87	75
5.5	83	72	0.0	88	76	9.0	84	67	0.0	88	75	0.0	87	74
1.0	86	71	0.0	88	76	24.0	85	64	27.0	84	72	10.0	88	75
7.3	90	72	0.0	89	75	5.0	82	64	0.0	87	75	0.0	86	75
9.6	82	74	0.0	87	76	7.0	86	75	14.0	86	73	0.0	89	76
0.0	83	72	0.0	90	76	3.0	85	76	9.0	86	73	0.0	89	77
0.0	89	76	18.0	90	72	9.0	87	75	5.0	84	72	0.0	88	77
0.0	87	78	0.5	90	72	1.0	88	75	0.0	89	71	8.0	88	75
0.0	89	74	0.0	83	70	12.0	87	74	0.0	88	73	15.0	87	74
12.0	93	75	0.0	84	69	17.0	88	75	18.0	87	73	10.0	87	75
0.0	86	76	0.0	89	72	13.0	86	73	0.0	88	74	0.0	87	75
0.0	91	74	0.0	90	76	0.0	88	74	21.0	87	75	0.0	88	76
0.0	92	75	0.0	92	77	0.0	84	74	13.0	87	75	0.0	89	76
6.0	83	70	0.0	92	78	0.0	84	75	0.0	84	75	0.0	89	76
–	–	–	0.0	92	76	2.0	85	73	7.0	86	74	0.0	89	75
0.0	80	73	0.0	89	68	16.0	82	74	0.0	86	74	0.0	89	75
0.0	86	67	0.0	89	70	0.0	87	74	17.0	88	75	13.0	89	75
0.0	84	70	0.0	88	72	0.0	90	84	0.0	85	74	22.0	87	74
0.0	84	69	0.0	90	72	19.0	86	76	11.0	87	75	9.0	86	74
0.0	85	67	0.0	91	73	0.0	89	74	31.0	86	73	2.0	87	75
0.0	84	66	7.0	91	75	0.0	90	76	30.0	84	75	0.0	87	75
0.0	87	67	0.0	92	73	17.0	88	75	27.0	84	73	0.0	87	75
0.0	88	67	0.0	92	68	0.0	89	75	16.0	87	74	0.0	88	75
0.0	89	73	0.0	91	69	0.0	85	76	3.0	87	72	4.0	88	74
0.0	92	72	11.0	90	67	11.0	84	75	7.0	88	75	10.0	88	74
–	–	–	17.0	89	64	0.5	82	74	2.0	88	75	0.0	89	75
0.0	92	73	17.0	82	74	29.5	90	78	13.0	87	75	0.0	89	75
0.0	87	74	5.0	83	65	0.0	–	–	9.0	88	74	6.0	89	76
			31.0	82	66				–	–	–	0.0	90	79
53.4	93	66	111.5	92	64	216.0	90	64	319.5	89	71	114.0	90	74
1696. mm.			1672. mm.			1674. mm.			1725. mm.			1682. mm.		

Contd. Daily rainfall, maximum and minimum temperatures

1961

Day of the Month	September			October			November			December		
	mm.	F°	F°	mm.	F°	F°	mm.	F°	F°	mm.	F°	F°
1	0.0	89	76	4.0	89	71	2.0	86	69	0.0	87	61
2	0.0	89	76	12.0	88	71	0.0	85	69	0.0	87	61
3	4.0	89	76	41.0	86	70	6.0	88	71	0.0	86	62
4	0.0	88	75	7.0	87	70	7.0	88	70	0.0	89	62
5	0.0	89	75	9.0	87	71	4.0	87	71	0.5	87	61
6	0.0	89	76	14.5	86	72	24.0	86	68	4.0	85	61
7	7.0	89	75	0.0	89	75	26.7	86	67	0.0	86	62
8	0.0	89	75	0.0	89	74	0.0	89	67	5.0	87	64
9	0.0	89	76	14.0	85	72	5.0	86	67	0.0	88	64
10	5.0	86	74	18.0	83	71	0.0	87	68	0.0	87	63
11	0.0	88	75	9.0	82	70	13.0	87	68	16.7	83	60
12	0.5	88	75	10.0	83	71	0.0	88	69	8.0	84	60
13	0.0	89	75	12.0	91	69	5.0	88	70	0.0	84	61
14	7.0	89	75	6.0	80	72	0.0	85	69	0.0	85	62
15	0.0	89	75	5.0	82	70	3.0	85	69	0.0	87	64
16	5.0	89	74	9.5	80	72	0.0	85	68	0.0	86	64
17	0.0	88	74	23.5	80	71	0.0	84	67	0.0	86	64
18	19.0	86	73	24.0	79	72	0.0	82	68	0.0	85	62
19	8.0	86	73	0.0	80	71	0.0	82	68	0.0	85	60
20	0.0	86	74	0.0	81	70	0.0	80	65	0.0	85	60
21	0.0	87	74	0.0	79	72	0.0	80	67	–	–	–
22	4.0	87	74	0.0	82	63	0.0	82	70	–	–	–
23	0.0	88	74	0.0	81	65	0.0	83	65	–	–	–
24	9.0	87	74	0.0	88	64	0.0	84	65	–	–	–
25	14.0	87	73	0.0	81	65	0.0	82	62	–	–	–
26	11.0	87	73	11.0	83	69	0.0	84	60	–	–	–
27	0.0	87	74	23.0	82	68	0.0	82	60	–	–	–
28	0.0	88	73	0.0	79	68	0.0	81	60	–	–	–
29	0.0	89	73	0.0	78	72	0.0	83	60	–	–	–
30	0.0	90	71	12.0	88	75	0.0	84	59	–	–	–
31				–	83	74				–	–	–
Monthly Total mm., max. & min. temp.	93.5	90	71	264.5	91	63	95.7	89	59	34.2	89	60
Rainfall, previous 12 months	1574. mm.			1674. mm.			1539. mm.			1514. mm.		

1962

January			February			March			April			May		
mm.	F°	F°	mm.	F°	F°	mm.	F°	F°	mm.	F°	F°	mm.	F°	F°
–	–	–	1.0	84	60	0.0	85	70	0.0	94	73	0.0	89	74
–	–	–	3.5	79	68	0.0	86	66	2.5	87	72	0.0	89	69
–	–	–	0.0	81	67	0.0	86	68	0.5	84	71	0.0	88	68
–	–	–	0.0	80	62	0.0	89	68	3.5	83	70	0.0	88	68
–	–	–	0.5	84	62	14.5	85	64	0.0	87	72	24.0	84	71
–	–	–	0.0	84	66	0.0	76	61	0.0	91	74	0.3	85	71
–	–	–	0.0	82	63	0.0	–	58	38.0	93	74	0.0	85	64
–	–	–	0.0	84	63	0.0	86	64	0.0	87	75	0.0	84	63
–	–	–	0.0	85	70	0.0	88	63	0.0	89	73	0.0	84	64
–	–	–	2.5	85	69	0.0	90	74	0.0	90	74	0.0	86	73
–	–	–	1.0	79	66	0.0	91	72	0.0	91	74	0.0	86	74
–	–	–	0.0	78	60	0.0	94	70	0.0	92	73	19.0	89	69
–	–	–	0.0	77	60	0.0	91	74	23.0	84	70	3.0	85	71
–	–	–	0.0	80	60	0.0	91	74	12.0	77	71	3.0	85	70
0.0	82	63	0.0	84	61	0.0	89	74	0.5	78	71	1.0	82	70
4.0	82	63	0.0	83	60	1.0	78	68	30.0	81	67	19.0	81	68
5.0	92	63	0.0	84	64	13.0	76	64	0.0	81	68	12.0	80	66
0.0	82	63	0.0	86	64	3.0	78	67	0.0	82	65	1.5	81	68
0.0	82	63	0.0	86	72	0.0	83	65	10.0	83	64	0.0	83	68
0.0	82	63	0.0	85	69	0.0	88	65	0.0	79	65	0.0	84	64
0.0	82	60	0.0	87	68	0.0	91	65	0.0	84	65	0.0	85	64
0.0	84	59	0.0	87	68	0.0	93	73	0.0	86	71	0.0	89	66
0.0	83	59	0.0	91	72	0.0	92	70	0.0	88	73	0.0	90	74
0.0	82	59	0.0	88	72	0.0	92	70	0.0	88	72	0.0	89	74
0.0	82	57	0.0	87	70	0.0	92	73	0.0	89	72	0.0	88	74
0.0	82	68	0.0	87	68	0.0	85	66	0.0	89	73	0.0	89	75
6.0	83	66	0.0	88	69	0.0	82	62	0.0	89	75	0.3	90	75
2.5	82	65	0.0	89	69	0.0	83	62	0.0	93	75	0.0	90	76
0.3	79	63				0.0	86	62	0.0	92	75	0.0	90	74
0.0	81	60				0.0	91	69	0.0	90	78	0.0	91	74
0.0	82	61				0.0	94	73				0.0	92	76
17.5	84	57	8.5	91	60	31.5	94	58	120.3	94	64	83.1	92	63
1419. mm.			1357. mm.			1360. mm.			1427. mm.			1398. mm.		

Contd. Daily rainfall, maximum and minimum temperatures

1962

Day of the Month	June			July			August			September		
	mm.	F°	F°	mm.	F°	F°	mm.	F°	F°	mm.	F°	F°
1	0.0	92	75	23.5	88	74	0.0	86	74	3.0	87	71
2	0.0	92	74	12.0	82	72	5.5	86	72	2.0	90	71
3	0.0	93	76	4.0	86	74	10.0	83	74	0.0	88	71
4	0.0	92	78	4.0	86	73	0.0	88	74	0.0	89	73
5	7.5	87	70	22.0	85	72	0.0	88	76	5.0	88	73
6	2.3	87	70	1.5	82	72	2.5	86	71	0.0	88	72
7	63.5	89	74	7.0	84	73	0.0	89	70	0.0	89	72
8	3.8	89	75	0.0	86	73	0.5	89	72	4.0	90	73
9	1.0	84	73	0.0	86	72	17.3	87	72	0.0	87	74
10	21.5	82	69	2.0	85	68	0.0	88	73	0.0	87	71
11	38.0	76	71	1.5	85	73	0.0	89	70	0.0	88	71
12	0.2	83	73	0.0	87	75	0.0	89	72	15.0	88	70
13	26.0	87	74	4.0	85	73	4.5	87	69	5.0	87	70
14	5.0	86	74	0.0	89	72	0.0	88	70	5.0	88	72
15	0.0	86	74	0.3	88	76	0.0	88	72	20.0	88	74
16	0.5	88	76	2.0	86	74	19.0	89	71	5.0	87	74
17	0.0	89	76	11.0	86	71	0.0	88	72	0.0	85	73
18	0.0	89	76	30.5	86	72	4.3	88	71	0.0	87	74
19	2.0	88	74	2.0	84	74	1.3	86	72	0.0	87	74
20	0.9	87	74	0.0	85	73	0.0	88	76	50.0	86	76
21	0.0	86	75	0.0	86	73	0.3	88	72	15.0	85	74
22	0.3	84	76	0.0	88	74	0.0	86	72	100.0	87	73
23	1.0	87	76	0.0	87	71	1.3	88	68	0.0	83	75
24	0.0	89	74	0.0	87	73	15.0	89	68	5.0	87	72
25	0.0	89	75	0.0	88	74	20.5	89	72	0.0	83	72
26	0.0	88	75	1.0	88	71	17.0	86	72	3.0	85	73
27	0.0	88	74	13.0	82	72	0.0	84	75	10.0	87	72
28	0.0	88	74	0.0	78	73	0.3	86	73	0.0	83	76
29	11.5	87	74	0.0	85	74	0.0	83	76	0.0	87	73
30	27.0	87	74	9.3	87	73	0.0	87	74	0.0	85	76
31				0.0	86	74	25.0	88	73			
Monthly Total mm., max. & min. temp.	212.0	93	69	150.6	89	68	144.3	89	68	247.0	90	70
Rainfall, previous 12 months	1394. mm.			1225. mm.			1256. mm.			1409. mm.		

1962 Day of the Month	October			November			December			1963 January		
	mm.	F°	F°	mm.	F°	F°	mm.	F°	F°	mm.	F°	F°
1	0.0	86	73	3.0	76	63	0.0	78	63	–	–	–
2	0.0	87	73	0.0	78	61	0.0	77	62	–	–	–
3	25.0	85	72	0.0	78	60	0.0	78	63	–	–	–
4	5.0	79	74	0.0	77	60	0.0	76	60	–	–	–
5	0.0	85	73	0.0	76	60	0.0	78	63	–	–	–
6	0.0	88	74	0.0	75	59	0.0	77	64	–	–	–
7	0.0	88	70	0.0	79	63	0.0	78	64	–	–	–
8	0.0	87	71	0.0	80	63	0.0	77	63	–	–	–
9	0.0	85	71	2.5	79	59	0.0	78	62	–	–	–
10	9.0	85	73	0.0	80	64	0.0	79	62	–	–	–
11	0.0	83	70	0.0	77	62	0.0	78	63	–	–	–
12	0.0	84	71	0.0	69	63	0.0	76	61	–	–	–
13	10.0	83	71	0.0	74	63	0.0	78	62	–	–	–
14	0.0	84	70	0.0	76	65	0.0	77	58	–	–	–
15	0.0	85	69	0.0	76	66	0.0	77	59	–	–	–
16	7.0	84	70	0.0	76	68	0.0	78	60	–	–	–
17	6.0	82	71	0.0	76	67	0.0	79	60	–	–	–
18	2.5	84	71	0.0	78	66	0.0	78	61	–	–	–
19	0.0	82	67	26.5	71	64	0.0	78	60	–	–	–
20	0.0	85	69	0.0	82	70	0.0	79	61	–	–	–
21	10.0	84	70	0.0	83	71	0.0	76	63	–	–	–
22	11.0	83	71	0.0	84	72	0.0	75	65	–	–	–
23	0.0	83	71	17.5	78	72	0.0	78	66	–	–	–
24	28.5	80	72	14.0	81	71	0.0	75	65	–	–	–
25	41.5	80	71	9.0	80	69	0.5	78	64	–	–	–
26	15.0	78	71	0.0	79	64	0.0	78	65	–	–	–
27	13.0	79	60	0.0	79	63	0.0	76	63	–	–	–
28	23.0	77	73	0.0	77	66	0.0	75	64	–	–	–
29	4.0	81	72	0.0	77	63	0.8	76	65	4.0	84	56
30	1.5	82	72	0.0	79	62	1.0	77	60	0.0	82	68
31	2.0	82	69				0.0	78	62	0.0	–	–
Monthly Total mm., max. & min. temp.	214.0	88	60	72.5	84	59	2.3	79	58	4.0	84	56
Rainfall, previous 12 months	1359. mm.			1336. mm.			1304. mm.			1290. mm.		

Contd. Daily rainfall, maximum and minimum temperatures

1963

Day of the Month	February			March			April		
	mm.	F°	F°	mm.	F°	F°	mm.	F°	F°
1	3.5	74	64	0.0	81	68	0.0	85	66
2	0.0	80	66	0.0	86	71	0.0	84	65
3	15.0	78	64	0.0	85	70	2.0	85	66
4	0.0	70	52	0.0	84	72	0.0	87	69
5	0.0	72	52	0.0	86	72	0.0	87	69
6	0.0	72	50	0.0	89	72	0.0	88	70
7	0.0	75	52	0.0	86	72	0.0	88	71
8	0.0	78	53	0.0	84	72	0.0	88	71
9	0.0	83	54	4.5	83	68	0.0	91	74
10	0.0	86	64	0.0	83	69	0.0	94	76
11	0.0	88	67	0.0	85	70	0.0	95	77
12	0.0	83	67	0.0	89	70	0.0	93	79
13	0.0	83	68	0.0	89	70	0.0	91	76
14	0.0	84	67	0.0	89	71	0.0	87	73
15	0.0	76	66	0.0	88	71	0.0	85	66
16	3.0	73	68	0.2	89	71	0.0	85	63
17	1.0	80	67	0.0	–	–	0.0	89	65
18	0.0	78	66	0.0	88	70	0.0	81	62
19	0.0	86	66	0.0	88	74	0.0	88	72
20	0.0	83	69	0.0	90	73	0.0	88	69
21	0.0	82	60	26.0	87	73	0.0	89	73
22	0.0	83	60	34.0	84	70	0.0	91	73
23	0.0	83	62	9.0	76	65	0.0	89	72
24	0.0	82	64	0.0	76	65	0.0	91	72
25	9.0	81	70	0.0	82	68	0.0	91	78
26	0.0	83	68	0.0	83	68	0.0	88	73
27	30.0	85	68	0.1	83	67	0.0	90	72
28	0.5	85	67	0.0	84	68	0.0	90	73
29				0.0	84	67	0.0	89	74
30				0.0	84	66	0.0	90	74
31				0.0	78	66			
Monthly Total mm., max. & min. temp.	62.0	88	50	73.8	90	65	2.0	95	62
Rainfall, previous 12 months	1344. mm.			1386. mm.			1268. mm.		

Day of the Month	May			June			July		
	mm.	F°	F°	mm.	F°	F°	mm.	F°	F°
1	0.0	92	73	0.0	88	72	9.0	81	73
2	0.0	92	73	0.0	92	72	2.0	84	74
3	0.0	95	73	0.0	92	72	trace	86	74
4	1.5	92	75	0.0	92	76	0.0	87	74
5	0.0	89	75	0.0	95	78	16.0	81	74
6	0.0	91	72	0.0	94	76	4.0	83	74
7	0.0	90	69	0.0	94	78	0.5	83	75
8	0.0	89	68	0.0	92	76	2.0	84	75
9	0.0	89	68	5.5	92	76	trace	88	78
10	0.0	88	68	0.0	96	80	5.0	84	73
11	0.0	88	66	29.0	94	78	4.0	85	75
12	0.0	90	67	7.5	90	78	0.5	86	74
13	0.0	92	70	0.0	94	78	0.0	88	75
14	0.0	92	73	29.0	93	76	0.0	88	73
15	0.0	91	70	0.0	92	77	0.0	89	73
16	0.0	92	70	0.0	90	76	0.0	91	76
17	0.0	91	75	0.0	90	78	26.0	87	73
18	0.0	91	76	1.0	88	75	15.0	87	73
19	0.0	90	76	0.5	85	76	11.0	80	75
20	0.0	92	75	0.0	89	76	1.0	80	74
21	0.0	91	76	0.0	91	78	3.5	84	75
22	0.0	84	74	62.5	87	76	2.0	82	73
23	0.0	87	73	1.5	90	75	14.5	85	73
24	0.0	89	74	2.0	82	74	14.0	83	74
25	0.0	92	72	0.0	89	74	1.5	82	75
26	0.0	92	74	0.0	84	72	0.0	87	72
27	0.0	92	76	0.0	87	75	trace	87	74
28	0.0	94	76	0.0	88	74	0.0	88	73
29	7.0	92	75	trace	88	75	trace	85	73
30	35.0	84	69	0.5	87	76	0.0	86	72
31	4.0	88	71				–	–	–
Monthly Total mm., max. & min. temp.	47.5	95	67	139.0	96	72	131.5	91	72
Rainfall, previous 12 months	1232. mm.			1159. mm.			1140. mm.		

APPENDIX B

SECTION 1

About nineteen miles (30 kilometers) south of Tikal is Lake Petén-Itzá, the largest lake in the Petén, ten miles long and nearly two miles wide. The city of Flores is on an island in the west end of the lake. Most of the population of the Petén is concentrated in Flores, in villages and numerous ranchos scattered along the lake shore, and in the extensive savannahs south of the lake. Open country is much more prevalent there than at Tikal, and the bird-life quite naturally includes species not found at Tikal. Forested areas are, nevertheless, substantial and where they occur are of the same types as found at Tikal. The area around Flores was studied from May to September 1932 by Alulah M. Taibel, director of experimental aviculture in Rovigo, Italy (Taibel 1955). He reported eighty-seven species, of which the following seventeen have not yet been found at Tikal or Uaxactún, (* designates migrants):

Snail or Everglade Kite (*Rostrhamus sociabilis*)
Black-collared Hawk (*Busarellus nigricollis*)
Pale-vented Pigeon (*Columba cayennensis*)
Plain-breasted Ground-Dove (*Columbigallina minuta*)
White-tipped Dove (*Leptotila verreauxi*)
Acorn Woodpecker (*Melanerpes formicivorus*)
Bare-crowned Antbird (*Gymnocichla nudiceps*)
Vermilion Flycatcher (*Pyrocephalus rubinus*)*
Fork-tailed Flycatcher (*Muscivora tyrannus*)*
White-throated Flycatcher (*Empidonax albigularis*)*
Common Tody-Flycatcher (*Todirostrum cinereum*)
Yellow-bellied Elaenia (*Elaenia flavogaster*)
Southern House Wren (*Troglodytes aedon*)*
Black Catbird (*Melanoptila glabrirostris*)
Yellow-billed Cacique (*Amblycercus holosericeus*)
Red-winged Blackbird (*Agelaius phoeniceus*)*
Grayish Saltator (*Saltator coerulescens*)

One additional record was made, by Jorge A. Ibarra, at La Libertad, 27 April 1956:

Olive Sparrow (*Arremonops rufivirgatus*)

SECTION 2

Josselyn Van Tyne (1935) included some one hundred and sixty records from a collection of birds made in the Petén by Harry Malleis (then a Field Assistant with the U. S. Bureau of Biological Survey) between 26 March and 15 May 1923. Eighteen species from the Malleis collection have not been found at Tikal, Uaxactún, or Lake Petén-Itzá. They are listed below, together with the names of the localities (see Map C) where the species were found. (Migrants are indicated by an *.)

Little Tinamou (*Crypturellus soui*), at Chuntuqui, Sacchich, Remate

Semipalmated Plover (*Charadrius semipalmatus*)*, at Remate

Lesser Yellowlegs (*Totanus flavipes*)*, at La Libertad

Spectacled Owl (*Pulsatrix perspicillata*), at Yaloch

Dusky Flycatcher (*E. oberholseri*)* (formerly called Wright's), at Remate

Slate-headed Tody-Flycatcher (*Todirostrum sylvia*), at San Miguel

Mangrove Swallow (*Tachycineta albilinea*), at Chuntuqui, Flores

Cactus Wren (*Campylorhynchus zonatus*), at Gavilán

Gray-breasted Wood-Wren (*Henicorhina leucophrys*), at Santa Rita

Blue-gray Gnatcatcher (*Polioptila caerulea*)*, at Remate, La Libertad

Gray-crowned Yellowthroat (*Geothlypis poliocephala*), at Chuntuqui, Gavilán

Red-eyed Cowbird (*Tangavius aeneus*), at Flores

Eastern Meadowlark (*Sturnella magna*), at La Libertad

Blue-gray Tanager (*Thraupis episcopus*), at Flores, La Libertad

Flame-colored Tanager (*Piranga bidentata*), at Pacomón

Yellow-faced Grassquit (*Tiaris olivacea*), at Macanché, La Libertad

Grasshopper Sparrow (*Ammodramus savannarum*)*, at La Libertad

Yellow-carpalled Sparrow (*Aimophila petenica*), at La Libertad

SECTION 3

Prior to the records cited in Sections 1 and 2, collectors of a much earlier period, in the years from about 1850 and 1860 on, reported a substantial number of species from the Petén. These were mainly from the pine ridges near Poctún, from the Lake Petén-Itzá area, from the savannahs south of that lake at a village then known as Sakluk (now Libertad), and from the "sources of the Río de la Pasión." Some of the localities are only vaguely described and cannot be reliably quoted. Map C shows all the sites of the Petén together with a few across the borders. From such records, as gathered in Salvin and Godman's *Biologia Centrali Americana* (Aves, vols. I, II, III, 1879–1904), have been culled the following sixteen species, which may be added to our list to bring the records of the Petén very close to completion. The sum total of Petén birds is then three hundred and thirty-three.

Chestnut-bellied Heron (*Agami agami*)
Black-crowned Night-Heron (*Nycticorax nycticorax*)
Muscovy (*Cairina moschata*)
American Coot (*Fulica americana*)*
Upland Plover (*Bartramia longicauda*)*
Inca Dove (*Scardafella inca*)
Red-billed Azurecrown (*Amazilia cyanocephala*)
Long-billed Starthroat (*Heliomaster longirostris*)
Ruby-throated Hummingbird (*Archilochus colubris*)*
Wedge-billed Woodcreeper (*Glyphorhynchus spirurus*)
Great Antshrike (*Taraba major*)
Crimson-collared Tanager (*Phlogothraupis sanguinolenta*)
Hepatic Tanager (*Piranga flava*)
Variable Seedeater (*Sporophila aurita*)
Rusty Sparrow (*Aimophila rufescens*)
Botteri's Sparrow (*Aimophila botteri*)

Of the fifty-two species listed in these appendices, but not recorded from the Tikal area, some may turn up there eventually. Others, because of the nature of their habitat, will probably never do so. Except for a few rare or elusive species, such as some of the hawks and owls, very few resident species not known from the Petén are likely ever to be recorded at Tikal. Among the migrants, especially in such groups as the shorebirds, additions to the list may be expected from time to time.

APPENDIX C

PAYNTER'S "ORNITHOGEOGRAPHY"

Paynter (1955) reported four hundred and twenty-nine species, plus fifty-eight races, from the Yucatán Peninsula. His study includes the Mexican states of Campeche, Yucatán, and Quintana Roo, the islands associated with them and the adjacent portions of the Gulf of Mexico and the Caribbean Sea. It does not include the Petén or British Honduras. The southern half of the area, roughly, is forested much like the Petén, and the rainfall approximates that of Tikal, but the climate becomes steadily drier as one goes north; the northernmost portion receives less than half the annual rainfall of Tikal. The changes in the habitat resulting from the gradient in climate are accompanied by changes in the birdlife, adding new species from area to area. The hundreds of miles of coastal habitat touching the Gulf of Mexico and the Caribbean Sea, the numerous islands along the coast, the shallow coastal waters, the large marshes such as the Laguna de Términos, all these harbor further new species. It is no wonder then that this vast area with its great variety of habitats produces many more birds than the two hundred and eighty-one found at Tikal. The wonder is, rather, that Tikal has produced such a large number within its twelve-mile radius.

One further comparison between the two areas is of interest. Paynter grouped two hundred and sixty-two "mainland breeding birds" of the Yucatán Peninsula into three categories (Table II, pp. 301–303). In group A he placed forty-five "species dependent on the presence of water," in the sense of *bodies* of water being present; in group B, one hundred and five "species characteristic of more humid areas," in the sense that there was atmospheric moisture and rainfall; in group C, one hundred and twelve "species characteristic of drier areas." While these groupings are arbitrary, when they are examined for birds which are duplicated at Tikal, we find that Tikal has 26 (58%) of those in group A; 92 (88%) of those in group B, and 59 (53%) of those in group C. The B group, those species of more humid, perhaps quasi-rainforest areas, show a very high degree of duplication of Tikal's birdlife.

APPENDIX D

PENSILE NESTS

Pensile nests of a unique type are built by numerous small fly-catchers. They are not found north of Mexico and are unfamiliar to many North Americans. They are distinguished by specialized methods of suspension, by being fully enclosed except for a small entrance, and by a matting together of the nest materials instead of weaving. All nests of this type have been referred to throughout this book as *pensile nests*. (The nest of the Rose-throated Becard is similarly hung and enclosed, but is more woven than felted.)

A typical pensile nest of the type under discussion is made by compacting vegetable material together, often with the help of cobwebs, into a more or less solid tangle about the size of a man's fist. The mass is penetrated by the bird, gradually pushing the fibers apart to form a small niche. The niche is then expanded into an inner chamber by pressure from within. As the work progresses material is added to the inside to thicken the walls and form a strong nest cavity. Material is also added to the outside to fasten the nest more securely to its anchor, and for other less obvious reasons. Each species has evolved details of structure and location which identify the builder.

The majority of pensile nests are freely pendant from the tip of a slim branchlet or similar anchor, the nest hanging as a dangling structure; some are slung purse-like, held by fibers carried over the top of the branchlet. The majority also have a *visor-like* projection just above the entrance; in one type the visor is greatly enlarged and is called an *apron;* in still another the entrance is a downwardly projecting tube and this type is referred to as a *retort.*

The following sketches illustrate a few of these unique nests and are accompanied by notes on the species known to build them.

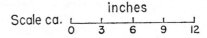

Scale ca.

inches

0   3   6   9   12

PENSILE NESTS WITH VISORS
BEGINNING WITH SIMPLEST

Sepia-capped Flycatcher (*Leptopogon amaurocephalus*)
P. 199. 5 in. long. Condor 46:1:6–8 (R. T. Moore).
Located rather low, in shadowy places such as recesses, shallow coves, and overhangs; one at Tikal, under the peak of roof of outhouse.
Color brown with much green moss also visible.
Eggs 2, pure white.
a-1¼, b-8, c-6, d-?, e-?, f-3, g-12 in.

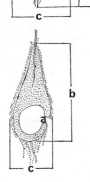

Ruddy-tailed Flycatcher (*Terenotriccus erythrurus*)
P. 185. 4 in. long. P.C.A. 34:534–538 (Skutch), nest pictured p. 535.
Located 5 to 15 ft. up; attached to tip of slender drooping support.
Color blackish; dried leaves added to outside.
Bird sits with reddish tail out of entrance.
Eggs 2, white, blotched heavily on larger end with brown lightly elsewhere.
a-?, b-7 to 9, c-3 in.; elongated as a pyramid.

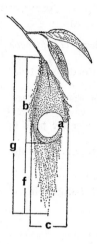

Common Tody-Flycatcher (*Todirostrum cinereum*)

Not at Tikal. 3½ in. long. P.C.A. 34:477–481 (Skutch), nest pictured pp. 478, 480.

Located 3 to 60 ft. up, mostly 6 to moderate heights; attached to some slender support.

Color brownish (sometimes green moss used); effect is one of wind-blown, ragged appearance.

Bird sits facing out.

Eggs 3 (sometimes 2), usually pure white.

a-?, b-6, c-2½ to 3½, d-?, e-?, f-?, g-7, 11, 12, 15 in., elongated.

Slate-headed Tody-Flycatcher (*T. sylvia*)

Not at Tikal. 3½ in. long. P.C.A. 34:491–492 (Skutch).

Located 6 to 10 ft. up; attached and constructed much like *T. cinereum*.

Color brown. Eggs 2, white with chocolate-colored wreath at large end, a sprinkling elsewhere.

Spotted Tody-Tyrant (*T. maculatum*)

Not at Tikal. Auk. 72:4:325–331 (Haverschmidt).

Located 1 to 9 ft. up; hung on a branch rather than from a tip-end, otherwise similar to nests of other Tody Flycatchers except that the "tail" of the nest is usually shorter.

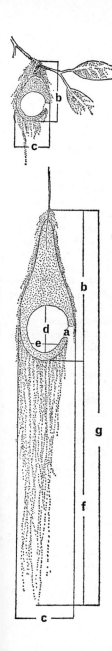

Northern Bentbill (*Oncostoma cinereigulare*)

P. 191. 4 in. long. P.C.A. 34:556–558 (Skutch).
Located low, about 2 ft. above ground.
Color pale brown with some green moss on top and sides.
Bird sits facing out.
Eggs 2, white (Alvarez del Toro).
a-?, b-4½ to 5½, c-2¾ to 3 in.

Southern Bentbill (*Oncostoma olivaceum*)

Not at Tikal. 4 in. long. P.C.A. 34:558–560 (Skutch); nest pictured p. 559.
Located 3 to 14 ft. up; very similar to Northern Bentbill's.
Bird sits facing out.
Eggs 2, white with small blotches and scrawls of pale brown about lower end, and a few such marks elsewhere.
a-?, b-5½, c-3 in.

Ochre-bellied Flycatcher (*Pipromorpha oleaginea*)

P. 200. 5 in. long. P.C.A. 34:565–568 (Skutch), nest pictured p. 566.
Located 2 to 12 ft. up; attached to tip-end of long drooping vine or aerial root; usually near flowing water (but still not an uncommon bird at Tikal); usually hangs free but also close to some solid tree trunk or rock; somewhat pear-shaped with very long beard of 2 to 3 ft.
Color usually green with much mossy cover, but brown in dry weather.
Bird sits facing out.
Eggs 3, less often 2, pure white.
a-1½, b-12 to 14, c-3½, d-4, e-2½, f-24 to 36 in., g-3 ft. to 4 ft.

Olive-striped Flycatcher (*Mionectes olivaceus*)

Not at Tikal. Nest very similar to *Pipromorpha*'s.

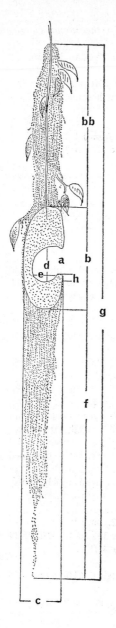

Royal Flycatcher (*Onychorhynchus coronatus*)

P. 187. 6½ in. long. P.C.A. 34:519–523 (Skutch), nest pictured p. 522.

Located 8 to 20 ft. up; attached to end of drooping branchlet or thin vine, preferably above running water (but still not uncommon at Tikal); may be anchored to lateral branchlets farther down, but nest niche is placed still lower and in freely swinging portion. Usually very long, but length varies from 3 ft. (or less) to 6 ft. There is no definite visor and only a very shallow nest cup.

Color brownish, the whole appearing like dead vegetable matter fallen from above and caught in a branch.

Bird sits with tail sticking out of the entrance.

Eggs 2, unusually colored, dark red-brown at the larger end shading to buff at small end.

a-3½ (by 1½ wide), b-about 12, bb-12 or more, c-about 5, d-4½, e-2½ inches, f-1 ft. or more, g-3 ft. to 6 ft. h(depth)-½ in.

PENSILE NESTS WITH "APRON"

Sulphur-rumped Flycatcher (*Myiobius sulphureipygius*) or (*M. barbatus*)

P. 186. 5 in. long. P.C.A. 34:540–544 (Skutch); nest pictured p. 543.

Located 6 to 35 ft. up, but usually fairly low; attached to tip of branchlet or dangling vine.

Color brownish.

Bird sits with tail out over the entrance.

Eggs 2, white, finely sprinkled chocolate brown, mostly as wreath at larger end.

a-small, circular, beneath apron, b-9, bb-may be 15, c-3½, d-?, e-?, f-?, g-extreme may be to 20 inches.

The sketches below, after Skutch (*ibid.*), pp. 541, 543, illustrate building sequence.

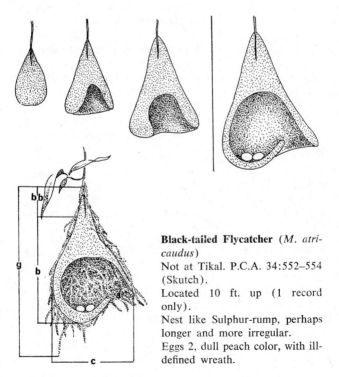

Black-tailed Flycatcher (*M. atricaudus*)

Not at Tikal. P.C.A. 34:552–554 (Skutch).

Located 10 ft. up (1 record only).

Nest like Sulphur-rump, perhaps longer and more irregular.

Eggs 2, dull peach color, with ill-defined wreath.

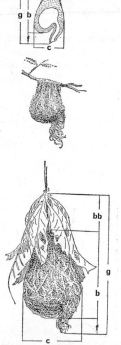

PENSILE NESTS OF "RETORT" TYPE

Yellow-olive Flycatcher or **Sulphury Flatbill** (*Tolmomyias sulphurescens*)
P. 189. 5½ in. long. P.C.A. 34:496–500 (Skutch), nest pictured p. 499.
Located 6 to 20 ft. up, sometimes near wasp nests, attached *purse-like* over a slender, usually leafy, twig. Entrance is a downward-opening tube, about 2 to 3 in. long. Color is black.
Bird sits with head above the entrance tube.
Eggs 2 or 3, white or creamy, sparingly speckled with pale brown.
a-?, b-5½, c-3½, d-?, e-?, f-2 to 3, g-7½ to 8¼ inches.

Yellow-vented Flatbill (*Tolmomyias flaviventris*)
Not at Tikal. Wilson Bull. 62:2:214–216 (Haverschmidt)
Nest similar to Yellow-olive Flycatcher's.

Eye-ringed Flatbill (*Rhynchocyclus brevirostris*)
P. 190. 6 in. long. P.C.A. 34:508–514 (Skutch).
Located 8 to 35 ft. up; attached to tip-end of a leafy branchlet or dangling vine; similar but much bulkier than Yellow-olive's and made of coarser materials; some have up to 6 in. of large papery leaves added over the top. Sleeping nests are also made, flimsier, the spout shorter or lacking.
Color is blackish in tone. Bird sits with head over the tube.
Eggs 2, pale red-brown, darker brown mottling at larger end.
a-?, b-11½, bb-6, c-5 × 6, d-?, e-?, f-2½, g-15 to 20 in.

Olivaceous Flatbill (*Rhynchocyclus olivaceus*)
Not at Tikal. P.C.A. 34:513, 514 (Skutch). Located 6 to 20 ft. up.
Very similar to Eye-ringed Flatbill's nest.

PLATE 36   The main road close to the author's camp at Tikal.

PLATE 37 The author and his assistant, José M. Marquéz, preparing specimens. Photograph courtesy of George Holton.

PLATE 38   The Posada de la Selva or Jungle Lodge at Tikal.

PLATE 39   A clearing in the jungle at Tikal.

APPENDIX E

The tabulation below of the annotated list of the birds of the Tikal area is subdivided into groups in accordance with their "status" as defined on page xxvii. An asterisk (*) denotes a sight record.

RESIDENTS (INCLUDING 4 SUMMER RESIDENTS, MARKED S.R.)

Great Tinamou
Slaty-breasted Tinamou
Rufescent Tinamou
Least Grebe
Bare-throated Tiger-Heron
* King Vulture
* Black Vulture
* Turkey Vulture
* Swallow-tailed Kite
Hook-billed Kite
Double-toothed Kite
Bicolored Hawk
Roadside Hawk
* Gray Hawk
White Hawk
Ornate Hawk-Eagle
Black Hawk-Eagle
Crane Hawk
Laughing Falcon
Collared Forest-Falcon
Barred Forest-Falcon
Orange-breasted Falcon
Bat Falcon
Great Curassow
Crested Guan

Plain Chachalaca
Spotted Wood-Quail
Singing Quail
Ocellated Turkey
Gray-necked Wood-Rail
Ruddy Crake
* American Jaçana
Scaled Pigeon
Short-billed Pigeon
Ruddy Ground-Dove
Blue Ground-Dove
Gray-headed Dove
Ruddy Quail-Dove
Olive-throated Parakeet
Brown-hooded Parrot
White-crowned Parrot
White-fronted Parrot
Red-lored Parrot
Mealy Parrot
Squirrel Cuckoo
Groove-billed Ani
Pheasant Cuckoo
Vermiculated Screech-Owl
Mottled Wood-Owl
Black-and-white Owl

Common Potoo
Pauraque
Yucatán Poorwill
Dusky-backed Swift
* Lesser Swallow-tailed Swift
Long-tailed Hermit
Little Hermit
Scaly-breasted Hummingbird
Wedge-tailed Sabrewing
White-necked Jacobin
* Green-breasted Mango
Fork-tailed Emerald
White-bellied Emerald
Fawn-breasted Hummingbird
Rufous-tailed Hummingbird
Purple-crowned Fairy
Slaty-tailed Trogon
Citreoline Trogon
Collared Trogon
Violaceous Trogon
Ringed Kingfisher
Pygmy Kingfisher
Tody Motmot
Blue-crowned Motmot
Rufous-tailed Jacamar
White-necked Puffbird
White-whiskered Puffbird
Emerald Toucanet
Collared Araçari
Keel-billed Toucan
Golden-olive Woodpecker
Chestnut-colored Woodpecker
Lineated Woodpecker
Golden-fronted Woodpecker
Black-cheeked Woodpecker
Smoky-brown Woodpecker
Pale-billed Woodpecker
Tawny-winged Woodcreeper
Ruddy Woodcreeper
Olivaceous Woodcreeper
Barred Woodcreeper
Ivory-billed Woodcreeper

Streak-headed Woodcreeper
Buff-throated Foliage-gleaner
Plain Xenops
Scaly-throated Leafscraper
Barred Antshrike
Russet Antshrike
Plain Antvireo
Dot-winged Antwren
Dusky Antbird
Black-faced Antthrush
Bright-rumped Attila
Rufous Mourner
Rufous Piha
Cinnamon Becard
Gray-collared Becard
Rose-throated Becard
Masked Tityra
Black-crowned Tityra
Red-capped Manakin
White-collared Manakin
Thrush-like Manakin
Tropical Kingbird
Piratic Flycatcher (S.R.)
Sulphur-bellied Flycatcher
  (S.R.)
Streaked Flycatcher (S.R.)
Boat-billed Flycatcher
Social Flycatcher
Great Kiskadee
Brown-crested Flycatcher
Yucatán Flycatcher
Dusky-capped Flycatcher
Tropical Pewee
Ruddy-tailed Flycatcher
Sulphur-rumped Flycatcher
Royal Flycatcher
White-throated Spadebill
Yellow-olive Flycatcher
Eye-ringed Flatbill
Northern Bentbill
Greenish Elaenia
Northern Beardless Tyrannulet

* Paltry Tyrannulet
Yellow-bellied Tyrannulet
Sepia-capped Flycatcher
Ochre-bellied Flycatcher
Gray-breasted Martin
Rough-winged Swallow
Black-and-blue Jay
Green Jay
Brown Jay
White-browed Wren
Spot-breasted Wren
White-breasted Wood-Wren
White-bellied Wren
White-throated Robin
Clay-colored Robin
Tropical Gnatcatcher
Long-billed Gnatwren
Green Shrike-Vireo
Yellow-green Vireo (S.R.)
Mangrove Vireo
Tawny-crowned Greenlet
Gray-headed Greenlet
Green Honeycreeper
Red-legged Honeycreeper
Gray-throated Chat
Golden-crowned Warbler
Montezuma Oropéndola
Giant Cowbird
Melodious Blackbird
Black-cowled Oriole
Yellow-tailed Oriole
Yellow-throated Euphonia
Olive-backed Euphonia
Masked Tanager
Yellow-winged Tanager
Rose-throated Tanager
White-winged Tanager
Red-crowned Ant-Tanager
Red-throated Ant-Tanager
Black-throated Shrike Tanager
Gray-headed Tanager
Black-headed Saltator

Black-faced Grosbeak
Cardinal
Blue-black Grosbeak
Blue Bunting
White-collared Seedeater
Thick-billed Seedfinch
Blue-black Grassquit
Orange-billed Sparrow
Green-backed Sparrow

RESIDENTS "FORMERLY"
(based on bones found at
Tikal)

*** Black-throated Bobwhite
*** Barn Owl
*** Ferruginous Pygmy Owl

*VISITORS (RESIDENT IN
PETÉN)*

* Olivaceous Cormorant
* Anhinga
Cattle Egret
Yellow-crowned Night Heron
* Boat-billed Heron
* Wood Stork
* Plumbeous Kite
* Common Black Hawk
Great Black Hawk
* Limpkin
* Purple Gallinule
Sungrebe
Black-necked Stilt
* Scarlet Macaw
Amazon Kingfisher
Green Kingfisher
Strong-billed Woodcreeper
Bananaquit
* Great-tailed Grackle
* Scrub Euphonia
Chipping Sparrow

TRANSIENTS AND WINTER RESIDENTS

* * Pied-billed Grebe (or Resident?)
* * Great Blue Heron (or Resident?)
* Green Heron (or Resident?)
* Little Blue Heron (or Resident?)
* * Reddish Egret
* * Common Egret (or Resident?)
* * Snowy Egret (or Resident?)
* * Blue-winged Teal
* Broad-winged Hawk
* American Kestrel
* * Sora
* Killdeer
* * Common Snipe
* Spotted Sandpiper
* Solitary Sandpiper
* Pectoral Sandpiper
* White-rumped Sandpiper
* * Common (?) Night Hawk
* Chuck-will's-widow
* Belted Kingfisher
* Yellow-bellied Sapsucker
* Scissor-tailed Flycatcher
* Eastern Kingbird
* Great-crested Flycatcher
* Olive-sided Flycatcher
* Eastern Wood-Pewee
* Yellow-bellied Flycatcher
* Traill's Flycatcher
* Least Flycatcher
* * Purple Martin
* Barn Swallow
* Catbird
* Wood Thrush
* Swainson's Thrush
* Gray-cheeked Thrush
* Veery
* * Cedar Waxwing
* White-eyed Vireo
* * Yellow-throated Vireo
* Red-eyed Vireo
* Philadelphia Vireo
* Black-and-white Warbler
* Prothonotary Warbler
* Worm-eating Warbler
* Blue-winged Warbler
* Tennessee Warbler
* Yellow Warbler
* Magnolia Warbler
* Myrtle Warbler
* * Townsend's Warbler
* Black-throated Green Warbler
* Cerulean Warbler
* Blackburnian Warbler
* Chestnut-sided Warbler
* Ovenbird
* Northern Waterthrush
* Louisiana Waterthrush
* Kentucky Warbler
* Mourning Warbler
* Common Yellowthroat
* Yellow-breasted Chat
* Hooded Warbler
* Pileolated Warbler
* American Redstart
* Bobolink
* Orchard Oriole
* Baltimore Oriole
* Summer Tanager
* Rose-breasted Grosbeak
* Blue Grosbeak
* Indigo Bunting
* Painted Bunting
* Dickcissel

APPENDIX F

NEW RECORDS FOR THE PETÉN

Some seventy-eight species appear to be "new" records for the Department of the Petén, Guatemala. Some of those listed below are recorded as present in neighboring departments (as Alta Verapaz), and in British Honduras, but I have found no clear evidence for their presence in the Petén. Map C includes my best effort to locate some of the sites of former records within the Petén and also some sites which border the Petén. An asterisk (*) denotes sight record.

RESIDENTS

Least Grebe (*Podiceps dominicus*)
Double-toothed Kite (*Harpagus bidentatus*)
Black Hawk-Eagle (*Spizaëtus tyrannus*)
Collared Forest-Falcon (*Micrastur semitorquatus*)
Barred Forest-Falcon (*Micrastur ruficollis*)
Orange-breasted Falcon (*Falco deiroleucus*)
Brown-hooded Parrot (*Pionopsitta haematotis*)
Black-and-white Owl (*Ciccaba nigrolineata*)
Lesser Swallow-tailed Swift (*Panyptila cayennensis*)
Scaly-breasted Hummingbird (*Phaeochroa cuvierii*)
Fawn-breasted Hummingbird (*Amazilia yucatanensis*)
Collared Trogon (*Trogon collaris*)
White-necked Puffbird (*Notharcus macrorhynchos*)
Barred Woodcreeper (*Dendrocolaptes certhia*)
Russet Antshrike (*Thamnistes anabatinus*)
Rufous Mourner (*Rhytipterna holerythra*)
Rufous Piha (*Lipaugus unirufus*)
Gray-collared Becard (*Pachyramphus major*)
Rose-throated Becard (*Platypsaris aglaiae*)
Piratic Flycatcher (*Legatus leucophaius*)
Great Kiskadee (*Pitangus sulphuratus*)

Yucatán Flycatcher (*Myiarchus yucatanensis*)
Northern Bentbill (*Oncostoma cinereigulare*)
* Paltry Tyrannulet (*Tyranniscus vilissimus*)
Yellow-bellied Tyrannulet (*Ornithion semiflavum*)
Green Shrike-Vireo (*Smaragdolanius pulchellus*)
Green Honeycreeper (*Chlorophanes spiza*)
Gray-throated Chat (*Granatellus sallaei*)
White-winged Tanager (*Piranga leucoptera*)

RESIDENT "FORMERLY"

Ferruginous Pygmy Owl (*Glaucidium brasilianum*)

VISITORS

Cattle Egret (*Bubulcus ibis*)
Yellow-crowned Night-Heron (*Nyctanassa violacea*)
* Wood Stork (*Mycteria americana*)
* Common Black Hawk (*Buteogallus anthracinus*)
Sungrebe (*Heliornis fulica*)
Black-necked Stilt (*Himantopus himantopus*)

TRANSIENTS AND WINTER RESIDENTS

* Great Blue Heron (*Ardea herodias*)
* Reddish Egret (*Dichromanassa rufescens*)
* Common Egret (*Casmerodius albus*)
* Snowy Egret (*Leucophoyx thula*)
* Blue-winged Teal (*Anas discors*)
Broad-winged Hawk (*Buteo platypterus*)
* Sora (*Porzana carolina*)
Killdeer (*Charadrius vociferus*)
* Common Snipe (*Capella gallinago*)
Pectoral Sandpiper (*Erolia melanotos*)
* Common (?) Nighthawk (*Chordeiles minor*)
Chuck-will's-widow (*Caprimulgus carolinensis*)
Belted Kingfisher (*Megaceryle alcyon*)
Yellow-bellied Sapsucker (*Sphyrapicus varius*)
Scissor-tailed Flycatcher (*Muscivora forficata*)
Eastern Kingbird (*Tyrannus tyrannus*)
Great-crested Flycatcher (*Myiarchus crinitus*)
Olive-sided Flycatcher (*Nuttallornis borealis*)

Yellow-bellied Flycatcher (*Empidonax flaviventris*)
Traill's Flycatcher (*Empidonax traillii*)
* Purple Martin (*Progne subis*)
Barn Swallow (*Hirundo rustica*)
Veery (*Hylocichla fuscescens*)
* Yellow-throated Vireo (*Vireo flavifrons*)
Philadelphia Vireo (*Vireo philadelphicus*)
Prothonotary Warbler (*Protonotaria citrea*)
Worm-eating Warbler (*Helmitheros vermivorus*)
Blue-winged Warbler (*Vermivora pinus*)
Tennessee Warbler (*Vermivora peregrina*)
Myrtle Warbler (*Dendroica coronata*)
* Townsend's Warbler (*Dendroica townsendi*)
Black-throated Green Warbler (*Dendroica virens*)
Cerulean Warbler (*Dendroica cerulea*)
Blackburnian Warbler (*Dendroica fusca*)
Chestnut-sided Warbler (*Dendroica pensylvanica*)
Pileolated Warbler (*Wilsonia pusilla*)
Bobolink (*Dolichonyx oryzivorus*)
Summer Tanager (*Piranga rubra*)
Rose-breasted Grosbeak (*Pheucticus ludovicianus*)

APPENDIX G

The following is a list of the only *sight records* which have been accepted for the Petén records:

Pied-billed Grebe (*Podilymbus podiceps*)
Neotropic Cormorant (*Phalacrocorax brasilianus*)
Anhinga (*Anhinga anhinga*)
Great Blue Heron (*Ardea herodias*)
Reddish Egret (*Hydranassa rufescens*)
Common Egret (*Egretta alba*)
Snowy Egret (*Egretta thula*)
Boat-billed Heron (*Cochlearius cochlearius*)
Wood Ibis (*Mycteria americana*)
Blue-winged Teal (*Anas discors*)
King Vulture (*Sarcoramphus papa*)
Black Vulture (*Coragyps atratus*)
Turkey Vulture (*Cathartes aura*)
Swallow-tailed Kite (*Elanoides forficatus*)
Plumbeous Kite (*Ictinia plumbea*)
Gray Hawk (*Buteo nitidus*)
Common Black Hawk (*Buteogallus anthracinus*)
Limpkin (*Aramus guarauna*)
Sora (*Porzana carolina*)
Purple Gallinule (*Porphyrula martinica*)
American Jaçana (*Jacana spinosa*)
Common Snipe (*Capella gallinago*)
Scarlet Macaw (*Ara macao*)
Common Nighthawk (*Chordeiles minor*)
Lesser Swallow-tailed Swift (*Panyptila cayennensis*)
Green-breasted Mango (*Anthracothorax prevosti*)
Paltry Tyrannulet (*Tyranniscus vilissimus*)
Purple Martin (*Progne subis*)
Cedar Waxwing (*Bombycilla cedrorum*)
Yellow-throated Vireo (*Vireo flavifrons*)
Townsend's Warbler (*Dendroica townsendi*)
Great-tailed Grackle (*Cassidix mexicanus*)
Scrub Euphonia (*Tanagra affinis*)

MAPS

MAP A is an insert on Map B and shows the location of Tikal, el Petén, Guatemala, in relation to the Yucatán Peninsula, Mexico, British Honduras, Honduras, Cuba, and the United States.

MAP B shows the main roads and the trails in Tikal and its immediate surroundings, the area to which the author's field work for this publication was limited.

MAP C shows most of the sites which have been reported by previous collectors within the Department of the Petén and many of those which border the Petén are shown on Map C. In order to make the references as complete as possible, the reports of Griscom (1932), those of Van Tyne (1935), and those of Salvin and Godman (1879–1904) have been analyzed. There is some confusion among those records, as is to be expected. Some sites which were not on any maps when Griscom wrote his gazetteer now appear on maps in positions which vary materially from his.

An example of a possible variance of this kind is Griscom's location of Finca Sepacuité at position number 35. Finca Sepacuité carries with it the locations of Chipoc, Chimoxán, Secanquim, and Sepur. Modern maps show a village named Sepacuité some twenty-five kilometers farther south. It is interesting to note that the village is in an area which agrees much more closely with the altitudes assigned by Griscom to the sites than does the area of his choice. Where questions of this nature occur, the site has been enclosed in brackets on Map C.

Altitudes above sea-level are approximations in most cases. They are given in meters. Towns and villages other than collecting sites occur on Map C, but the following lists include only those reported in the references cited above. They are tabulated separately for the Petén and for the bordering portions of Alta Verapaz, Huehuetenango, El Quiché, and Izabal. Numbers which precede some names are as recorded by Griscom (ibid.).

LOCATIONS IN PETÉN

Bocamonte (Pacomón)
(170 m.)
Chantuqui (Chuntuqui)
(220 m.)
Dolores
Dos Arroyos
El Cimarrón (Cimarrón)
El Gallo (El Galla, Guyo)
El Remate (Remate) (130 m.,
325 m. on cliffs)
Flores (130 m.)
Gavilán (El Gavilán) (250 m.)
Ixtinto (Ixtinta, Ixtinte)
(150 m.)
Juntecholol (150 m.)
Laguna Petén-Itzá (Lake of
Petén) (120 m.)
La Libertad (Sakluk) (170 m.)
Macanché (Macambie)
Nueva Aguada
Pacomón (see Bocamonte)
Paso Subín (Subín) (150 m.)
Plancha de Piedra
Poptún (Poctun) (500 m.)
Rancho Tuilhá (300 m.)
Remate (see El Remate)
Río de la Pasión
Río Sarstún (Río Sarstoon)
Sacchich (200 m.)
Sakluk (see La Libertad)
San Andrés
San Benito (130 m.)
San Francisco (Chachaclún)
San Luis (400 m.)
San Miguel (120 m.)
Santa Ana (200 m.)
Santa Rita (300 m.)
Santo Toribio (350 m.)
Sotz (El Zotz) (Laguna del
Zotz) (190 m.)

Subín (see Paso Subín)
Tikal (200 to 250 m.)
Uaxactún (200 m.)
Yaloch (Yaloche) (170 m.)
Yaxhá (Yashá)

LOCATIONS IN ALTA VERAPAZ

3 Aquil (Achil) (600 m.)
Cahabón (220 m.)
12 Cantoloc (Candoloc, Can-
toöloc) (200 m.)
Cobán (1300 m.)
14 Chamá (350 m.)
Chahal (Chialal) (220 m.)
20 Chimoxán (460 m.)
Chimuchuch (200 m.)
21 Chimuy (200 m.)
22 Chipoc (620 m. but only
250 m. where shown)
Chiriquyu (not shown, near
Cobán)
Chisec (200 m.)
23 Choctum (370 m.)
30 Finca Concepción
(1140 m.)
35 Finca Sepacuité (1000 m.
but only 500 m. where
shown)
Gubilguitz (Cubilguitz)
(300 m.)
41 Kampamak
Kokak (not shown, near
Lanquín)
46 Lanquín (Langín, San Agus-
tín Lanquín) (400 m.)
Raxché (Rasché) (local
mountain range)
Río Chixoy (Río Negro)
48 Salinas (Las Salinas)
(130 m.)

San Pedro de Carchá (Carchá) (780 m.)

Sayuchil (not shown, near Gubilguitz)

Secanquim (500 m.)

Sepacuité (1000 m.)

Sepur (not shown, near Finca Sepacuité) (900 m.)

53 Tuilá (310 m.) (see Rancho Tuilhá to north)

77 Yaxcabnal (Yaxcamnal) (250 m.)

LOCATIONS IN HUEHUE-TENANGO

Barillas (Barrillos) (1600 m.)

LOCATIONS IN EL QUICHÉ

34 Finca La Perla (1350 m.)

LOCATIONS IN IZABAL

Lívingston

Lago de Izabal

Puerto Barrios

Río Chocón (Río Chocan)

Río Dulce

67 Santo Tomás

BIBLIOGRAPHY

REFERENCES

Reference has been made throughout this publication to many sources of information, derived from individuals, technical papers, monographs, periodicals, journals, and even complete books. In each case the reference has been headed by an identifying name. The names are listed below, in alphabetical order, together with additional clarifying material.

Allen 1961. *Birds of the Caribbean,* Robert P. Allen; The Viking Press, New York, N. Y.

Alvarez del Toro 1964. *Lista de las Aves de Chiapas,* Miguel Alvarez del Toro; Instituto de Sciencias y Artes de Chiapas, Tuxtla Gutierrez, México.

AOU 1957. *Check-list of North American Birds,* 5th ed.; The American Ornithologists' Union, Box 8669, Louisiana State University, Baton Rouge, La. 70803.

Animal Kingdom. *Animal Kingdom,* a bimonthly Bulletin of the New York Zoological Society, 630 Fifth Avenue, New York, N. Y. 10020.

Ardea. *Ardea,* a quarterly, Nederlandsche Ornithologische Vereeniging, Leiden, The Netherlands.

Audubon Magazine. *Audubon Magazine,* a bimonthly publication of the National Audubon Society, 1130 Fifth Avenue, New York, N. Y. 10028.

Auk. *The Auk,* a quarterly journal of The American Ornithologists' Union (see AOU).

Austin 1961. *Birds of the World,* Oliver L. Austin, Jr.; Golden Press, New York, N. Y.

Aveledo 1958. *Aves de Caza,* Gines y Ramón Aveledo; Monografía Numero 4, Sociedad Venezolana de Ciencias Naturales, Caracas, Venezuela.

Basch 1959. *Land Mollusca of the Tikal National Park, Guatemala,* Paul F. Basch; Occ. Papers, No. 612, Univ. Mich. Mus. Zool., Ann Arbor, Mich.

Bent. *Life Histories of North American Birds,* A. C. Bent; 20 volumes, 1924–1958, U. S. Natl. Mus. Bull.; reprinted by Dover Publications, New York, N. Y.

Biología Centrali Americana. See Salvin and Godman.

Bird Songs. *Birds of the Tropics,* Paul Schwartz; recordings, Instituto Neotropical, Caracas, Venezuela; Lab. of Ornith., Cornell Univ., Ithaca, N. Y. 14850.

Blake 1953. *Birds of Mexico,* Emmet R. Blake; The Univ. of Chicago Press, Chicago, Ill. 60605.

Bond 1961. *Birds of the West Indies,* James Bond; Houghton Mifflin Co., Boston, Mass.

Boucard 1883. "On a Collection of Birds from Yucatán," Adolphe Boucard; *Zool. Soc. London, Proc.* 51:434–462.

Brewster and Chapman 1895. "Notes on Birds Observed in Trinidad," Wm. Brewster and Frank M. Chapman; *Auk* 12:3:208–211.

Chapman 1929. *My Tropical Air Castle,* Frank M. Chapman; D. Appleton & Co., New York, N. Y. (out of print)

Cole 1906. "Aves," in *Vertebrata from Yucatan,* L. J. Cole; Bull. 50:109–146, Mus. Comp. Zool., Cambridge, Mass. 02138.

Condor. *The Condor,* a bimonthly journal of the Cooper Ornithological Society, Berkeley, Calif. 94720.

Cruz 1939. *Lexico de la Fauna Yucateca,* S. Pacheco Cruz; Imprenta Oriente, Mérida, Yucatán, México.

Davis, L. Irby. See Mexican Bird Songs.

de Schauensee 1964. *The Birds of Colombia,* R. Meyer de Schauensee; The Academy of Natural Sciences of Philadelphia; Livingston Publishing Co., Narberth, Pa.

Dick 1957. *The Warblers of America,* Ludlow Griscom, Alexander Sprunt, Jr., and others; illustrated by John Henry Dick; The Devin-Adair Co., New York, N. Y.

Dilger. "Ecology of Thrushes," Wm. C. Dilger; *Wilson Bull.* 68:3:171–199.

Edwards 1955. *Finding Birds in Mexico,* Ernest P. Edwards; E. P. Edwards & Co., Amherst, Va.

Edwards 1959. "Nesting of Lesser Swallow-tailed Swift in Guatemala"; *Auk* 76:3:358–359.

Eisenmann 1952. *Annotated List of Birds of Barro Colorado Island,* Eugene Eisenmann; Smithsonian Misc. Coll. 117:5, pub. no. 4058, Smithsonian Inst., Washington 25, D. C.

Eisenmann 1955. *The Species of Middle American Birds,* Eugene Eisenmann; Trans. of the Linnaean Soc. of N. Y., Vol. 7, c/o Am. Mus. Nat. Hist., New York, N. Y. 10024.

Field Mus. *The Birds of El Salvador,* D. R. Dickey and A. J. van Rossem; Zool. Ser. 23 (1938), Pub. 406 (out of print), Field Mus. Nat. Hist., Chicago, Ill. 60605.

Friedmann, Griscom, and Moore 1950. See P.C.A. 29.

Gilliard 1958. *Living Birds of the World,* E. Thomas Gilliard; Doubleday & Co., Garden City, N. Y.

Greenewalt 1960. *Hummingbirds,* Crawford H. Greenewalt; Doubleday & Co., Garden City, N. Y.

Griscom 1932. *The Distribution of Bird-Life in Guatemala,* Ludlow Griscom; Bull. 64, Am. Mus. Nat. Hist., New York, N. Y. 10024.

Handbuch der Oölogie. *Handbuch der Oölogie,* Parts 1–9 issued, Max Schönwetter and Wilhelm Meise; Akademie Verlag, Berlin, Germany.

Haverschmidt. "The breeding habits of *Panyptila cayennensis,*" F. Haverschmidt; *Auk* 75:2:121–130; and other references.

Hellmayr. *Catalogue of Birds of the Americas,* C. B. Cory, C. E. Hellmayr, and B. Conover; Zool. Ser. 13, various volumes, Field Mus. Nat. Hist., Chicago, Ill. 60605.

Herklots 1961. *The Birds of Trinidad and Tobago,* Geoffrey A. C. Herklots; Collins Clear-Type Press, London, England.

Holdridge 1956. "Middle America," in *A World Geography of Forest Resources,* Leslie R. Holdridge; The Ronald Press Co., New York, N. Y.

Holdridge 1957. "The Vegetation of Mainland Middle America," in *Proc. 8th Pacific Congress,* Vol. 4:148–161.

Hundley. Mrs. Margaret H. Hundley, Florida Audubon Soc., in litt.

Ibis. *The Ibis,* a quarterly journal of the British Ornithologists' Union, c/o Bird Room, British Mus. (Nat. Hist.), London, S.W. 7, England.

Jour. für Ornith. *Journal für Ornithologie,* quarterly, Deutschen Ornithologen-Gesellschaft, West Berlin, Germany.

K. de Phelps 1953. *Aves Venezolanas,* Kathleen Deery de Phelps; Talleres de Cromotip, Caracas, Venezuela.

Lack 1947–48. "The Significance of Clutch Size," David Lack; *Ibis* 89:April:303.

Lancaster. "Life History of the Boucard Tinamou in British Honduras," Douglas A. Lancaster; *Condor* 66:3:165–181 and 66:4:253–276.

Lanyon. Reports on genus *Myiarchus,* Wesley E. Lanyon; *Condor* 62:5:341–350 and 63:6:421–449.

Lundell 1937. *The Vegetation of Petén,* Cyrus Longworth Lundell;

Publication No. 478, Carnegie Institution of Washington, Washington 5, D. C.

Mason. C. Russell Mason, Director Florida Audubon Soc., in litt.

Mexican Bird Songs. *Mexican Bird Songs,* recordings by L. Irby Davis, Laboratory of Ornithology, Cornell Univ., Ithaca, N. Y. 14850.

Miller, Friedmann, Griscom, and Moore 1957. See P.C.A. 33.

Monroe 1963. *Notes on Avian Genus Arremonops, etc.,* Burt L. Monroe, Jr.; Occ. Papers No. 38, Louisiana State Univ., Baton Rouge, La. 70803.

Murphy and Amadon 1953. *Land Birds of America,* Robert Cushman Murphy and Dean Amadon; McGraw-Hill Book Co., New York, N. Y.

Nature. *Nature Magazine,* formerly pub. by American Nature Assoc.; now incorporated with *Natural History,* the journal of the Am. Mus. of Nat. Hist., New York, N. Y. 10024.

Northwest Science 1945. "The Migration of Swainson's Hawks Through Costa Rica," Alexander F. Skutch; *Northwest Science* 19:4:80–89, State College of Washington, Pullman, Wash.

Novitates 1950, No. 1450. "Dimorphic Plumage of Female White-necked Jacobin," in *Studies of Peruvian Birds,* John T. Zimmer; Am. Mus. Nat. Hist., New York, N. Y.

Novitates 1962, No. 2094. *Notes on Nighthawks, etc.,* Eugene Eisenmann; Am. Mus. Nat. Hist., New York, N. Y.

Oölogists' Record 1952. "Eggs of the *Falconinae*," N. B. Coltart; *Oölogists' Record* 26:3:43.

P.C.A. 29. *Distributional Check-List of Birds of Mexico,* Part 1, 1950, Herbert Friedmann, Ludlow Griscom, and Robert T. Moore; Pacific Coast Avifauna, No. 29, Cooper Ornith. Soc., Berkeley, Calif. 94720.

P.C.A. 31. *Life Histories of Central American Birds,* 1954, Alexander F. Skutch; Pacific Coast Avifauna, No. 31, Cooper Ornith. Soc.

P.C.A. 33. *Distributional Check-List of the Birds of Mexico,* Part 2, 1957, Alden H. Miller, Herbert Friedmann, Ludlow Griscom, and Robert T. Moore; Pacific Coast Avifauna, No. 33, Cooper Ornith. Soc.

P.C.A. 34. *Life Histories of Central American Birds,* 1960, Alexander F. Skutch; Pacific Coast Avifauna, No. 34, Cooper Ornith. Soc.

Paynter 1955. *The Ornithogeography of the Yucatán Peninsula,* Raymond A. Paynter, Jr.; Bull. No. 9, Yale Univ., Peabody Mus. of Nat. Hist., New Haven, Conn.

Paynter 1957. "Rough-winged Swallows of the race *stuarti,* etc.";
    Condor 59:3:212, 213.

Peters. *Check-list of Birds of the World,* James Lee Peters and
    others; Volumes 1–7, 9, 10, 15 published (1931 to 1964), Har-
    vard Univ. Press, Cambridge, Mass. 02138.

Peterson 1947. *A Field Guide to the Birds* (East of the Rockies),
    Roger Tory Peterson; Houghton Mifflin Co., Boston, Mass.

Peterson 1960. *A Field Guide to the Birds of Texas,* Roger Tory
    Peterson; The Texas Game and Fish Commission; Houghton
    Mifflin Co., Boston, Mass.

Peterson 1961. *A Field Guide to Western Birds,* Roger Tory Peter-
    son; Houghton Mifflin Co., Boston, Mass.

Pough 1953. *Audubon Guides,* Richard H. Pough; Doubleday &
    Co., Garden City, N. Y.; combines *Audubon Bird Guide (Small
    Land Birds)* (1940) and *Audubon Water Bird Guide (Water,
    Game, and Large Land Birds)* (1951).

Puleston, Dennis E., member of staff of Tikal Project, in litt.

Rand 1956. *American Water and Game Birds,* Austin L. Rand;
    E. P. Dutton & Co., New York, N. Y.

Ridgway. *The Birds of North and Middle America,* Robert Ridg-
    way and H. Friedmann; various volumes, 1901–1950; Bull. 50,
    U. S. Natl. Mus., Smithsonian Institution, Washington 25, D. C.

Russell 1964. *A Distributional Study of the Birds of British Hon-
    duras,* Stephen Russell; Monograph No. 1 of the American Orni-
    thologists' Union (see AOU).

Salvin and Godman 1879–1904. "Biología Centrali Americana,"
    Osbert Salvin and Frederick D. Godman; *Aves,* 3 vols. of text,
    1 of plates, London, England (out of print).

Sapper 1937. "Mittelamerika," Karl Sapper; *Handbuch der Region-
    alen Geologie,* Heft 29:8:1–160; and other papers.

Saunders 1951. *A Guide to Bird Songs,* Aretas A. Saunders;
    Doubleday & Co., Garden City, N. Y.

Schwartz, Paul. See Bird Songs, *Birds of the Tropics.*

Sick. "Nests of *Panyptila cayennensis,*" Helmut Sick; *Auk*
    75:2:217–220.

Skutch, Alexander F. Numerous life histories and reports; also
    frequently quoted "in litt."; see P.C.A. 31 and P.C.A. 34.

Slud 1964. *The Birds of Costa Rica,* Paul Slud; Bull. 128, Am.
    Mus. of Nat. Hist., New York, N. Y. 10024.

Smith, Neal G. Reports, in litt.; see King Vulture and Black Hawk-
    Eagle.

Smithe and Land 1960. "First records of Cattle Egrets in Guate-
    mala," Hugh C. Land; *Auk* 77:2:219.

Smithe and Paynter 1963. *Birds of Tikal, Guatemala,* Frank B. Smithe and Raymond A. Paynter, Jr.; Bull. 128, No. 5, pp. 245–324, Mus. Comp. Zool., Cambridge, Mass. 02138.

Stein. "Isolating Mechanisms Between Populations of Traill's Fly-catchers," Robert Carrington Stein; *Proc. Am. Phil. Soc.,* Vol. 107:1:21–50, Philadelphia 6, Pa.

Sutton 1951. *Mexican Birds,* George Miksch Sutton; Univ. Oklahoma Press, Norman, Okla.

Taibel 1955. "Uccelli del Guatemala, ecc.," Alulah M. Taibel; extract from the Proceedings of the Societá Italiana di Scienze Naturali, Vol. 94:1:15–84 and plates; Milano, Italy.

Trik. Aubrey Trik, in litt., Field Dir. Tikal Project, and member of staff of The University Museum, Philadelphia, Pa. 19104.

Van Tyne 1929. *The Life History of the (Keel-billed) Toucan,* Josselyn Van Tyne; Misc. Pub. No. 19:1:1–43, Univ. Mich. Mus. Zool., Ann Arbor, Mich.

Van Tyne 1935. *The Birds of Northern Petén, Guatemala,* Josselyn Van Tyne; Misc. Pub. No. 27:1–47, Univ. Mich. Mus. Zool.

Van Tyne 1950. *Bird Notes from Barro Colorado Island,* Josselyn Van Tyne; Occ. Papers No. 525:1–12, Univ. Mich. Mus. Zool.

Van Tyne and Berger 1959. *Fundamentals of Ornithology,* Josselyn Van Tyne and Andrew J. Berger; John Wiley & Sons, Inc., New York, N. Y.

Wagner. "Notes on the Life History of the Emerald Toucanet," Helmuth O. Wagner; *Wilson Bull.* 56:2:65–76.

Wildlife Survey 1950. *A Fish and Wildlife Survey of Guatemala,* George B. Saunders, Ancil D. Holloway, and Charles O. Handley, Jr.; Special Scientific Report: Wildlife No. 5; U. S. Dept. of Int., Fish and Wildlife Service, Washington, D. C.

Willis. "A study of Ant-Tanagers in British Honduras," Edwin Willis; *Condor* 62:2:73–87 and 63:6:479–503; also reports, in litt.

Wilson Bull. *The Wilson Bulletin,* a quarterly pub. of The Wilson Ornithological Soc., West Virginia Univ., Morgantown, W. Va.

INDEX

FRANK B. SMITHE has long been an amateur archeologist and ornithologist. Requested by local authorities to make a comprehensive study of the birds of Tikal, he spent over eight years assembling the information for this volume. A graduate of Columbia University, with a degree in Mechanical Engineering, Mr. Smithe has now retired and is living in Douglaston, New York.